Structure

Dearborn
Home Inspection

This publication is designed to provide accurate and authoritative information in regard to the subject matter covered. It is sold with the understanding that the publisher is not engaged in rendering legal, accounting, or other professional service. If legal advice or other expert assistance is required, the services of a competent professional person should be sought.

President: Roy Lipner
Publisher and Director of Distance Learning: Evan M. Butterfield
Senior Development Editor: Laurie McGuire
Content Consultant: Alan Carson
Acting Editorial Production Manager: Daniel Frey
Creative Director: Lucy Jenkins
Graphic Design: Neglia Design Inc.

Published by Dearborn™ Real Estate Education
a Division of Dearborn Financial Publishing, Inc.®
a Kaplan Professional Company®
30 South Wacker Drive
Chicago, IL 60606-7481
www.dearbornRE.com

Printed in the United States of America.

03 04 05   10 9 8 7 6 5 4 3 2 1

INTRODUCTION

Welcome! This home inspection training program has two primary goals:

- To provide you with a sound introduction to the components, materials and mechanics of house systems that you will encounter and evaluate as a home inspector;

- To provide you with a solid understanding of inspection processes, strategies and standards of practice that will help define the scope of your inspections.

We hope you enjoy this training program and develop a good understanding of the various house systems as you proceed. Good luck!

FEATURES OF THIS PROGRAM

This program is structured to help you learn and retain the key concepts of home inspection. It also will help you form a set of best practices for conducting inspections. A number of features are included to help you master the information and put your knowledge into practice:

- Topics are organized into evenly paced Study Sessions. Each Session begins with learning objectives and key words to set up the important concepts you should master by the end of the Session. Each Session concludes with Quick Quizzes to help you test your understanding. Answers to Quick Quizzes are provided so you can check your results.

- Scope and Introduction sections present the ASHI® (American Society of Home Inspectors) Standards of Practice for each major topic. Standards help you define a professional, consistent depth and breadth for your inspections.

- An Inspection Checklist at the end of each section summarizes the important components you will be inspecting and their typical problems. You can use this as a set of field notes during your own inspections.

- The Inspection Tools list will help you build your toolkit of "must have" and optional tools for the job.

- An Inspection Procedures section provides some general guidelines to conducting your inspection of each major house system. This feature will help you develop a methodology to complement your technical knowledge.

- Field Exercises give you an opportunity to turn your knowledge into real world experience.

SUMMARY

The road we have paved for you is designed to be easy and enjoyable to follow. We trust it will lead you quickly to your destination of success in the home inspection profession.

ACKNOWLEDGMENTS

Thanks to Kevin O'Malley for his inspiration, advice and guidance. Thanks also to James Dobney for his invaluable input and encouragement. Special thanks are extended to Dan Friedman for his numerous and significant contributions.

We are grateful for the contributions of: Duncan Hannay, Richard Weldon, Peter Yeates, Tony Wong, Graham Clarke, Ian Cunliffe, Joe Seymour, Charles Gravely, Graham Lobban, Dave Frost, Gerard Gransaull, Jim Stroud, Diana DeSantis, David Ballantyne, Shawn Carr and Steve Liew.

Special thanks are also extended to Susan Bonham, Dearbhla Lynch, Lucia Cardoso-Tavares, Jill Brownlee, Ida Cristello and Rita Minicucci-Colavecchia who have brought everything together. Thanks also to Jim Lingerfelt for his invaluable editing assistance.

► FOOTINGS AND FOUNDATIONS

► FLOORS

► WALL SYSTEMS

► ROOF FRAMING

1

FOOTINGS AND FOUNDATIONS

Structure

MODULE

► TABLE OF CONTENTS

► **1.0 OBJECTIVES**

During this section you will learn –
• the various foundation configurations
• the different material types used for foundations
• the key components of a foundation and the basics of foundation construction
• the common problems found with foundations
• how to identify these conditions
• the causes and implications of these conditions

Not The
Last Word

This program is not an in-depth Structure course and you should not assume that you have all the knowledge of a professional engineer, architect, designer, carpenter, mason, etc. after studying this material. This program does not qualify you to design or build homes. There are many places to go to learn more and we encourage you to continue expanding your knowledge.

Structure
M O D U L E

STUDY SESSION 1

1. This Session covers the scope of the inspection as set out in the ASHI®/CAHI Standards of Practice.
Note: ASHI® stands for American Society of Home Inspectors
CAHI stands for Canadian Association of Home Inspectors

2. At the end of this Session you should be able to –

- List six structural elements that must be observed in a Standard inspection.
- List six structural elements that must be described in a report
- Describe in one sentence when probing is required
- Describe in one sentence when attics or crawlspaces should be entered

3. Before you start, watch the Footings and Foundations part of Structure Video. Don't worry if you don't understand everything. We just want to get you thinking about foundations for now. After you have watched it, rewind the tape to the beginning, we will ask you to watch it again.

Done with the Video? Okay, let's move on.

4. This is a short section and it should only take about 30 minutes to complete.

5. Quick Quiz 1 is at the end of the section.

Key Words:
- *Foundations*
- *Floor structure*
- *Columns*
- *Wall structure*
- *Ceiling structure*
- *Roof structure*
- *Attics*
- *Crawlspaces*
- *Probe*
- *Dangerous*
- *Readily accessible*
- *Significantly deficient*
- *Engineering Service*

► 2.0 SCOPE AND INTRODUCTION

2.1 SCOPE

These are the following components of the ASHI® Standards of Practice, effective, January, 2000 :

- Purpose and Scope
- Structural System
- General Limitations and Exclusions
- Glossary

► THE ASHI® STANDARDS OF PRACTICE

2.0 PURPOSE AND SCOPE

2.1 The purpose of these Standards of Practice is to establish a minimum and uniform standard for private, fee-paid home *inspectors* who are members of the American Society of Home Inspectors. *Home Inspections* performed to these Standards of Practice are intended to provide the client with information regarding the condition of the *systems* and *components* of the home as inspected at the time of the *Home Inspection*.

2.2 The *inspector* shall:

A. *inspect:*
  1. *readily accessible systems* and *components* of homes listed in these Standards of Practice.
  2. *installed systems* and *components* of homes listed in these Standards of Practice.
B. *report*:
  1. on those *systems* and *components* inspected which, in the professional opinion of the *inspector*, are *significantly deficient* or are near the end of their service lives.
  2. a reason why, if not self-evident, the *system* or *component* is *significantly deficient* or near the end of its service life.
  3. the *inspector's* recommendations to correct or monitor the reported deficiency.
  4. on any *systems* and *components* designated for inspection in these Standards of Practice which were present at the time of the *Home Inspection* but were not inspected and a reason they were not inspected.

2.3 These Standards of Practice are not intended to limit *inspectors* from:

A. including other inspection services, *systems* or *components* in addition to those required by these Standards of Practice.
B. specifying repairs, provided the *inspector* is appropriately qualified and willing to do so.
C. excluding *systems* and *components* from the inspection if requested by the client.

3.0 STRUCTURAL SYSTEM

3.1 The *inspector* shall:

A. *inspect:*
1. the *structural components* including foundation and framing.
2. by probing a *representative number* of structural components where deterioration is suspected or where clear indications of possible deterioration exist. Probing is NOT required when probing would damage any finished surface or where no deterioration is visible.

B. *describe:*
1. The foundation and *report* the methods used to *inspect* the *under-floor crawl space.*
2. the floor structure
3. the wall structure
4. the ceiling structure
5. the roof structure and *report* the methods used to *inspect* the attic

3.2 The *inspector* is NOT required to:

A. provide any *engineering service* or *architectural service.*
B. offer an opinion as to the adequacy of any *structural system* or *component.*

13. GENERAL LIMITATIONS AND EXCLUSIONS

13.1 General limitations:

A. Inspections performed in accordance with these Standards of Practice
1. are not *technically exhaustive.*
2. will not identify concealed conditions or latent defects.
B. These Standards of Practice are applicable to buildings with four or fewer dwelling units and their garages or carports.

13.2 General exclusions:

A. The *inspector* is not required to perform any action or make any determination unless specifically stated in the Standards of Practice, except as may be required by lawful authority.
B. *Inspectors* are NOT required to determine:
1. the condition of *systems* or *components* which are not *readily accessible.*
2. the remaining life of any *system* or *component.*
3. the strength, adequacy, effectiveness, or efficiency of any *system or component.*
4. the causes of any condition or deficiency.
5. the methods, materials, or costs of corrections.
6. future conditions including, but not limited to, failure of *systems* and *components.*
7. the suitability of the property for any specialized use.
8. compliance with regulatory requirements (codes, regulations, laws, ordinances, etc.).

9. the market value of the property or its marketability.

10. the advisability of the purchase of the property.

11. the presence of potentially hazardous plants or animals including, but not limited to wood destroying organisms or diseases harmful to humans.

12. the presence of any environmental hazards including, but not limited to toxins, carcinogens, noise, and contaminants in soil, water, and air.

13. the effectiveness of any *system installed* or methods utilized to control or remove suspected hazardous substances.

14. the operating costs of *systems or components*.

15. the acoustical properties of any *system or component*.

C. *Inspectors* are NOT required to offer:

1. or perform any act or service contrary to law.

2. or perform *engineering services*.

3. or perform work in any trade or any professional service other than *home inspection*.

4. warranties or guarantees of any kind.

D. *Inspectors* are NOT required to operate:

1. any *system* or *component* which is *shut down* or otherwise inoperable.

2. any *system* or *component* which does not respond to *normal operating controls*.

3. shutoff valves.

E. *Inspectors* are NOT required to enter:

1. any area which will, in the opinion of the *inspector*, likely be dangerous to the *inspector* or other persons or damage the property or its *systems* or *components*.

2. the *under-floor crawlspaces* or *attics* which are not *readily accessible*.

F. *Inspectors* are NOT required to *inspect*:

1. underground items including, but not limited to underground storage tanks or other underground indications of their presence, whether abandoned or active.

2. *systems* or *components* which are not *installed*.

3. *decorative* items.

4. *systems* or *components* located in areas that are not entered in accordance with these Standards of Practice.

5. detached structures other than garages and carports.

6. common elements or common areas in multi-unit housing, such as condominium properties or cooperative housing.

G. *Inspectors* are NOT required to:

1. perform any procedure or operation which will, in the opinion of the *inspector*, likely be dangerous to the *inspector* or other persons or damage the property or its *systems or components*.

2. move suspended ceiling tiles, personal property, furniture, equipment, plants, soil, snow, ice, or debris.

3. *dismantle* any *system* or *component*, except as explicitly required by these Standards of Practice.

GLOSSARY OF ITALICIZED TERMS

Alarm Systems

Warning devices, installed or free-standing, including but not limited to; carbon monoxide detectors, flue gas and other spillage detectors, security equipment, ejector pumps and smoke alarms

Architectural Service

Any practice involving the art and science of building design for construction of any structure or grouping of structures and the use of space within and surrounding the structures or the design for construction, including but not specifically limited to, schematic design, design development, preparation of construction contract documents, and administration of the construction contract

Automatic Safety Controls

Devices designed and installed to protect systems and components from unsafe conditions

Component

A part of a system

Decorative

Ornamental; not required for the operation of the essential systems and components of a home

Describe

To report a system or component by its type or other observed, significant characteristics to distinguish it from other systems or components

Dismantle

To take apart or remove any component, device or piece of equipment that would not be taken apart or removed by a homeowner in the course of normal and routine homeowner maintenance

Engineering Service

Any professional service or creative work requiring engineering education, training, and experience and the application of special knowledge of the mathematical, physical and engineering sciences to such professional service or creative work as consultation, investigation, evaluation, planning, design and supervision of construction for the purpose of assuring compliance with the specifications and design, in conjunction with structures, buildings, machines, equipment, works or processes.

Further Evaluation

Examination and analysis by a qualified professional, tradesman or service technician beyond that provided by the home inspection

Home Inspection

The process by which an inspector visually examines the readily accessible systems and components of a home and which describes those systems and components in accordance with the Standards of Practice.

Household Appliances
Kitchen, laundry, and similar appliances, whether installed or free-standing

Inspect
To examine readily accessible systems and components of a building in accordance with these Standards of Practice, using normal operating controls and opening readily openable access panels

Inspector
A person hired to examine any system or component of a building in accordance with these Standards of Practice

Installed
Attached such that removal requires tools

Normal Operating Controls
Devices such as thermostats, switches or valves intended to be operated by the homeowner

Readily Accessible
Available for visual inspection without requiring moving of personal property, dismantling, destructive measures, or any action which will likely involve risk to persons or property

Readily Openable Access Panel
A panel provided for homeowner inspection and maintenance that is within normal reach, can be removed by one person, and is not sealed in place

Recreational Facilities
Spas, saunas, steam baths, swimming pools, exercise, entertainment, athletic, playground or other similar equipment and associated accessories

Report
To communicate in writing

Representative Number
One component per room for multiple similar interior components such as windows and electric outlets; one component on each side of the building for multiple similar exterior components

Roof Drainage Systems
Components used to carry water off a roof and away from a building

Significantly Deficient
Unsafe or not functioning

Shut Down
A state in which a system or component cannot be operated by normal operating controls

Solid Fuel Burning Appliances

A hearth and fire chamber or similar prepared place in which a fire may be built and which is built in conjunction with a chimney; or a listed assembly of a fire chamber, its chimney and related factory-made parts designed for unit assembly without requiring field construction

Structural Component

A component that supports non-variable forces or weights (dead loads) and variable forces or weights (live loads)

System

A combination of interacting or interdependent components, assembled to carry out one or more functions

Technically Exhaustive

An investigation that involves dismantling, the extensive use of advanced techniques, measurement, instruments, testing, calculations, or other means

Under-floor Crawl Space

The area within the confines of the foundation and between the ground and the underside of the floor

Unsafe

A condition in a readily accessible, installed system or component which is judged to be a significant risk of personal injury during normal, day-to-day use. The risk may be due to damage, deterioration, improper installation or a change in accepted residential construction standards

Wiring Methods

Identification of electrical conductors or wires by their general type, such as "non-metallic sheathed cable" ("Romex"), "armored cable" ("bx") or "knob and tube," etc.

► NOTES ON THE STANDARDS

The Standards ask us to inspect all of the basic foundation components with the exception of footings. Footings are excluded because, in most houses, you can't see the footings.

Ceilings

One of the items that has been included relatively recently in the Standards and one that confuses some people is **ceilings**. For many people, ceilings are not a structural component. Depending on your definition, ceilings may or may not contribute to holding up the house. In a house with a conventional steep roof and rafters, there are ceiling joists which serve to tie the outer walls and rafter ends together. They support the insulation and ceiling plaster or drywall, although these are not structural functions, according to some.

If there are cathedral ceilings or flat roofs, the **roof joists**, **rafters** or **trusses** may support finish ceilings. These are structural components.

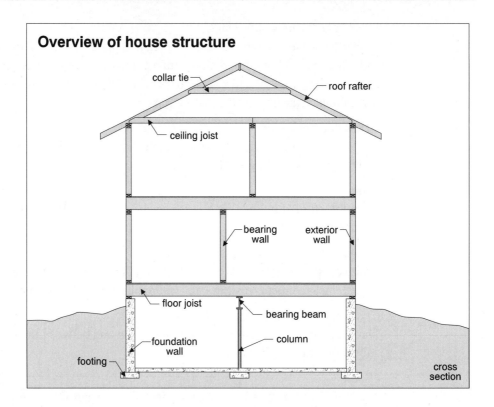

Overview of house structure

Labels: collar tie, roof rafter, ceiling joist, bearing wall, exterior wall, floor joist, bearing beam, foundation wall, column, footing, cross section

Foundations   You are asked to describe the type of foundations. You should describe the material and configuration, where visible. The foundation, in many cases, will be a perimeter strip foundation wall. In other cases, it may be piers, often with grade beams spanning between. The foundations could also be driven piles, although you may not know this.

Probing   We are required to probe structural components where deterioration is suspected. While it doesn't say so, we take this to mean wooden components, for the most part. In some cases, you may wish to probe concrete or masonry foundation materials as well if you suspect deterioration. Mortar which may be falling off masonry units is one example. Don't damage drywall, plaster or paneling, for example, when probing.

Crawlspaces   We are required to report how we inspected crawlspaces and attics. We are not
And Attics   required to enter these areas, although you have to report whether or not you did. We also explain why, if we did not enter these areas. Reasons may include –

• The access is blocked
• You might damage the property
• It might be dangerous

What Is Obstructed Access?
Different inspectors have different impressions of what obstructed access means. For some people, unscrewing a cover door or pulling off a nailed-on panel is normal routine. Most inspectors would not do it. Our practice is, when there is risk of damaging a cover or interior finishes, we will not do it. Also, if there is a question of whether or not we'd be able to get the panel back in place securely, we don't do it.

Damaging Property
Although it's tough to envision a condition when entering a crawlspace might damage the property, it's easy to envision with attics. If you're crawling across an insulated attic, you may

- Crush concealed ductwork
- Put your foot through the ceiling
- Pinch an electrical wire on top of a joist buried below insulation.

These are only a few examples of damage you might cause.

Dangerous Situations
Dangerous situations in crawlspaces would include evidence of animals (e.g., rats, snakes, scorpions, raccoons), and standing water in the crawlspace, which may be raw sewage. There may be live electrical wires lying in the water.

Crawlspaces Are Problem Areas
We find lots of problems in crawlspaces, and wherever it's physically possible, we get into them. Our inspectors carry paper coveralls and boots to avoid getting our clothes dirty, then tracking dirt through the home.

Not A Design Review
The structure inspection does not include calculations or design review to determine strength or adequacy of components. We are evaluating performance based on visual inspection.

Life Expectancy And Costs
You aren't required to give a life expectancy of any component, nor are you required to provide a cost estimate for repairs, although some inspectors do.

Rot And Insect Damage
You don't have to report on the presence of wood destroying organisms (rot or insects, such as termites and carpenter ants) although, again, many inspectors do. Since you have to inspect the structural components, our conclusion here is that you have to report any wood damage but don't have to say whether it's caused by rot, insects or chain saws.

Accessible
You only have to inspect components that are **readily accessible**. You don't have to move ceiling tiles, furniture, carpeting, equipment, etc. to look at the structure.

Deficient or Worn Out
You have to report on components that are **significantly deficient** (unsafe or not functioning). This would include broken floor joists and bowing foundation walls, for example. You also have to report on components near the end of their service life. This does not apply to structural components for the most part, which are intended to last the life of the building.

Explain Why
Unless it's self-evident, you have to explain the implications of a problem. For example, you should explain in your report why it's important that the endbearing for the joists are ½ inch (way too small).

Direct Client

Where you find problems, you have to tell people what to do about them, in general terms. This means telling clients that they need to have a condition repaired, but not how to repair it.

House and Garage Only

You don't have to inspect any outbuildings except garages.

2.2 INTRODUCTION

This Module will follow **The Home Reference Book** Structure Section and we encourage you to review that material before starting this Module. **The Basics of Structures** provides a good introduction to the structural inspection.

General Strategy

Home inspectors are often guilty of superficial structural inspections, because structural defects are less common than defects in other areas. However, structural conditions are often the most serious and expensive to correct. In some cases, correction cannot be accomplished cost effectively and the home may be lost.

Not A Design Review

Your work as a home inspector is to evaluate the performance of the house structure. On new houses, there isn't much performance over time that you can evaluate, and so you must default to generally accepted building practices, and point out deviations therefrom. While home inspectors don't do code inspections,

Not Code Inspection

a knowledge of code requirements for residential construction is very helpful. Home inspectors may offer their professional opinion, which can be more or less stringent than standard building practice or minimum code requirements, depending on the situation and the inspector's experience.

House Stays Put

In houses that have been around a few years, you will be looking to see whether the structure is responding satisfactorily. In most cases, this means staying put. While all structures move slightly (they must to carry their loads), the amount of movement should not –

- Cause failure of interior finishes
- Put undue stress on joints or individual components
- Affect the usability and operation of house systems (windows shouldn't jam, pipes shouldn't be broken, electrical wires shouldn't be pulled, etc.)

Support Live Loads

Perhaps most importantly, the structure should safely support the live loads imposed upon it. Structures that are unsound may allow people to fall, or may crush people.

Not An Engineering Design Course

We're going to talk about footings and foundations from a performance standpoint. We're looking to see whether they're doing their job. We are not going to figure out how to design buildings, we're not going to learn to be soils engineers and, most of all, we're not going to pretend we have X–ray vision.

Don't Draw Conclusions From Less Than Complete Information
Having said that, the single most common mistake that we see on home inspection reports is people describing a structure as **sound**. Since you can't see the whole thing, you don't really know. Do yourself a favor, just report what you saw. If you see no evidence of movement, say that. If you see evidence of movement, tell them what it is, where it was and how much movement.

Don't Go Out On A Limb
While it's terrific customer service to be able to discuss the causes of the movement, the implications and whether or not corrective actions are necessary, these things are risky when we're talking structure, especially if you're guessing. Even more risky is telling people how quickly they ought to do it and exactly how much it's going to cost. All of this can get you into trouble.

Like all parts of a home inspection, while there's stuff we can't do, there's lots that we can. Just remember that when we're talking about footings and foundations, you typically see absolutely none of the footings, and only part of the foundations.

Structure
MODULE

QUICK QUIZ 1

☑ INSTRUCTIONS

- You should finish reading Study Session 1 before doing this Quiz.
- Write your answers in the spaces provided.
- Check your answers against ours at the end of this section.
- If you have trouble with the Quiz, re-read the Session and try the Quiz again.
- If you do well, move on to Study Session 2.

1. According to the ASHI® Standards of Practice, an inspector must inspect all structural components. Two components are listed. What are they?

   _____

   _____

2. According to the ASHI® Standards of Practice, which structural elements must be **described** in your report?

   _____

   _____

   _____

3. You are required to probe structural elements where deterioration is suspect. When would probing not be required?

   _____

4. Under what conditions are you not required to inspect crawlspaces?

    _____

5. Under what conditions would you not enter the attic? Give some examples.

    _____

    _____

    _____

6. Do the Standards require you to explain how you inspected the crawlspace or an attic?
    Yes ☐　No ☐

7. Do the Standards require you to inspect a foundation footing?
    Yes ☐　No ☐

8. If the client is able to produce building drawings, are you required to look at the drawings to see if the foundation footing size is correct for your area?
    Yes ☐　No ☐

If you had no trouble with the Quiz, you are ready for Study Session 2!

Key Words:

- *Foundations*
- *Floor structure*
- *Columns*
- *Wall structure*
- *Ceiling structure*
- *Roof structure*

- *Attics*
- *Crawlspaces*
- *Probe*
- *Dangerous*
- *Readily*
  accessible

- *Significantly*
  deficient
- *Engineering*
  Service

Structure
M O D U L E

STUDY SESSION 2

1. You should have finished Study Session 1 and Quick Quiz 1 before starting this Session.

2. This Session includes an Introduction to Structure inspections and the functions, types and materials of footings and foundations.

3. By the end of this Session, you should be able to –

   • List two functions of footings and foundations
   • Define dead loads and live loads in one sentence each
   • List seven common soil types in order of strength
   • Describe in one sentence how frost can affect foundations
   • List three common foundation configurations
   • List three common slab-on-grade arrangements
   • Define in one sentence each – spread footings
                                    – pad footings
                                    – pilasters
                                    – piles
                                    – piers
                                    – grade beams

4. Read sections 1.0 to 4.0 of the Structure chapter of **The Home Reference Book** before starting this Session.

5. This Session may take an hour and a half to complete.

6. At the end there is a Quick Quiz to refresh your memory.

Key Words:
- *Transfer loads*
- *Live load*
- *Dead load*
- *Frost*
- *Soil types*
- *Basement*
- *Crawlspace*
- *Slab-on grade*
- *Spread footing*
- *Pilaster*
- *Pad footing*
- *Piles*
- *Piers*
- *Grade beams*
- *Caissons*
- *Raft foundation*
- *Mat foundation*
- *Preserved wood foundation*
- *Post-tensioned slabs*

► 3.0 FUNCTIONS, TYPES AND PROBLEMS

Functions

To put it simply, the function of a structure is to do nothing. The most successful structures stay still. That's the goal of the exercise. Getting slightly more technical, we can look at footings and foundations as having two functions:

Transfer Loads

1. to transfer the live and dead loads of the building to the soil over a large enough area so that neither the soil nor the building will move, and

Resist Frost

2. in areas where frost occurs, prevent frost from moving the building.

Dead Loads

Dead loads are the weight of the building materials and the soil surrounding the foundations.

Live Loads

Live loads include the weight of people, furniture, snow, rain and wind. Wind may be a vertical force downward, a horizontal force, or an uplift force.

A live load may also be exerted by water in the soil around the foundations. Wet soil exerts much more force than dry soil. Frozen soil exerts much more force than wet soil.

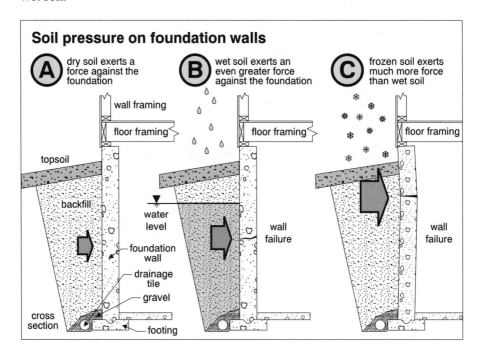

Soil pressure on foundation walls

A dry soil exerts a force against the foundation

B wet soil exerts an even greater force against the foundation

C frozen soil exerts much more force than wet soil

wall framing

floor framing

topsoil

backfill

water level

foundation wall

drainage tile

gravel

cross section

footing

wall failure

Direction of Loads

The weight of objects is caused by gravity and results in a vertical downward load. Wind can be in any direction, as mentioned earlier. The soil exerts forces in all directions, but foundations usually see the horizontal thrust of the soil on the outside of the foundation wall. The forces of frost are also in all directions. Most frost failures in buildings include horizontal movement (foundation walls cracking, bowing or collapsing inwards) and frost heaving (upward movement of the building as the soil under the building expands due to frost).

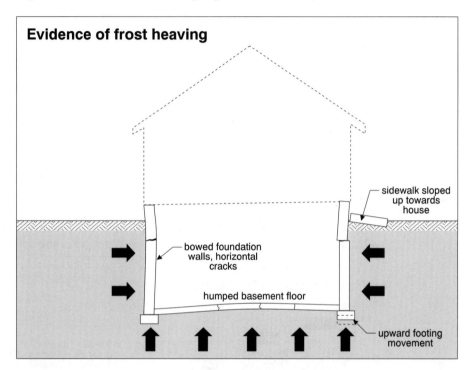

Evidence of frost heaving

sidewalk sloped up towards house

bowed foundation walls, horizontal cracks

humped basement floor

upward footing movement

SOILS

Soil Quality Is The Key

Buildings rely on the soil beneath them to stay put. If the soil under the house moves up, down or sideways, the house is in trouble. Designers of homes may know quite a bit about the soil conditions at a site and may design the building exactly for those. More commonly, soil conditions are assumed to be a certain type, and footings and foundations are designed with a margin of safety to account for adverse soil conditions, within reasonable limits. Occasionally we guess wrong and the building moves, but for an average site, it costs more to find out how good the soil is over the whole site than to design a system that will work on most soils.

Soil Types   While we won't be talking about any soils engineering or geology, and we certainly don't encourage you to offer soil testing as part of your home inspection, let's just give you some very crude rules, and rank soil types in order of their bearing capacity. You should understand that many soils are a combination of these types, and many building sites contain more than one soil type. The soil profile can change as you move across a site from side to side, and can change as you go down into the soil. With all those qualifiers, here is a ranking of soil types from strongest to weakest.

Strong   1. Bedrock
2. Gravel
3. Coarse sand
4. Fine sand
5. Clay
6. Silt
Weak   7. Organic material

With the exception of organic material, all of the soil types can be built on, given appropriate consideration for the soil type.

Again, while it's beyond our scope to get specific, the soil bearing capacity changes with moisture levels for most soil types, in some cases dramatically.

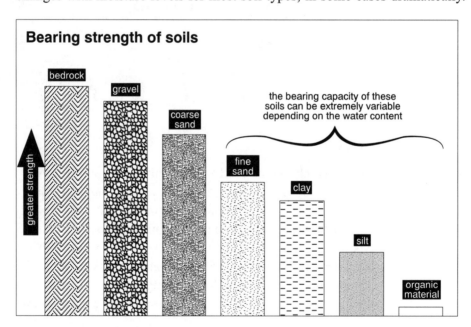

Function Depends On Location   The function of footing and foundation systems varies with location. Perimeter foundations have to resist the lateral thrust of soil outside the foundation wall. Interior foundations and footings under columns, for example, see more purely vertical loads.

FROST

The Strategy Varies

Have you ever wondered why there are basements in houses in the northern part of North America but not in the southern parts? Many of you probably know that the answer lies in one word – **frost**. Frost expands soil and exerts tremendous pressure. Frost induced pressures can lift houses up or push foundation walls in. If you are building in the north, you have to dig down far enough to get below the **frost line** – this is depth to which frost penetrates into the soil. That's where the footings should be. The foundations have to be tall enough to extend up through the soil above the grade, so we can put the house on top of the foundation. Since we have to dig a trench for the footings and foundations, we may as well create a hole and use the below grade space. That's how basements were invented.

Basements Where There's Frost

Slab-On-Grade Or Crawlspaces Where There's No Frost

If the building is not likely to see frost to any great depth, there's little risk of the building heaving. As a result, the weight of the building can be spread out on footings near the surface. Adding a basement becomes quite expensive. Most of the living space is above grade in areas where frost is not an issue. Incidentally, when we build at grade level in southern climates, we remove the organic soil (top soil) from the surface, since it is not very stable. While we might scrape off the surface, that's different from digging holes to get below the frost line.

Exceptions

No Frost In Cold Areas

Since this is home inspection, there are always exceptions to the rule. If you build on bedrock in frost areas, frost is not an issue and you don't have to put footings down below the frost line. Similarly, if you build on gravel or coarse sand that is free-draining, and the water table is far enough down, frost isn't likely to be a problem. Good draining soils allow the water from rain and melting snow to fall through very quickly and as long as the water doesn't stick around, it doesn't matter how cold the sand and gravel gets, it won't expand if there's no water in it.

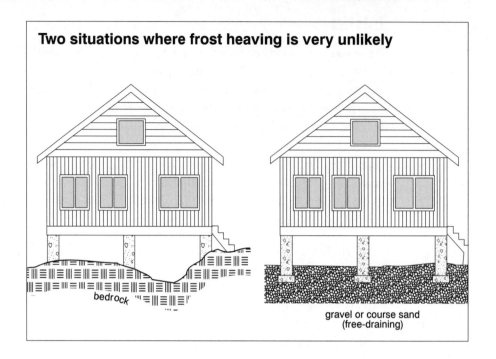

Two situations where frost heaving is very unlikely

bedrock

gravel or course sand
(free-draining)

Homes With
Basements
Need Heat

For those of you who live in frost areas, it's important to understand that once you dig a hole and make a basement, you've got to keep the building heated. We're trying to stop the frost from getting under the building. As long as we keep the inside of the building heated, frost can't get down under the basement floor. As long as the foundations are deep enough to extend below the frost line outside, the frost can't get under the building from the outside either.

Unheated
Houses
Can Heave

A problem arises when we have a house with a basement that is left unheated over the winter. If the frost depth in an area penetrates three to four feet into the soil, the footings have to be at or below that depth. An unheated house allows frost to penetrate the soil 3 to 4 feet **under the basement floor**. If there is adequate moisture in the soil, it will heave, picking the whole house up with it, or more commonly, parts of the house. Very serious structural damage can result.

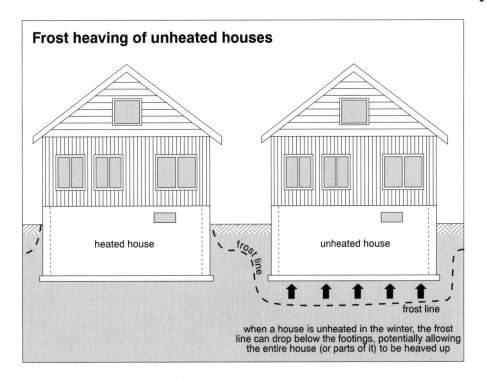

Frost heaving of unheated houses

heated house

unheated house

frost line

frost line

when a house is unheated in the winter, the frost line can drop below the footings, potentially allowing the entire house (or parts of it) to be heaved up

3.1 BASEMENTS, CRAWLSPACES, SLAB-ON-GRADE

Three Common Configurations

We've just been talking about **basements**, one of the common foundation configurations. **Crawlspaces** are another, which you can think of as short basements. **Crawlspaces** are used in areas where holes have to be dug to a slight depth to get below organic material or frost depth, but the area is not tall enough to create a basement, or basement space is not desirable. **Crawlspaces** may be built very similar to basements. They may have continuous perimeter foundations or they may have piers.

Slab-on-grade

The third common configuration is **slab-on-grade** construction. A concrete floor slab is poured at grade level. These slabs may be supported on continuous foundations, piers or piles and grade beams, or grade beams directly on isolated footings, for example. These foundations often serve as the building floor, as well as the support for the house loads.

Floor slabs may be:

Floating
1. Floating – supported by the ground and independent of perimeter foundations.

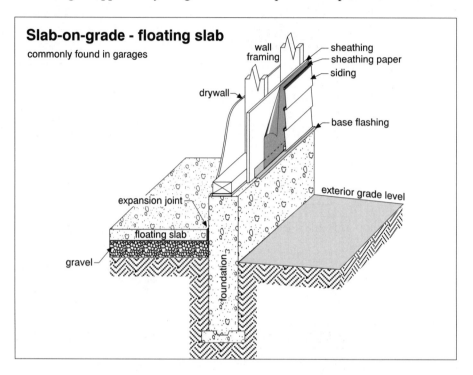

Supported
2. Supported – the floor slab may be integrated into the foundation system for the building. In this case, the foundations support the slab.

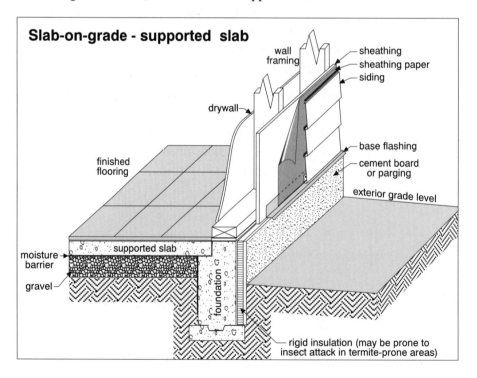

Monolithic   Monolithic – the slab may be an integral part of the footing.

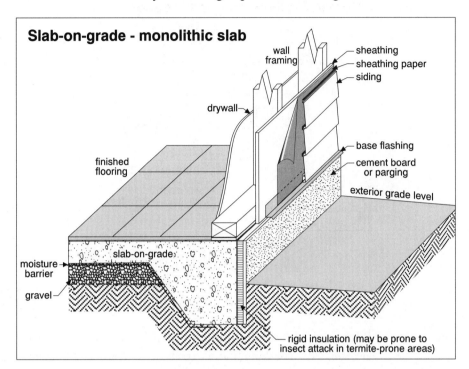

Slab-on-grade - monolithic slab

- wall framing
- sheathing
- sheathing paper
- siding
- drywall
- base flashing
- cement board or parging
- exterior grade level
- finished flooring
- slab-on-grade
- moisture barrier
- gravel
- rigid insulation (may be prone to insect attack in termite-prone areas)

Slabs are typically concrete and may be reinforced, depending on how they're built. Slabs may be thickened, typically on the underside, to support the weight of interior loadbearing members such as columns. Alternatively, the column may go through the slab, and a separate footing may be provided for the column.

3.2 FOOTING AND FOUNDATION TYPES

Spread Footings   This leads us to the configuration of footings. Houses may have spread footings (strip footings) that support the perimeter walls. These footings are wide pads that are continuous around the perimeter of the house. In some cases, the pads may be widened and/or thickened to accommodate concentrated loads from fireplaces, pilasters, etc.

Pilasters   A **pilaster** is a thickening of a foundation wall. It may be thickened to receive the concentrated load of a beam resting on top of the pilaster, or it may be acting as a stiffener to prevent the foundation wall from bowing inward.

Pad Footings   Pad footings are similar to continuous footings except they are usually under a single pier or column. Pad footings spread the load out, usually in a square, with the column or pier sitting in the middle of the square. It's common for houses to have strip footings around the perimeter and pad footings on the building interior under columns.

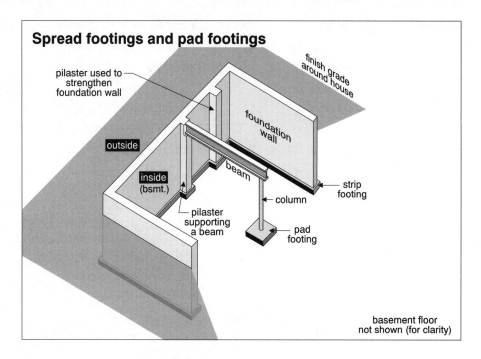

Spread footings and pad footings

pilaster used to strengthen foundation wall

finish grade around house

foundation wall

outside

inside (bsmt.)

beam

strip footing

column

pilaster supporting a beam

pad footing

basement floor not shown (for clarity)

Piles

Piles are used instead of footings, typically where the soil quality is poor. They are, generally speaking, more expensive to install and have to be driven into the ground with specialized equipment. They can work one of two ways:

Endbearing

1. Piles can be driven down to a point where they bear on bedrock or other sound substrate.

Friction

2. Piles can be driven into soil far enough that the friction of the soil against the sides of the pile is enough to resist any downward movement.

Incidentally, if a house is supported on piles, they probably won't be visible and you may not know it.

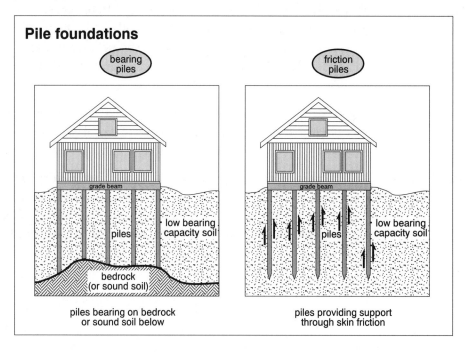

Pile foundations

bearing piles

friction piles

grade beam

piles

low bearing capacity soil

bedrock (or sound soil)

piles bearing on bedrock or sound soil below

grade beam

piles

low bearing capacity soil

piles providing support through skin friction

Piers   **Piers** are columns that may be completely concealed in the soil, or may project above. Most of you will be familiar with the piers that are commonly used to build exterior wood decks and porches. These piers may be poured concrete, often with the concrete poured into a cardboard cylinder in a hole dug in the ground. Piers usually, but not always, have footings. Piers can either be thought of as posts or columns, or can be thought of as short piles that bear on their ends.

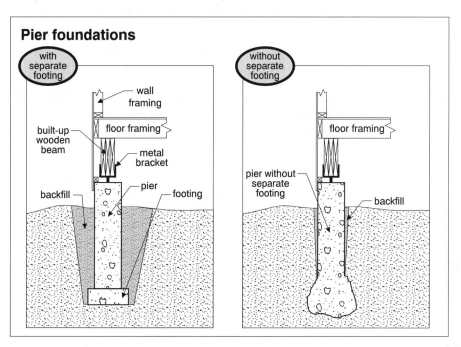

Grade Beams   **Grade beams** are usually concrete beams that are supported on footings, piles or piers and are located at grade. In some cases, they extend below grade, and usually extend only slightly above grade. Grade beams transfer the loads from the building down to the footings or piles.

Caissons   **Caissons** are foundation systems created by drilling holes and filling them with concrete. A caisson pile is a cast-in-place pile that has a hollow tube driven into the ground. The earth is excavated from the tube, and concrete is poured into the tube. Some caisson piles are flared out at the bottom to create a larger bearing surface. These are sometimes called bell caissons.

By now it should be clear that footings and foundations are –

- Important to the stability of the house
- Expensive
- Mostly out of sight

Materials   Footings and foundations should be strong so they can transfer loads and durable with respect to exposure from air, water, soil and insect attack. Most modern footings are concrete (sometimes reinforced.) Footings on older buildings may be brick or stone. While we won't talk much about preserved wood foundation systems, these systems sometimes employ a wood footing.

Foundations   Foundations may be concrete, concrete block, cinder block, brick, hollow clay tile (terra cotta), stone (either dry laid or laid in mortar) or wood. Wood was common on very old buildings and has become common again to the extent that preserved wood foundations are used.

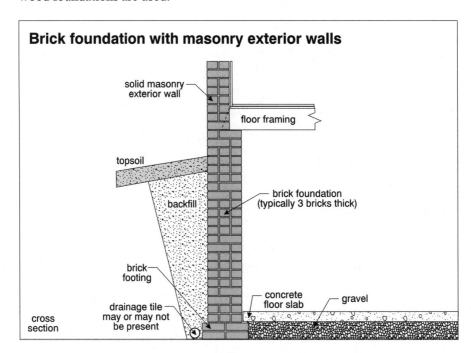

Brick foundation with masonry exterior walls

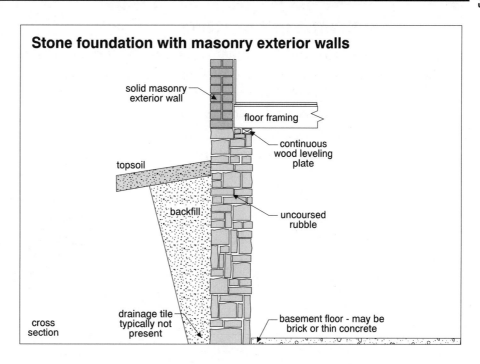

Stone foundation with masonry exterior walls

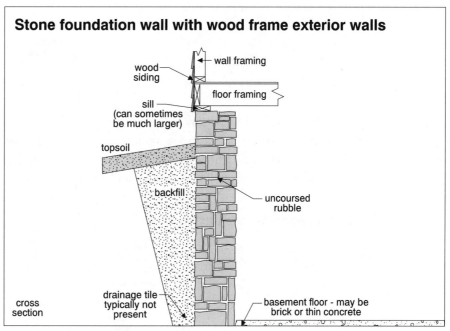

Stone foundation wall with wood frame exterior walls

Piles	Piles are typically concrete, steel or wood. Again, you likely won't see these.
Piers	Piers might be wood, concrete, concrete block, brick or stone.

SPECIAL FOUNDATIONS

Raft Or Mat
Foundations

These foundation systems are described briefly in **The Home Reference Book**. They are not common and you would not usually know that is what you're looking at in the field. Their construction materials and failure modes are the same as what we will be looking at, in any case. So we won't go into more detail.

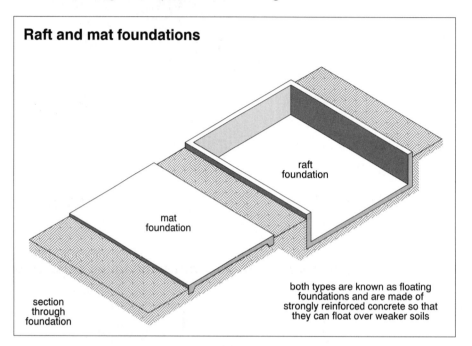

Raft and mat foundations

raft foundation

mat foundation

section through foundation

both types are known as floating foundations and are made of strongly reinforced concrete so that they can float over weaker soils

Preserved
Wood
Foundations

This type of foundation system has become popular in some areas over the last few years. Wood in a below grade, damp soil environment has historically not had a long life, particularly as a structural member. As a result, there are several design challenges with respect to wood foundations.

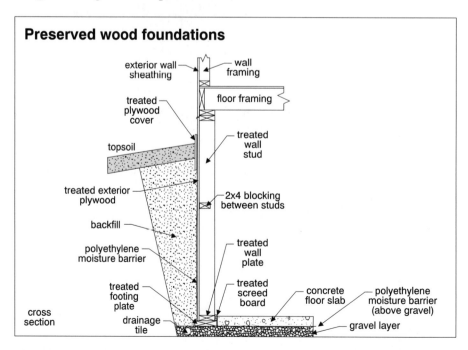

Preserved wood foundations

exterior wall sheathing

wall framing

treated plywood cover

floor framing

topsoil

treated wall stud

treated exterior plywood

2x4 blocking between studs

backfill

polyethylene moisture barrier

treated wall plate

treated footing plate

treated screed board

concrete floor slab

polyethylene moisture barrier (above gravel)

cross section

drainage tile

gravel layer

Rot And Insects

They are more likely to be successful in dry soils than wet soils. For the most part, their modes of failure will be similar to what we will look at on most other foundation systems, with a couple of exceptions. Since wood is less brittle or more flexible than concrete, for example, cracking is likely to be less common and bowing may be prevalent. Rot and insect damage are obviously possibilities with wood foundations, while these are not issues with most other foundation and footing materials.

In most cases, the interiors of preserved wood foundations are finished as living space and it may be difficult to identify the foundation system, let alone inspect it.

Post-tensioned Foundations

Some areas have expansive soils that make it risky to use conventional footings and foundations. A special reinforcement technique for concrete grade beams and floor slabs is sometimes used to resist the forces of the soil, and prevent differential movement of the structure.

Cables or Tendons

Post-tensioned slabs and grade beams use steel cables or tendons that are laid in place before the concrete is poured. The cables are most often surrounded by a plastic sheathing. After the concrete is poured, jacks are used to pull the cables tight, strengthening the assembly. You may be able to see the anchors and cable ends on the exterior of foundations near grade level. These post-tensioned cables sometimes snap, and in some cases, shoot out from the foundation or come up through floor slabs. Fortunately this problem is rare, at least so far.

INSPECTION TIPS

No Access Into Crawl Spaces

If there is no access to a part of a house structure that you ordinarily would see, this should be a red flag. You should document the limitations to your inspection and make your client understand that you couldn't do everything you normally do. This is important because problems in living spaces or highly visible areas tend to get addressed. Those that are concealed, tend to get ignored. If you can't get into the crawlspace, chances are no one has been in there. There may be considerable damage or distress that has developed over time. If you fail to make it clear to clients that you couldn't get into a crawlspace, which is important, you'll probably regret it eventually.

Macro And Micro

It's very important to look at the structure from far away and up close. Step back from the house and look at it from every angle. Where possible, line up the walls of the house you're looking at with adjacent houses or structures. Do the corners line up or is one of the buildings leaning?

Look Inside And Out

You have to look at the outside and inside to complete your stucture inpspection. In many cases, after having looked outside, you'll see something inside. There is nothing wrong with going back outside to have a second look.

Structure
M O D U L E

QUICK QUIZ 2

☑ INSTRUCTIONS

- You should finish reading Session 2 before doing this Quiz.
- Write your answers in the spaces provided.
- Check your answers against ours at the end of this section after the final test.
- If you have trouble with this Quiz, re–read the Session and try the Quiz again.
- If you do well, move on to Session 3.

The following questions assume that you have read sections 1.0 to 4.0 of the Structure chapter in **The Home Reference Book**. If you have not, do that now. All finished? Very good – now let's try the Quiz.

1. What is the function of a footing? – a foundation?

   _____

   _____

2. List the 3 common foundation configurations and footing types.

   _____   _____   _____

3. What is the difference between a strip footing and a pad footing and where would each be used?

   _____

   _____

4. Explain the difference between a full structural review and a performance based inspection.

    _____

    _____

5. There are several different materials that a foundation might be made of. List as many as you can.

    _____ _____ _____

    _____ _____ _____

    _____ _____ _____

6. As long as the footing is below the frost line, it is not a problem to let the temperature in the basement go below freezing.
    True ☐   False ☐

    Explain:

    _____

    _____

    _____

7. Why is it critical to document how the crawlspace was inspected?

    _____

    _____

    _____

8. Explain the difference between a live load and a dead load. Give examples.

    _____

    _____

    _____

9. What is the difference between a pilaster and a pier?

    _____

    _____

    _____

10. When a foundation is supported on piles, are the piles typically visible for inspection?

_____

_____

_____

If you had no trouble with the Quiz, you are ready to move on to Study Session 3.

Key Words:

- **Transfer loads**
- **Live load**
- **Dead load**
- **Frost**
- **Soil types**
- **Basement**
- **Crawlspace**
- **Slab-on grade**
- **Spread footing**
- **Pilaster**
- **Pad footing**
- **Piles**
- **Piers**
- **Grade beams**
- **Caissons**
- **Raft foundation**
- **Mat foundation**
- **Preserved wood foundation**
- **Post-tensioned slabs**

Structure

MODULE

STUDY SESSION 3

1. You should have completed Study Sessions 1 and 2 before starting this Session.

2. This session lists some common foundation problems and includes the first part of foundation cracks discussion.

3. By the end of this Session, you should be able to –

- List twelve common foundation problems
- List four types of cracks
- Describe in one sentence the cause and implication of shrinkage cracks
- List four characteristics of shrinkage cracks
- Define control joint
- Distinguish between uniform and differential settlement in two sentences.
- List eight causes of differential settlement
- List two reasons soil bearing capacity may change after the house is built
- List five soil problems that can cause differential settlement

4. You should be able to finish in 30 minutes.

5. Quick Quiz 3 is at the end of this Session.

Key Words:

- *Cracks*
- *Shrinkage*
- *Settling*
- *Heaving*
- *Spalling*

- *Cold joints*
- *Honeycombing*
- *Laterally unsupported*

- *Uniform settlement*
- *Differential settlement*

Now, let's look at some common problems found on foundations.

3.3 CONDITIONS

1. Cracks
   • Shrinkage
   • Settling
   • Heaving
   • Horizontal forces
2. Bowed, bulging or leaning
3. Mortar deterioration
4. Spalling material
5. Rot
6. Piers moving or deteriorating
7. Pilasters or buttresses pulling away
8. Cold joints
9. Honeycombing
10. Prior repairs
11. Foundation too short
12. Foundation too thin (laterally unsupported)

While there are many problems that may be found on foundations, the most common is cracking. We'll look more closely at all of the conditions, but let's start with cracking.

3.3.1 CRACKS

Four Types of Cracks

We'll look at four typs of foundation wall cracks:

• Shrinkage cracks
• Settlement cracks
• Heaving cracks
• Horizontal force cracks

3.3.1.1 Shrinkage cracks

Causes

Shrinkage cracks are caused by the natural curing of concrete. Some mixes will crack more than others, and cracking may be more pronounced if the concrete dries too quickly. This is common in hot weather. Overwatering the concrete or allowing it to freeze before it cures will also increase cracking. A 20 foot long wall might shrink 1/8 of an inch as it cures.

Implications

There are usually no structural implications to shrinkage cracks. The foundation wall may leak through shrinkage cracks which is a nuisance, but not a major structural problem.

Strategy

Shrinkage cracks are common with poured concrete foundation walls and floors. The cracks usually occur early in the life of the building when the concrete is still curing. While concrete cures for a number of years after it is poured, the majority of the curing takes place early on. Shrinkage cracks usually show up within the first year.

Vertical And Diagonal Cracks Are Common

The most common foundation wall shrinkage cracks are vertical or diagonal. The bottom part of the foundation is restrained by the footing and is less likely to open up due to shrinkage cracking.

Identifying Shrinkage Cracks

Shrinkage cracks typically do not extend into footings or into the structure above. They are not reflective of movement of the overall building, simply movement of the foundation component.

Shrinkage cracks do not necessarily have corresponding cracks elsewhere in the building. Cracks due to differential settlement usually do have corresponding cracks in two different locations.

Below Windows

Shrinkage cracks, as well as settlement cracks, usually occur at stress concentration points in the wall. Cracks most often radiate down from corners of basement windows.

Crack Size

Shrinkage cracks are usually relatively small, less than $1/8$ inch in width.

Control Joints

On large buildings or long walls, control joints are sometimes built into the wall. These are designed weak spots in the wall that allow the shrinkage cracks to form at these points. The walls are pre-patched during original construction, usually from the outside, anticipating the cracks. This prevents leakage and is a good practice, but is not common.

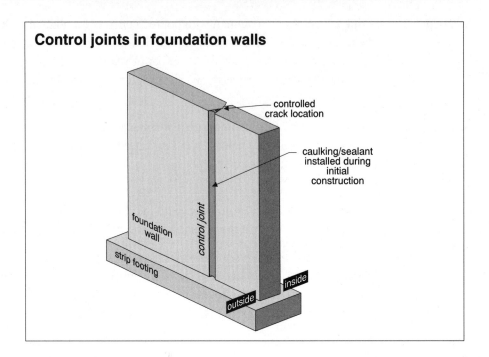

Control joints in foundation walls

controlled
crack location

caulking/sealant
installed during
initial
construction

foundation
wall

control joint

strip footing

outside

inside

3.3.1.2 Differential settlement cracks

Differential Settlement

When one part of the house settles and the rest does not, or two parts settle at different rates, cracking develops. This can be alarming and may or may not be a serious structural problem.

Uniform Settlement

Differential settlement cracks are the result of one part of a house moving relative to another. All houses settle when they are built. If the settlement is uniform, there are usually no problems that develop. The house settles slightly as a unit, and since everything moves together, there is no internal stress and no cracking.

Severe Uniform Settlement

Occasionally, uniform settlement can be a problem when the settlement is so dramatic that gas, water and electrical lines are strained and may break. In very severe cases of uniform settlement, the foundations may drop to a point where the bottom of the walls may get their feet in the dirt. Rot can result. This kind of dramatic uniform settlement is rare.

Tipping

There is a type of settlement that is not uniform, but not typically differential either. When a building tips, one part of the building settles more than another; however, the building holds together and no cracks develop. In some cases, no major structural problems develop, although if the building leans to a point where it is no longer stable, or the floors slope to the point where the usability of the house is affected, it can be serious.

Tower of Pisa

The Leaning Tower of Pisa is a good example of a building that tipped, but did not crack much. Eventually, the tipping got to a point where this tall slender building became unstable and had to be resupported.

Again, in severe cases, service lines may be strained and wood/soil contact may be created.

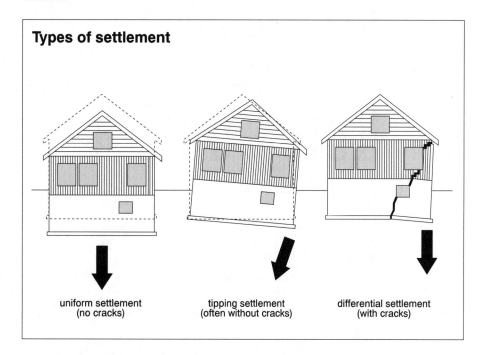

Types of settlement

uniform settlement
(no cracks)

tipping settlement
(often without cracks)

differential settlement
(with cracks)

Causes   There are several reasons for differential settlement:

Footing   • Footings are – missing
Problems   – undersized
                             – deteriorated

Soil   • Soil under the footings is – disturbed, on original construction, by tree roots or
Problems   when lowering floors or building additions for
                                              example
                                           – weak (poor bearing capacity)
                                           – expansive
                                           – eroding or slipping
                                           – freezing and heaving then settling

Load   • Loads increase due to – snow and ice
Problems   – building additions (e.g. adding a second floor)

To summarize, differential settlement occurs when the weight of the building exceeds the bearing capacity of the soil under part of the building.

Structure
MODULE

QUICK QUIZ 3

☑ INSTRUCTIONS

- You should finish reading Study Session 3 before doing this Quiz.
- Write your answers in the spaces provided.
- Check your answers against ours at the end of this Section after the Final Test.
- If you have trouble with this Quiz, re-read the Session and try the Quiz again.
- If you do well, move on to Study Session 4.

1. Name four causes of cracks in foundation walls.

   _____

   _____

   _____

   _____

2. Explain the difference between uniform settlement and differential settlement.

   _____

   _____

   _____

3. What is a shrinkage crack and what causes it?

   _____

   _____

4. Describe a typical shrinkage crack.

_____

_____

5. What is the main implication of a shrinkage crack?

_____

_____

6. Make a list of typical causes of differential settlement.

_____

_____

_____

If you had no trouble with the Quiz, you are ready for Study Session 4

Key Words:

- **Cracks**
- **Shrinkage**
- **Settling**
- **Heaving**
- **Spalling**

- **Cold joints**
- **Honeycombing**
- **Laterally unsupported**

- **Uniform settlement**
- **Differential settlement**

Structure
MODULE

STUDY SESSION 4

1. You should have completed Study Sessions 1, 2 and 3, before starting Session 4.

2. This Session covers – causes, implications and inspection strategy for differential cracks as well as some common corrective actions.

3. By the end of this Session you should be able to:

- List nine implications of differential cracks
- Define the maximum lot slope
- Describe in two sentences cut and fill lots
- Describe in two sentences how crack size can be misleading
- Describe three planes of differential movement that result in cracks
- Describe in one sentence pyramid cracks
- Describe in one sentence V-shaped cracks
- List four things you may recommend to clients with respect to cracks
- List six structural repair strategies

4. This Session may take about an hour to complete.

5. Quick Quiz 4 is included at the end of this Session.

Key Words:

- *Differential settlement cracks – implications*
- *Sloping lots*
- *Cut and fill lots*
- *Ravine lots*
- *Mud jacking*
- *Piles*

- *Planes of movement*
- *Horizontal*
- *Rotational*
- *Vertical*
- *Rate of movement*
- *Underpinning*

3.3.1.2 Differential Settlement Cracks – continued

Implications   The implications of settlement cracking depend on the extent of movement. Possible implications include –

1. None, if the cracks are not noticed
2. Cosmetic issues that make the house appear unstable to the lay person
3. Leakage through the cracks
4. Sloped or uneven floors
5. Utility lines being stressed or broken (plumbing, heating and gas pipes may break)
6. Flashings for chimneys and pipes may be moved at the roofline, resulting in leakage
7. Chimneys have become unstable or may develop dangerous openings in their flues
8. Floor, roof and ceiling joists and rafters losing their end bearing (which is usually only about an inch and one half) leading to possible floor or roof collapse
9. Collapse of floors, walls and roof if there is enough movement

These implications apply to most of the conditions we'll discuss in this Module.

Strategy   **Neighborhood Conditions**

Check Neighborhood   As you drive toward the house, look for structural problems in other homes in the neighborhood. Structural problems are often neighborhood specific, especially if they are related to soil conditions.

Topography   Check the general topography. Is the land flat or hilly? Is the home you are going to inspect near the top of a hill, on the side of a hill or near the bottom?

Age   How old is the neighborhood? Older neighborhoods that don't show structural problems are more reliable indicators of stability than newer neighborhoods that have not yet stood the test of time.

Soil Condition Research   Talk to municipal building inspectors, home builders, septic tank and sewer people about soil conditions they come across. Is your area known to have weak or expansive soils? Is the problem localized or is it a general problem?

Also ask about high water tables and underground streams. Ask about any areas built on fill or reclaimed land. This will help you identify and understand settlement problems.

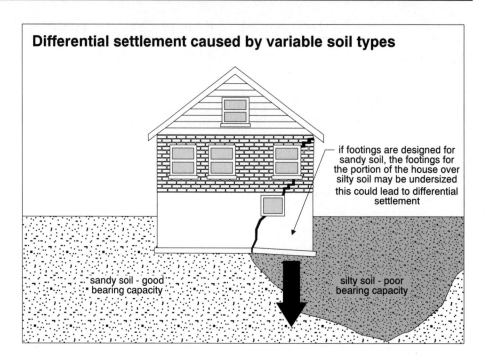

Differential settlement caused by variable soil types

if footings are designed for sandy soil, the footings for the portion of the house over silty soil may be undersized this could lead to differential settlement

sandy soil - good bearing capacity

silty soil - poor bearing capacity

Sloping Areas   Watch for structural problems in hilly areas. If the lots are predominately sloped, problems are more likely to arise.

Maximum Slope   Generally speaking, the maximum slope for a lot should be 1 in 2. That means for every two feet of horizontal distance along the surface, the ground should not rise or fall by more than one foot. This will be a function of the soil type and, to a certain extent, the rainfall amount and intensity. Many unstable soils can be washed out with heavy rains or flash floods. Houses that have stayed in place for years can be swept down hills if unstable soils are suddenly saturated.

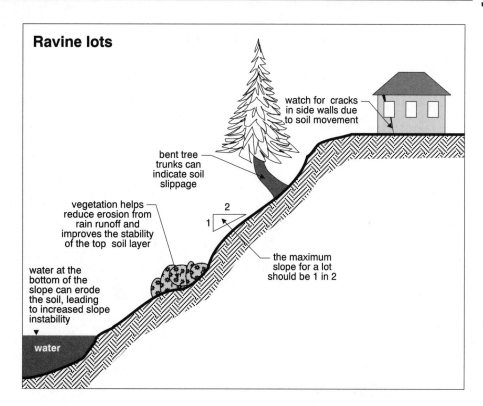

Ravine lots

watch for cracks
in side walls due
to soil movement

bent tree
trunks can
indicate soil
slippage

vegetation helps
reduce erosion from
rain runoff and
improves the stability
of the top soil layer

2

1

the maximum
slope for a lot
should be 1 in 2

water at the
bottom of the
slope can erode
the soil, leading
to increased slope
instability

water

Cut And
Fill Lots

When builders have to work on sloping lots, it is common to create a flat building pad by cutting back into the hill to form the pad for the uphill half of the house. The material that was removed is often deposited on the downhill slope and built up to form an extension of the pad that has been cut in.

You end up with the uphill half of the house built on undisturbed soil, and the downhill half of the house built on fill. Differential settlement cracks are very common here where the downhill half of the house wants to move and the uphill half wants to stay put.

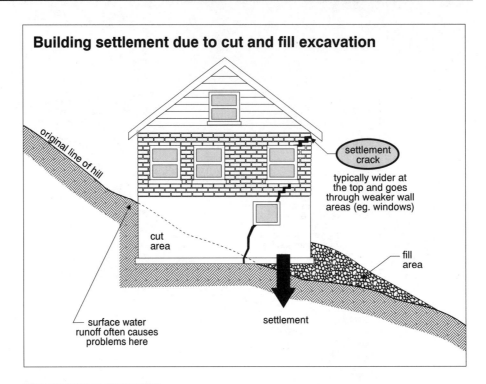

Building settlement due to cut and fill excavation

original line of hill

settlement crack

typically wider at the top and goes through weaker wall areas (eg. windows)

cut area

fill area

surface water runoff often causes problems here

settlement

FOOTING ISSUES

Usually More Than One Crack

If the cracks are due to **differential settlement**, there is usually more than one. If, for example, a corner of a building is settling, it will pull away from the walls on either side of the corner. If the downhill half of the house is sliding away from the uphill half, there will usually be cracks in both sidewalls.

Differential settlement cracks usually extend down through the footings and up through the structure. Unlike shrinkage cracks, they will not be restricted to the foundations.

Direction Of Cracks

Most cracks due to differential settlement are vertical or diagonal, including stepped cracks. Horizontal cracks are usually caused by lateral thrust. We'll talk about those in a little bit.

Crack Size People often grasp at straws to analyze cracks, based on size. This is very danger-ous, since there are several things that may confuse you. For example, which of these situations is worse?

- A one–quarter inch wide crack in a wall
- Sixteen cracks each 1/16 of an inch wide

Obviously, the several smaller cracks indicate more movement than the one large crack.

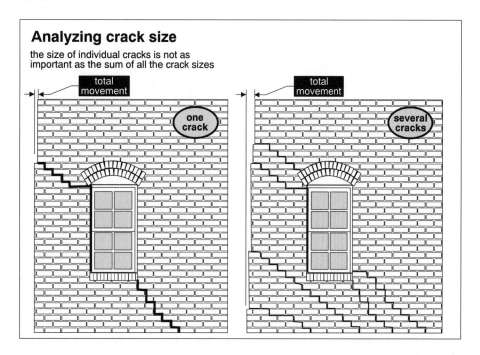

Analyzing crack size
the size of individual cracks is not as
important as the sum of all the crack sizes

total movement

one crack

total movement

several cracks

Planes Of Movement Horizontal You have to think of movement in all three dimensions. In the previous paragraph, we were talking about cracks that indicate that adjacent sections of the wall are pulling apart. One part of the building may be moving horizontally rel-ative to another.

Rotational A variation on this is a rotational crack, for example. There will be horizontal movement, but the higher up in the building you go, the more movement there will be, usually. The rotation is usually centered around the footing.

Vertical Shear One part of the building may drop relative to another. In this case, the crack width may be less than 1/16 of an inch. However, there can be significant dislocation. One side of the house could drop one inch relative to another and you still wouldn't have a very wide crack. You would have a serious structural problem though.

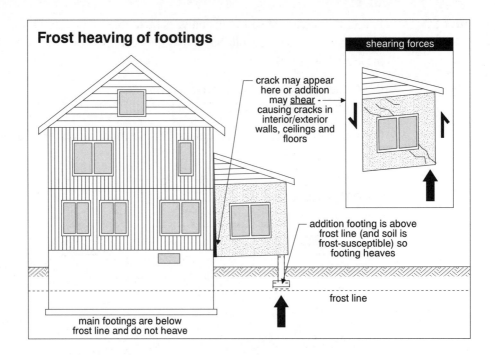

Frost heaving of footings

shearing forces

crack may appear here or addition may <u>shear</u> - causing cracks in interior/exterior walls, ceilings and floors

addition footing is above frost line (and soil is frost-susceptible) so footing heaves

frost line

main footings are below frost line and do not heave

Into/out Of The Wall Space — You may also end up with movement toward or away from you as you stand looking at a wall surface. One part of the wall may be falling away from you, or part of the wall may be falling toward you.

Think In 3-D — Look for movement in three dimensions. Don't just focus on crack width. Generally speaking, the more planes of movement, the more serious the problem.

Crack Shapes — It's dangerous to oversimplify, and there are text books written about crack analysis in buildings. Having said that, it's almost impossible to resist the temptation to give you a couple of general rules. So here we go.

Pyramids Fall — We've already said that vertical or diagonal cracks are usually related to differential settlement. Cracks often form a pyramid. If two diagonal cracks make a pyramid, most often, the inside of the triangle or the pyramid itself is dropping.

Vees May Be Heaving — If the cracks form an inverted pyramid, this may well be a heaving problem and not related to differential settlement at all. However, this could also be shrinkage or rotation, so be careful. Crushing of material is usually an indicator of heaving rather than shrinkage or rotation. We'll talk about heaving cracks later.

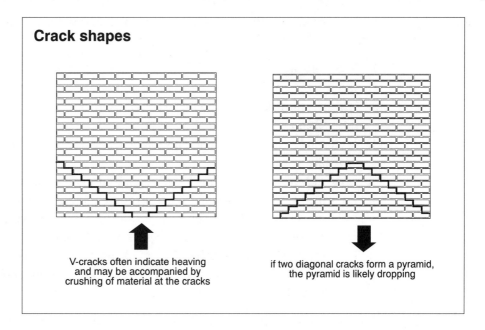

Crack shapes

V-cracks often indicate heaving
and may be accompanied by
crushing of material at the cracks

if two diagonal cracks form a pyramid,
the pyramid is likely dropping

Are The
Cracks In
Mortar Joints?
Some people feel that, if the cracks go through the brick or concrete block rather than follow the mortar joints, the cracks are more severe. This is not necessarily true. Whether the cracks follow the mortar joints or go through the masonry units is a function of mortar strength and the bond strength between the mortar and the masonry. If the mortar is stronger than the block and bonds to the masonry in a strong fashion, the wall will crack through the block. Walls will always break at their weakest link, and there isn't much useful information to be determined from whether the cracks go through the mortar joints.

Are The
Cracks Active?
This is one of the greatest challenges that you'll face as a home inspector. You've identified a crack, it looks dramatic. Your client is concerned; what does it all mean? As people look to you for the definitive answer, it's a good time to say that looking at a crack on a one-time visit is kind of like looking at a photograph of a golf ball on a green and knowing whether the ball is moving. We know it moved to get there, but we can't tell if it's moving, and if so, how fast, whether it's speeding up or slowing down.

Clues
There are some clues that may help, but, be careful about being conclusive.
- If the crack has been patched and opened again, it's more likely to be active, especially if the patching is recent.
- If the crack is in a painted wall and you can see paint inside the crack, the crack may not be recent, especially if the paint is very old.
- If there is a lot of dirt and debris inside the crack, it may have been there for a long time.
- If the corners of the crack are worn and rounded, it's more likely to be an old crack than if the edges are sharp.

However, none of these is conclusive.

Rate Of
Movement

It gets even worse. Even if we know that the crack is active, now we have to determine –

1. When did the crack develop?
2. Is it still moving?
3. If so, is it moving at a constant rate? This might indicate weak soil or an undersized footing.
4. Is the movement accelerating? This might indicate a soil erosion problem, for example.
5. Is the movement decelerating? This might be the case if we built on disturbed soil which is being compacted to a denser soil as the movement carries on.
6. Is the movement cyclical? This might be the case if the movement is due to frost, moisture changes or thermal expansion and contraction.
7. Is the movement unpredictable? This might be the case if it is the result of land slides or mud slides during heavy rains, or as the result of only very deep frost which occurs occasionally.

The message is pretty clear here; don't guess. Report what you see and then tell your client what to do.

Recommended
Actions

You might tell your client several things:

1. **Do nothing.** Only do this if you're absolutely sure that the problem is trivial.
2. **Monitor the situation.** We can often only learn if the movement is active by watching the crack over time. There are several ways to measure crack movement.
3. **Do further investigation.** Sometimes you will advise your client to engage a foundation or soils engineer to check into the situation and do more analysis and testing. In some cases, this can be expensive and disruptive.
4. **Take corrective action.** Sometimes it's clear that the amount of movement requires repair, re-supporting or replacement of components.

POSSIBLE CORRECTIONS

Possible
Corrective
Actions

There are several things that can be done with buildings that are settling. All of these are expensive. Let's look at some corrective actions including –
• mud jacking
• underpinning
• adding piles
• foundation irrigation systems
• remove and replace footings or foundations
• steel rods, cables or channels

Mud Jacking　**1.** If there has been soil erosion or a weak soil condition locally, sometimes grout (concrete slurry) can be pumped in below the footings to provide support. This is known in some areas as **mud jacking**.

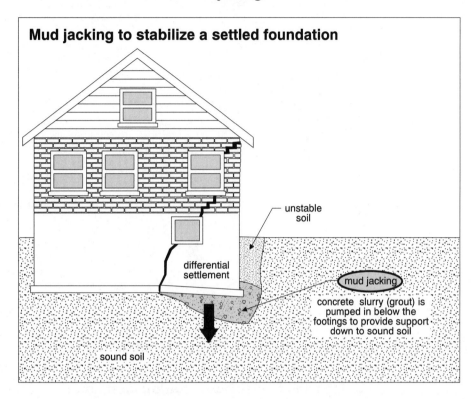

Mud jacking to stabilize a settled foundation

unstable soil

differential settlement

mud jacking

concrete slurry (grout) is pumped in below the footings to provide support down to sound soil

sound soil

Underpinning　**2.** Footings can sometimes be widened and/or deepened by underpinning.
Helical　Some underpinning options include using helical screw anchors that are
Anchors　turned into the ground below the footings and attached to the footings at various locations to support them.

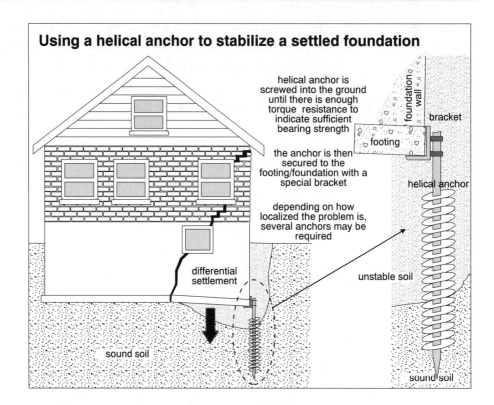

Using a helical anchor to stabilize a settled foundation

helical anchor is screwed into the ground until there is enough torque resistance to indicate sufficient bearing strength

foundation wall

bracket

footing

the anchor is then secured to the footing/foundation with a special bracket

helical anchor

depending on how localized the problem is, several anchors may be required

differential settlement

unstable soil

sound soil

sound soil

Piles

3. Sometimes piles can be added to help support the footings.

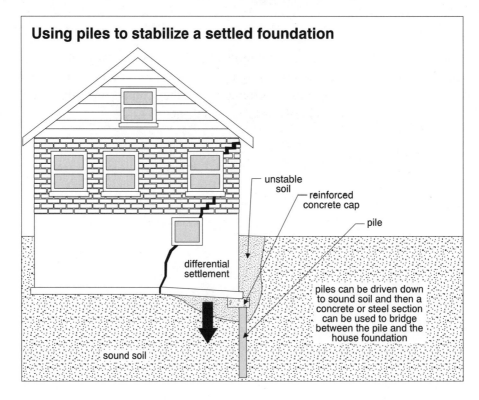

Using piles to stabilize a settled foundation

unstable soil

reinforced concrete cap

pile

differential settlement

piles can be driven down to sound soil and then a concrete or steel section can be used to bridge between the pile and the house foundation

sound soil

Foundation Irrigation

4. In cases where expansive clay soils may shrink as they dry, foundation irrigation systems are considered. This keeps expansive clay soils wet and since the soils don't change volume, the building won't move up and down. This is more common as preventative than corrective action.

Remove And Replace

5. Sometimes you have to remove part of the foundation and footing system and rebuild them.

Cables, Rods And Channels To Hold Building Together

6. If the building walls, floors and roof have moved to a point where their bearing is in question, stabilizing of the superstructure may be necessary. This may include running steel rods or cables through buildings, secured to large plates on the exteriors of opposite walls. Steel beams or channels may be added to the building, secured in several ways.

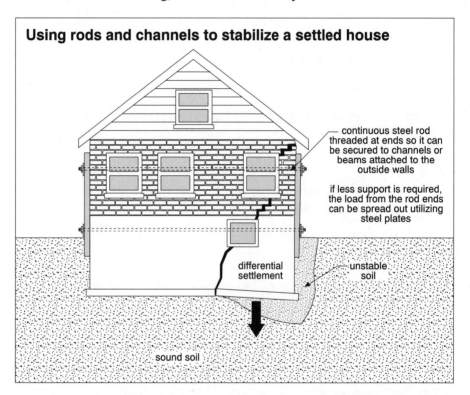

Using rods and channels to stabilize a settled house

continuous steel rod threaded at ends so it can be secured to channels or beams attached to the outside walls

if less support is required, the load from the rod ends can be spread out utilizing steel plates

differential settlement

unstable soil

sound soil

Demolition

7. In some cases, movement of the building is extensive enough that it's not cost effective to stabilize the building. The building may have to be demolished. While this is not common, it can be the case where houses are built on very poor soil or on sloping lots. The importance, size and quality of the building may determine whether it is worth saving. Most people wouldn't spend $30,000 to stabilize a garage moving down a hill, but $30,000 to stop a $2,000,000 home from moving is a different issue.

Structure
MODULE

QUICK QUIZ 4

☑ INSTRUCTIONS

- You should finish reading Study Session 4 before doing this Quiz.

- Write your answers in the spaces provided.

- Check your answers against ours at the end of this Section, after the Final Test.

- If you have trouble with this Quiz, re–read the Session and try the Quiz again.

- If you do well, move on to Study Session 5.

1. If you identify a foundation crack, is it possible to determine the rate of movement at the time of the inspection?

    _____

    _____

2. In your own words, explain what a cut and fill lot is and what implications this might have on building settlement.

    _____

    _____

    _____

3. It is a good idea to inspect the neighborhood as you are arriving at an inspection. What kinds of things should you look for and how can they help you in your inspection.

    _____

    _____

    _____

4. In general, which crack would be more serious? A crack that has moved in one plane or a crack that has moved in two different planes.

    _____

    _____

    _____

5. In the text, we have listed a number of clues that might indicate to you that the crack is active. List as many as you can.

    _____

    _____

6. What is underpinning and in what situation would it be used?

    _____

    _____

If you had no trouble with the Quiz, you are ready for Study Session 5!

Key Words:

- **Differential settlement cracks – implications**
- **Sloping lots**
- **Cut and fill lots**
- **Ravine lots**
- **Mud jacking**
- **Piles**
- **Planes of movement**
- **Horizontal**
- **Rotational**
- **Vertical**
- **Rate of movement**
- **Underpinning**

Structure
MODULE

STUDY SESSION 5

1. You should have completed Study Sessions 1 through 4 before starting this Session.

2. After completing this Session:

   • You should know about footing types
   • Understand the implications of lowering a basement floor

3. This Session should only take about half an hour.

4. Quick Quiz 5 and Field Exercise 1 await you at the end.

Key Words:
* *Footing size*
* *Step footings*
* *Bench footings*
* *Underpinning*
* *Non-shrink grout*
* *Control joints*
* *Concentrated loads*

FOOTING ISSUES

Footing Sizes   There are all kinds of rules for sizing footings, and these vary with types and building size. We won't get into great detail because home inspectors don't get to see the footings. You'll see the results of their failures though. Generally speaking, for a small house, the footings might be 6 inches thick and 16 inches wide around the perimeter. Some footings have steel reinforcement, others do not. Again, you won't be able to tell. Column pad footings for a one story house might be 2 feet by 2 feet by 1 foot thick.

Step Footings   Houses built on sloped lots often have footings that step down the slope. Look
And   for vertical cracks at each step. Rotational problems are common in this
Foundations   configuration. Generally speaking, steps should be at least 2 feet apart and, depending on a number of factors, each step should be no more than 16 to 24 inches high. Rather than memorizing numbers, it's better just to look for success or failure. Is there diagonal, vertical or horizontal cracking at the steps? (On new houses, the numbers become important because the house hasn't had a chance to prove itself under loads and over time.)

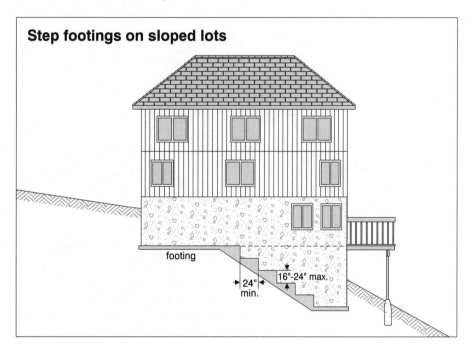

Step footings on sloped lots

footing

24" min.

16"-24" max.

LOWERED BASEMENTS

*Lowered
Basements*

Lowered basements are often problem areas, structurally. There are two general approaches to lowering basements.

1. Bench footings   In this approach, a curb is built inside and below the existing foundation. The footing itself is not undermined.

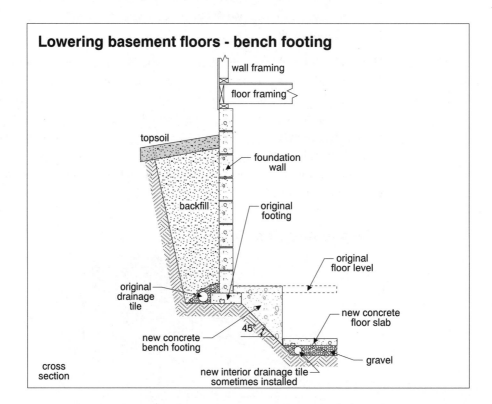

Lowering basement floors - bench footing

wall framing

floor framing

topsoil

foundation wall

backfill

original footing

original floor level

original drainage tile

new concrete floor slab

new concrete bench footing

45°

gravel

cross section

new interior drainage tile sometimes installed

2. Underpinning   This is a more expensive basement lowering strategy. The footings are cut off on the inside edge and new foundations and footings are built immediately below the existing ones. Since you can't hold the house up in the air while you do this, it has to be done in several small segments around the perimeter of the house. The work is time consuming, disruptive and challenging.

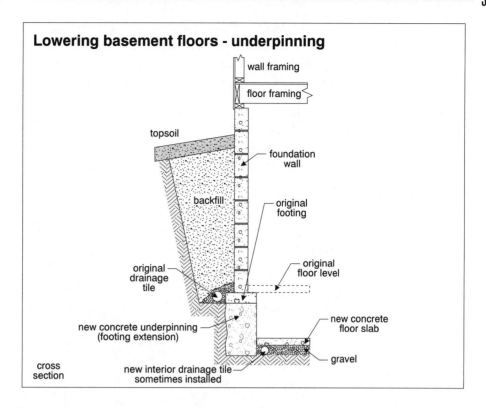

Lowering basement floors - underpinning

wall framing

floor framing

topsoil

foundation wall

backfill

original footing

original drainage tile

original floor level

new concrete underpinning (footing extension)

new concrete floor slab

gravel

cross section

new interior drainage tile sometimes installed

How Can You Tell If The Basement's Been Lowered?

There are several clues that a floor has been lowered:
- Curbs around the perimeter indicating bench footings.
- The foundation wall material changing part way down. This indicates underpinning.
- Unusually high basement ceilings.
- New basement stairs.
- Furnaces or other equipment on raised floor pads.
- Utility lines entering or leaving the house above the floor level.
- Sump pumps or sewage ejector pumps.
- Interior foundation drains.
- Basement floor heights different from other houses in the area.

Common problems with lowered basements

1. Bench footings may undermine the original footings if the vertical leg is bigger than the horizontal leg.

45° Angle

If you look at the bottom of a footing, you can trace the force it exerts on the soil below by drawing 45° lines down away from each corner of the footing. (This assumes conventional soils. Angles may change if soils are particularly sandy, for example.) Because of this 45° angle, the vertical leg of the bench footings should never be larger than the horizontal leg.

2. When underpinning, if conventional concrete is used below the original footing, it will shrink as it cures. This may allow the whole building to settle slightly onto its new foundation and footing system. This movement is often differential and can lead to considerable cracking.

Non-shrink Grout

Where underpinning has been done, look for a 2 to 3 inch wide band of a different colored concrete at the point of intersection between the old footing and new foundation. This indicates non-shrinking grout packed between the bottom of the old footing and the top of the new foundation.

Joints Every 2 To 4 Feet

Look also for vertical joints every 2 to 4 feet in the lowered section of the foundation. This is a typical result of an underpinning procedure because the new foundations and footings can only be put in 2 or 3 foot segments at a time, with 8 to 12 feet between individual segments, typically.

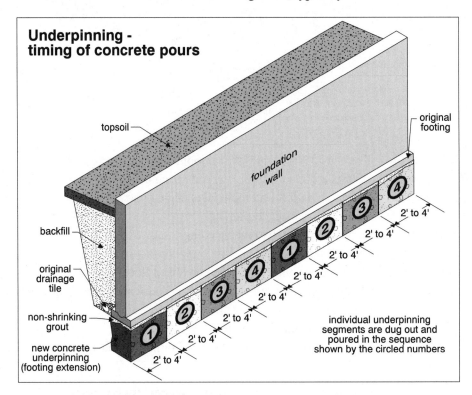

Underpinning - timing of concrete pours

topsoil

original footing

foundation wall

backfill

original drainage tile

non-shrinking grout

new concrete underpinning (footing extension)

2' to 4'

individual underpinning segments are dug out and poured in the sequence shown by the circled numbers

Drainage Tile Ineffective

3. While not a structural problem, moisture in lowered basements is a very common problem. The deeper the basement, the closer we are to the water table. Lowering the floor makes the perimeter drainage tile outside the foundation too high to be helpful. Interior drains are often added to help control leakage.

OTHER CRACK CAUSES AND LOCATIONS

Control Joints In Foundation Walls

We talked earlier about control joints built into foundation walls. Don't mistake these for settlement cracks.

Cracks In Floors

Cracks in concrete floors are not necessarily indicative of structure problems. They are most often the result of concrete shrinkage during curing. In houses with basements, for example, the concrete floor is not an integral part of the foundation. With slab-on-grade construction, the floor may or may not be an integral part of the foundation. Since you may not be able to tell with slab-on-grade construction, you should report cracks in the flooring and recommend monitoring or further investigation, unless you can be certain that there is no structural impact. The absence of slab displacement on either side of the crack suggests a less serious condition, but is not conclusive.

Cracks are Clues

Floor cracks concentrated around columns may indicate settling or heaving of the column. Floor cracks in one corner of the home may indicate settling or other differential movement in this part of the home. Cracks in garage floors, around the perimeter may suggest settlement of backfilled soil around the foundation. The slab doesn't settle in the center section where it rests on undisturbed soil.

Cracks At Additions

It is common for vertical or rotational cracks to form where additions join original houses. These cracks develop because all buildings settle when they are first constructed. If the original house has settled, and an addition is built, it will settle too. As the addition settles, it moves slightly relative to the original part of the house. In most cases, these cracks can be patched once the addition has settled (normally within the first two or three years). If the addition is new, you have no way of knowing how severe the cracking might get and when it might stop. Monitoring would be a reasonable recommendation in this situation.

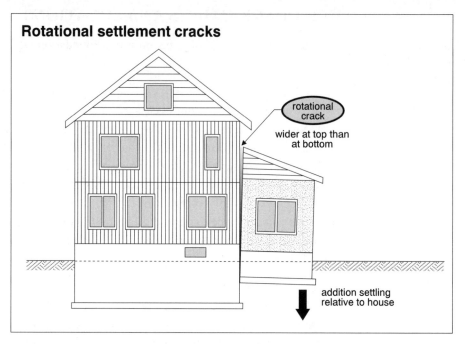

*Look For
Concentrated
Loads*

Where you see cracks, they are often close to large loads from the structure above. This may be below the end point of a long beam, or near a chimney, for example. If you can attribute the cracking to a single concentrated load, you have at least defined the extent of the problem.

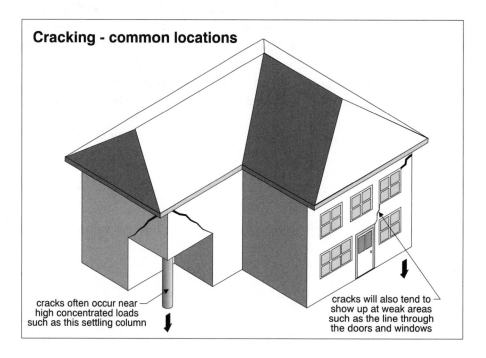

*Look For The
Weak Link*

Watch for a weakness in the foundation. For example, if a basement door has been cut in a foundation, that removes a good part of the foundation wall. Combining that weak opening with a concentrated load may allow you to explain a crack pattern.

*Garages
Often Settle*

Garage foundations are often not as substantial as house foundations. It is common to find that the attached garage has pulled away slightly from the house. Again, in new construction, it will be difficult to know how severe this movement may be. If the garage is twenty years old or more, the odds are better that the movement has stopped. Again, however, there are no guarantees. Frost heaving of attached garages is another common problem in cold climates.

*New Homes
Without
Cracks*

When looking at a relatively new house, you often see no cracking. Be careful about drawing any conclusions with respect the structure. It may simply be that the house has not seen enough live loading or been around long enough to start to move differentially.

As we discussed earlier, you should never be discussing a house as being **sound** anyway. You should only describe what you see.

Structure

MODULE

QUICK QUIZ 5

☑ INSTRUCTIONS

• You should finish reading Study Session 5 before doing this Quiz.

• Write your answers in the spaces provided.

• Check your answers against ours at the end of this Section, after the Final Test.

• If you have trouble with this Quiz, re-read the Session and try the Quiz again.

• If you do well, it is time for Field Exercise 1.

1. Where would a step footing be used and where would you look to find cracks?

   _____

   _____

2. How can you tell if the basement has been lowered? In the text there are 9 hints – list as many as you can.

   _____   _____   _____

   _____   _____   _____

   _____   _____   _____

3. What problems could result from lowering a basement floor?

   _____

   _____

4. Often there will be a settlement crack at the joint between an old house and an addition. Why would this crack develop?

_____

_____

5. What is a concentrated load?

_____

_____

If you had no trouble with the Quiz, you are ready for Field Exercise 1.

Key Words:
- *Footing size*
- *Step footings*
- *Bench footings*
- *Underpinning*
- *Non-shrink grout*
- *Control joints*
- *Concentrated loads*

Structure
MODULE

FIELD EXERCISE 1

☑ INSTRUCTIONS

You should complete everything up to Quick Quiz 5 before doing this Exercise. Allow yourself eight to ten hours to complete this exercise. You'll need access to several houses. Friends and relatives may be willing to let you look at their homes.

Exercise A

In this Exercise you will be inspecting foundations on existing homes. Try to look at ten, at least. Look for houses with an unfinished basement or sub-grade area.

For each foundation:
1. What type of foundation is it? (full basement, crawlspace or slab on grade?)

_____

2. What is the foundation material?

_____

3. How much of the foundation is visible on the exterior?

_____

4. How much of the foundation is visible on the interior?

_____

5. Look for any cracks in the foundation. If you find any, make a note of their location.

    _____

6. Make a sketch of the configuration of the cracks, size, and the planes of movement.

Exercise B

The purpose of this Exercise is to determine if there are any conditions that you should be cautious of in your area. Contact a building official or another inspector in your area. Ask the following questions:

1. What are the typical soil types in your area?

    _____

2. Are there any areas that have unstable soils?

    _____

3. Are there any developments that were built on land-fill sites?

    _____

4. Are there any areas with high water tables or underground streams?

    _____

5. What is the typical frost depth in your area?

    _____

6. How deep are footings usually placed to be sure they are below the frost depth?

    _____

Exercise C

The purpose of this Exercise is to familiarize yourself with what a footing looks like and what a foundation typically looks like when it is being constructed.

Contact a builder in your area. Ask if there are any building sites where the footing has just been poured.

Obtain permission to visit the site.

Make note of the depth of the footing, and the approximate size, width and thickness.

Look for pad footings that will support posts.

Are there any areas where the footing is wider?

Why might this be done?

Structure
MODULE

STUDY SESSION 6

1. You should have completed Study Sessions 1 through 5 before starting this Session.

2. By the end of this Session, you should know:

- The causes of heaving
- How to identify heaving cracks
- The implications of cracks due to heaving

3. This Session may take about 45 minutes.

4. At the end, there is a Quick Quiz.

Key Words:
- ***Frost heaving***
- ***Adfreezing***
- ***Expansive soils***
- ***Hydrostatic pressure***
- ***Basement walk-outs***

3.3.1.3 Cracks due to heaving

Causes

There are four common causes of heaving cracks –
- Frost heave
- Adfreezing
- Expansive soils
- Hydrostatic pressure

1. Frost heave

This may be the result of –

- Footings that are too shallow because of
  - An original condition
  - A change in the exterior grade height
  - The addition of an outside basement stairwell or walk-out
- Saturated soils
- The basement walls have been insulated, allowing greater frost depth around the house
- Leaving the house unheated during freezing weather

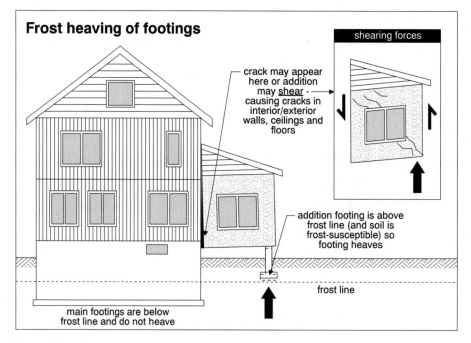

Frost heaving of footings

shearing forces

crack may appear here or addition may <u>shear</u> - causing cracks in interior/exterior walls, ceilings and floors

addition footing is above frost line (and soil is frost-susceptible) so footing heaves

frost line

main footings are below frost line and do not heave

2. Adfreezing

Frost Attaches To Foundation

Adfreezing is a situation where the ground beside the foundation freezes, attaching itself to the foundation. As the ground heaves up, it picks up the top part of the foundation wall and the entire house with it! The result is a horizontal crack which gets larger in the winter and smaller in the spring and summer, when the frost leaves the ground. The crack doesn't usually close all the way because bits of foundation and dirt get into the crack.

Horizontal Cracks And Inward Movement

When there is a horizontal fracture, the foundation can't resist the lateral soil pressure as well as before. Some horizontal displacement often results. The top part of the foundation wall not only moves up and down, but is often pushed inward over time. The bottom part may also move inward.

3. Expansive Soils

Expand By 10 Percent

We talked about expansive soils that dry out and shrink, causing settlement. Similarly, dry expansive soils will expand when they get wet. It's not unusual for expansive soils to expand by 10% of their volume.

Soils might get wet because of –

• a rising water table
• a sump pump malfunction
• perimeter drainage tile malfunction
• moisture added by air conditioner condensate drains
• supply or waste plumbing leakage under or around the building
• poor control of roof and surface water run off

4. High Water Table Causing Hydrostatic Pressure From Below

This can heave floor slabs, foundations, footings and entire buildings. This is often accompanied by leakage problems.

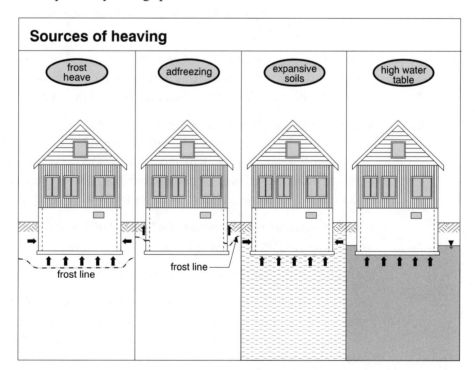

Sources of heaving

frost heave — adfreezing — expansive soils — high water table

Implications The implications of heaving include –

1. No implications if the cracks are so slight they are not noticed
2. Small cracks may only be cosmetic issues
3. Cracks may result in leakage
4. Heaving cracks may cause uneven floors and leaning walls
5. Service lines, interior pipes, wires and ducts may be strained
6. Chimneys may be disconnected
7. Flashing problems may be experienced at plumbing and chimney roof penetrations, for example
8. Floor, roof and ceiling joists and rafters losing their end bearing supports
9. In the most severe cases, structural collapse may occur

Strategy
Local
Research

You've done some local research into soil conditions, so you should know whether you are in an area of expansive soils. You should also learn the depth of frost in your area and the common building practices with respect to footing depth.

Is It Settling
Or Heaving?

The simple answer is, if it's going down, it's settling and if it's going up, it's heaving. However, it isn't always easy to tell. If there is a large hump in the center of the house, is it because the interior columns are heaving or because the perimeter is settling? It could be either. There are some things you can watch for:

Cracks
Opening Or
Crushing

1. If cracks are open, things are moving apart. If there is crushing around cracks, things are moving together or sliding against each other. Check as many reference points as you can.

Sidewalks
And Driveways

2. If driveways, sidewalks and patios around the house have an unnatural slope down toward the house, settlement of the home would be suspected. If these surfaces slope up toward the house, heaving is more likely.

Check Floor
Slab

3. If the central part of the house seems to be humped, but there is no cracking or displacement of the floor slab around the columns, it's probably not the columns heaving, but the perimeter settling. On the other hand, if the floor around the central columns shows lots of cracks and the floor slopes up toward the columns all the way around, it's more likely to be heaving.

4. Look at overhead wires coming to the house. Are they at a significantly different angle than neighboring houses?

5. Look at adjacent houses for neighborhood trends.

6. Look at soil lines against buildings. If the front door sill is below grade level, odds are pretty good the house is sinking. If you can see a dirt line six inches above the existing grade line around the perimeter of the house, chances are the house has heaved.

Subtle And Complex

Don't Guess

Most situations will not be dramatic or simple. Your investigative and deductive reasoning powers will be tested. As always, if you're not sure, don't guess. Simply report to your client exactly what you saw and advise the client that the information is inconclusive. Recommend further investigation if the movement is dramatic, or monitoring if the movement is less severe.

Frost Heave

When looking at cracking, there are some clues that frost heave may be the culprit. The movement is often a combination of upwards and inwards. Floors, footings and foundations may be lifted, almost always differentially by the frost around the building. Also, the frost pressure against foundation walls may push the foundation walls inward. We'll talk about the horizontal movement later, but understand that freezing soil exerts pressure in every direction.

Footing Depth

If you see evidence of the building moving up and/or foundation walls being pushed inwards, look at the depth of footings. The top of the footing is usually at the bottom of the basement floor slab.

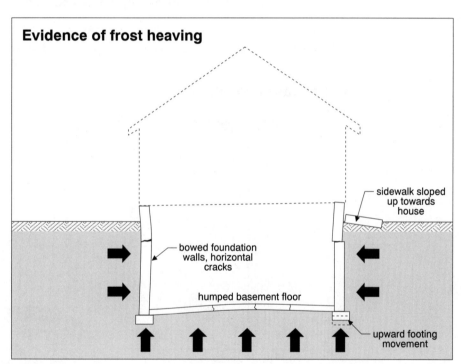

Evidence of frost heaving

sidewalk sloped up towards house

bowed foundation walls, horizontal cracks

humped basement floor

upward footing movement

On sloping lots, the frost footings may not have been deep enough initially. Footings may not be deep enough because –

• There was an original construction mistake.
• The footing depth was limited by a water table problem.
• The excavation was stopped when what seemed like bedrock was hit. Sometimes these are only large boulders not bedrock.

Changing Exterior Grade Height

• The exterior grade height may have changed. If the grade is lowered to put in a patio, for example, the frost depth may extend below the footings.

Adding Basement Walk-outs

• Adding an outside basement stairwell is another condition that allows frost to get deeper than it used to. This can cause localized heaving problems. While underpinning the footing around a basement stairwell is one option, a more common and cost effective option is to insulate under and around the basement stairwell to keep the frost out of the soil under and adjacent to the house.

Again, you won't be able to see whether footings are underpinned or whether insulation was buried, but you will see the results of failure to do something.

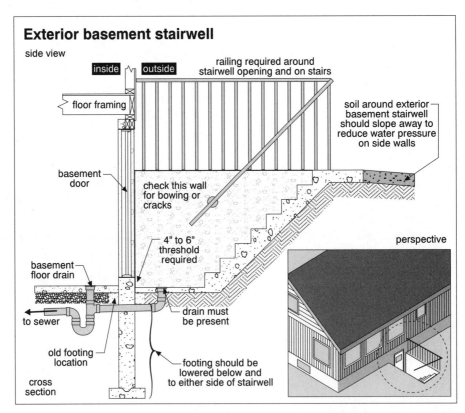

Exterior basement stairwell

side view

inside | outside

railing required around stairwell opening and on stairs

floor framing

soil around exterior basement stairwell should slope away to reduce water pressure on side walls

basement door

check this wall for bowing or cracks

4" to 6" threshold required

perspective

basement floor drain

to sewer

old footing location

drain must be present

cross section

footing should be lowered below and to either side of stairwell

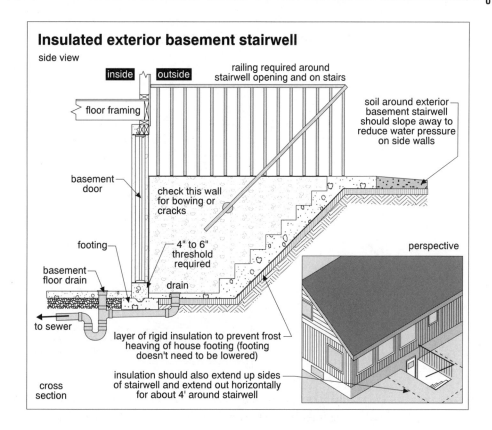

Insulated exterior basement stairwell

side view

inside | outside

railing required around stairwell opening and on stairs

floor framing

soil around exterior basement stairwell should slope away to reduce water pressure on side walls

basement door

check this wall for bowing or cracks

footing

4" to 6" threshold required

perspective

basement floor drain

drain

to sewer

layer of rigid insulation to prevent frost heaving of house footing (footing doesn't need to be lowered)

cross section

insulation should also extend up sides of stairwell and extend out horizontally for about 4' around stairwell

Must Have Moisture In Soil To Heave

Even if footings are too shallow, no heaving cracks will develop unless there is moisture in the soil. It is the soil moisture expanding as it freezes that exerts all the pressure. If the house is surrounded with perfectly dry gravel, it doesn't matter how cold it gets, there won't be any heaving or added lateral thrust exerted by the soil since there's no frozen water in it.

Soil Gets Wet

Problems can develop in a house if the soil has been relatively dry, historically, but becomes saturated due to adverse grading conditions that may have been created during landscaping, or even as a result of normal settlement. Soils may also be saturated by leaking or disconnected gutters and downspouts.

Basements Are Insulated

Frost heave may occur after basements are insulated. On many old houses, the basements are uninsulated. Heat loss from the basement during the winter months keeps the soil near the building warm enough to prevent freezing. However, if the basement is insulated, the soil around the basement may freeze, heaving the floors and pushing the foundation walls in.

Unheated Houses

We've discussed how frost acts on unheated houses. If the basement is unheated, the frost penetration depth starts at the basement floor and goes down. If there is any moisture in the soil underneath the house, this will almost certainly result in frost heaving.

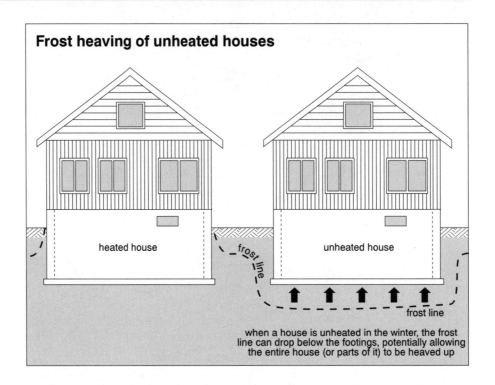

Frost heaving of unheated houses

heated house

unheated house

frost line

frost line

when a house is unheated in the winter, the frost line can drop below the footings, potentially allowing the entire house (or parts of it) to be heaved up

Adfreezing   When the moisture in soil freezes, it usually forms lenses of ice. These ice lenses will sometimes freeze to wet foundation walls. As the soil expands, the only directions it can move are up or sideways into the basement. It's possible for frozen soil adhered to a house to pick up the top half of the foundation and the entire house above. While it's hard to imagine the forces required to do this, frozen soil is very capable of picking up a house.

How To Spot It   This phenomenon is identified by the characteristic horizontal cracks that open in the winter and partially close in the summer. As we discussed, adfreezing is often accompanied by inward movement of the top part of the foundation wall.

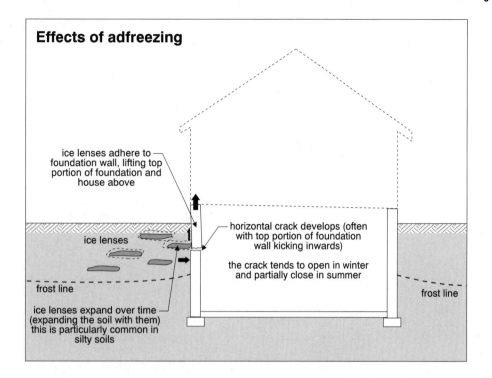

Effects of adfreezing

ice lenses adhere to foundation wall, lifting top portion of foundation and house above

ice lenses

horizontal crack develops (often with top portion of foundation wall kicking inwards)

the crack tends to open in winter and partially close in summer

frost line

frost line

ice lenses expand over time (expanding the soil with them) this is particularly common in silty soils

Remove The Moisture

Drainage Layer Or Slip Sheet

Adfreezing is usually controlled by reducing the soil moisture adjacent to the house. This is done by improving drainage, controlling roof water run-off, etc. Another approach is to provide external insulation or a drainage layer on the outside of the foundation wall. This keeps the outside of the foundation wall dry and the insulation or drainage layer acts as a slip sheet, allowing the soil to move without carrying the foundation with it.

Exterior basement insulation is becoming more common than interior insulation in new construction. Many of the insulation systems allow water to flow quickly down to the tile system. This minimizes hydrostatic pressure or frost pressure against the wall during cold weather.

*Concrete
Piers For
Exterior Decks*

Those in freezing climates have seen the effect of frost heave on piers for wood decks. Even though the piers extend down below the frost line, they usually don't have much of a footing. The frost in the top two or three feet of the ground sometimes grabs the pier and lifts the whole thing up out of the ground with the deck above. Some use plastic slip sheets around these piers to prevent this.

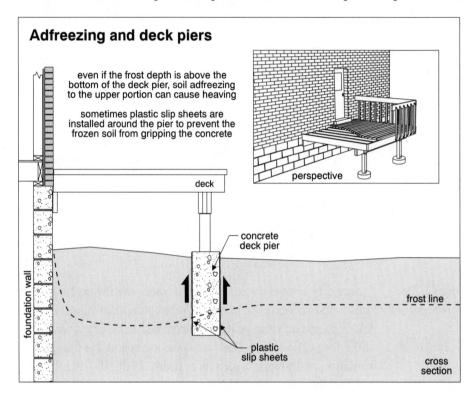

Adfreezing and deck piers

even if the frost depth is above the bottom of the deck pier, soil adfreezing to the upper portion can cause heaving

sometimes plastic slip sheets are installed around the pier to prevent the frozen soil from gripping the concrete

perspective

deck

concrete deck pier

foundation wall

frost line

plastic slip sheets

cross section

Decks Make Frost Go Deeper

Wood decks can cause frost heaving problems on a house. Snow is an insulator. Snow on the ground keeps the soil from getting colder even though the air temperature may be very cold. When you prevent snow from accumulating, the depth of frost may increase. People often keep decks shoveled clear of snow. Even if they don't, the snow sits on the deck which may be two or three feet above the ground. If the cold air can get in around the sides of the deck to the ground below, the ground has lost its insulating layer of snow and the depth of frost can be much greater.

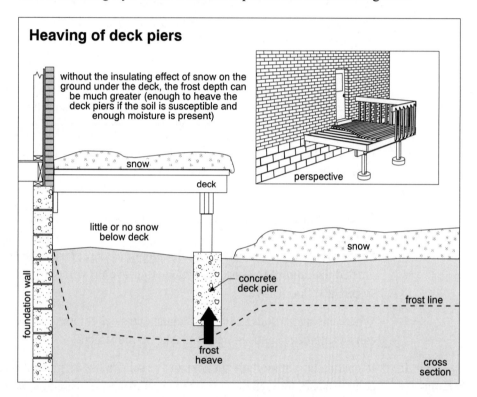

Heaving of deck piers

without the insulating effect of snow on the ground under the deck, the frost depth can be much greater (enough to heave the deck piers if the soil is susceptible and enough moisture is present)

snow

deck

perspective

foundation wall

little or no snow below deck

snow

concrete deck pier

frost line

frost heave

cross section

Driveways May Have

Driveways kept clear of snow may have much greater frost depth under them than in snow covered areas.

Deeper Frost Too

The amount of protection that snow offers against frost is a function of which comes first – the snow or the very cold weather. If there's a lot of snow and then the weather gets cold, the frost depth is usually not great. If there is a prolonged period of cold weather without much snow, the frost depth can be great. If considerable snow comes after that, the snow will insulate the ground and the frost will stay in the ground longer. In the northern United States and Canada, there are lots of areas where frost can penetrate six or seven feet into the ground.

Building Without Frost Footings	Sometimes we can build without frost footings in cold areas by – • Building on bedrock • Building on dry soils that are free–draining and never get wet • Insulating the soil around the building to prevent frost penetration
Expansive Soils	Clay soils that expand and contract as they get wet and then dry can be very troublesome. It's not unusual for expansive soils to move three inches up and down over a five foot depth. If this expansion and contraction is uniform over a large area, there may be no problems. However, in most cases, the movement is not uniform because the soil types change slightly or because the water levels are different.
Risky To Keep Soil Wet	In non-freezing areas, if the expansive soils are kept wet all the time, there will be no settlement or heaving. However, in frost areas, keeping the soils wet is a risky strategy since this moisture may freeze, creating considerable frost pressure.
Dry Soil Better In Cold Climates	In freezing areas, it is better to keep the clay soils dry by controling roof and surface water run-off.
Allowing For Heaving	Construction techniques in some areas allow for movement due to expansive soils. Basement walls are sometimes hung from the first floor, with a gap below the bottom of the wall concealed by a floating baseboard, for example. A slip joint is created that allows the basement floor to move up without pushing up the wall system and floor above. Where expansive soils are found, adjustable steel columns are often used. These can be lengthened and shortened to take up movement.
Slip Joint At Column-Floor Joint	It's particularly important with expansive soils to have a good slip joint where the column passes through the concrete floor. Foam pipe insulation makes a good joint material. If the floor slab heaves, it won't take the column up with it.
Special Forces Require Special Measures	The forces exerted by the expansive clay soils can be dramatic and, in some cases, the components can't be held in place. Stiffening foundation walls, improving lateral support for tops of foundation walls and allowing for differential movement among structural components are common strategies. It goes well beyond the scope of a home inspection to predict whether these measures will be required or effective.
Post-tensioned Concrete	We discussed post-tensioning earlier, as a way to strengthen foundations and floor slabs in areas of expansive soil.

High Water Table

The hydrostatic pressure on a foundation and footing system can be significant. For example, if the water table rises to two feet above the basement floor level, you probably have some leakage issues to contend with. Perimeter drainage tile may not be capable of lowering the water table below the footings. These may even be flooding issues.

If we manage to keep the water out the structural issues remain. Every square foot of water pushing on the bottom of the basement floor exerts 2 times 62.4 = 125 pounds of pressure on the underside of the floor (a cubic foot of water weighs 62.4 pounds, and a 2 foot high column has 2 cubic feet). If the footprint of the house is 500 square feet, the upward force on the house is about 62,000 pounds. This is about 31 tons. The hydrostatic pressure can push the house up dramatically. In most cases, the weak components heave. This would typically include the basement floor slab.

High water tables are serious problems since it is difficult to change the water table. Chronic and serious basement leakage is often the indicator of these problems. Heaved floor slabs may be the result of hydrostatic pressure, frost heave, or expansive soils. Be careful drawing conclusions about the cause of floor heaving.

Corrective Actions

Depending on what is causing the problem, several corrective actions are possible. These usually fall into one of two general strategies. Again, we do not recommend that you specify repairs for your clients.

1. **Remove soil moisture**

   If there is little or no moisture in the soil, frost won't make the soil heave. If it's an expansive soil but is dry, it won't expand. If there's no saturated soil under the building, there will be no hydrostatic pressure.

2. **Protect the footings against freezing**

   This can be done by raising the grade if it's too low, insulating the ground around the house, or removing insulation from basement walls to allow basement heat to prevent freezing of the soil.

Structure
M O D U L E

QUICK QUIZ 6

☑ INSTRUCTIONS

• You should finish reading Study Session 6 before doing this Quiz.

• Write your answers in the spaces provided.

• Check your answers against ours at the end of this Section, after the Final Test.

• If you have trouble with this Quiz, re-read the Session and try the Quiz again.

• If you do well, move on to Study Session 7.

1. Is adfreezing a condition that acts directly on the footing, the bottom of the foundation, or the sides of the foundation? Explain.

    _____

2. Give two causes of frost heaving.

    _____

    _____

3. It is sometimes difficult to distinguish between a settlement problem and a heaving problem. Give a few examples of how you would distinguish between the two.

    _____

    _____

4. Frost heaving will only exert a force in a vertical direction.
    True ☐   False ☐

5. Explain how adding an exterior basement stairwell can cause a frost heaving problem.

_____

_____

_____

6. There must be moisture in the soil to have frost heaving
   True ☐   False ☐

7. We can change the conditions on the outside of the house to create frost heaving problems. Give two examples.

_____

_____

8. It is not possible for a high water table to cause heaving because the drainage tile around the house will handle the water.
   True ☐   False ☐

If you had no trouble with the Quiz, you are ready for Study Session 7.

Key Words:

- **Frost heaving**
- **Adfreezing**
- **Expansive soils**
- **Hydrostatic pressure**
- **Basement walk-outs**

Structure

MODULE

STUDY SESSION 7

1. You should have completed Study Sessions 1 through 6 before starting this Session.

2. By the end of this Session, you should know:

- How to identify cracks due to horizontal forces
- The implications of such cracks
- Typical causes of horizontal forces

3. This Session may take roughly 45 minutes to complete.

4. As always, there is a Quiz at the end.

Key Words:

- *Bowing*
- *Bulging*
- *Lateral support*
- *Foundation irrigation*
- *Premature backfilling*
- *Buttress*
- *Pilaster*
- *Helical anchors*
- *Sister walls*

3.3.1.4 Cracks due to horizontal forces (lateral thrust)

These cracks are often serious structural problems. As a general rule, horizontal foundation cracks are more serious than vertical or diagonal cracks.

Causes

Causes include –
- Frost pressure (including adfreezing)
- Wet soil
- Vehicle loads adjacent to building
- Expansive soils
- Tree roots
- Impact damage (from careless backfilling, or backfilling with large rocks)

Implications

The implication of cracks due to horizontal forces may be –

- Insignificant
- Cosmetic
- Leakage
- Structural distress and ultimately collapse

Strategy

Foundation walls that are pushed out of place are not able to carry their vertical or horizontal loads. Any foundation wall that has been pushed out of plumb should be addressed by a specialist.

Cracks, Bulges, Bowing And Leaning

Horizontal cracks in foundation walls are often accompanied by bowing, bulges or leaning.

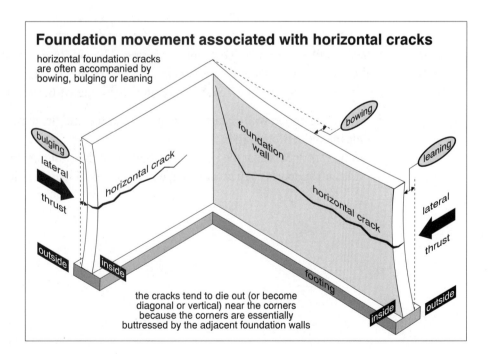

Foundation movement associated with horizontal cracks

horizontal foundation cracks are often accompanied by bowing, bulging or leaning

bowing

bulging

foundation wall

lateral

leaning

horizontal crack

thrust

horizontal crack

lateral

thrust

outside inside

footing

inside outside

the cracks tend to die out (or become diagonal or vertical) near the corners because the corners are essentially buttressed by the adjacent foundation walls

Foundations
Are Floors

Foundation walls are really floors on their side. You can think of a foundation wall as a floor with respect to holding up the soil outside (you have to tilt your head sideways to envision this but that's exactly what it is). The foundation wall needs to be supported at the bottom by the footing and basement floor and at the top by the connection to the floor and wall systems. This is the same as floors which must be supported at both ends.

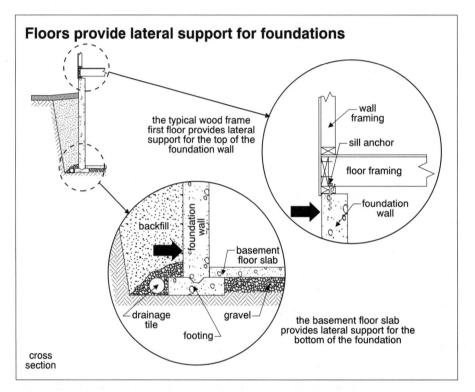

Floors provide lateral support for foundations

the typical wood frame first floor provides lateral support for the top of the foundation wall

wall framing

sill anchor

floor framing

foundation wall

backfill

foundation wall

basement floor slab

drainage tile

footing

gravel

the basement floor slab provides lateral support for the bottom of the foundation

cross section

Top, Middle
Or Bottom
May Move

When a wall cracks, it's like a floor breaking. The ability to transfer the loads to the ends of the joists or beams (top and bottom of the foundation wall) is lost. Horizontal cracks and movement may appear in one of three different ways:

1. If the foundation wall cracks horizontally near the middle, it may kick in near the midpoint of its height.
2. If the wall shears near the bottom, the bottom of the wall may kick in.
3. If lateral support is lost at the top, the top of the wall may kick in.

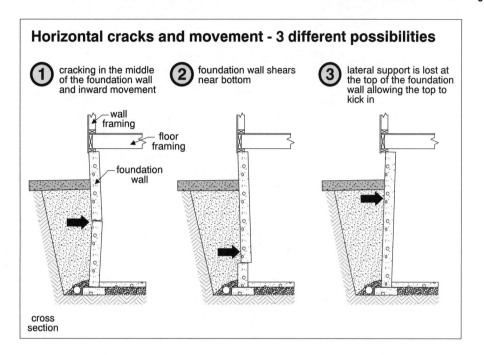

Horizontal cracks and movement - 3 different possibilities

① cracking in the middle of the foundation wall and inward movement

② foundation wall shears near bottom

③ lateral support is lost at the top of the foundation wall allowing the top to kick in

wall framing

floor framing

foundation wall

cross section

Bowing And Bulging

If the forces are applied slowly and over a long period of time, materials that we normally think of as brittle will flow and bend. Masonry and concrete walls can deform. These **bows** or **bulges** in walls, even if they do not have cracks, indicate movement and often require resupporting.

Common Crack Patterns

Walls subjected to horizontal forces often develop horizontal cracks. However, since these walls are usually restrained at the corners (the corner walls act as buttresses) the cracks may die out at the corners. In many cases, the cracks will be diagonal up toward the corner near either end of the wall. Vertical cracks may also appear near the middle of the wall length.

Beams Stick Out Through The Wall

When foundation walls bow inward, beams may punch through the top of the foundation wall. In extreme cases, the beam may actually project outside.

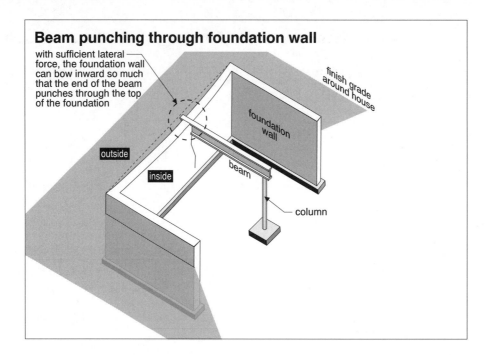

Beam punching through foundation wall

with sufficient lateral force, the foundation wall can bow inward so much that the end of the beam punches through the top of the foundation

finish grade around house

foundation wall

outside

inside

beam

column

Brick Overhang

Solid masonry or brick veneer walls above the foundation wall may not move inward. (Wood frame walls with siding are more flexible, and more likely to move with the foundation wall.) If the foundation wall bows inward, the masonry wall may not move with it! This leads to a significant overhang. Generally speaking, a one inch overhang is all that is acceptable. If the overhang is more than this, there is risk of the masonry wall collapsing.

Look From Outside

Look at the base of masonry and veneer walls from outside, If the overhang is most pronounced near the midpoint of the wall and disappears at either end, this suggests that the foundation wall is bowing inward.

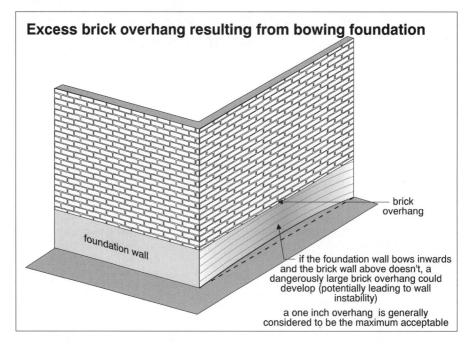

Excess brick overhang resulting from bowing foundation

brick overhang

foundation wall

if the foundation wall bows inwards and the brick wall above doesn't, a dangerously large brick overhang could develop (potentially leading to wall instability)

a one inch overhang is generally considered to be the maximum acceptable

Some Bowing Not Visible From Outside

The wall may be bowing with no indication from the outside along the top. If the top of the wall is adequately restrained (laterally supported), the foundation wall may not bow at the top and there may be no bow along the length of the wall. The bow or bending of the wall may occur between the top and bottom, with the maximum movement about half-way up the wall. The bowing disappears toward the end of the walls because of the buttressing effect of the foundations at the corners.

Loss Of Lateral Support

Walls may lean in at the top as joists rot at their ends. If the connection between the top of the foundation wall and the flooring system becomes weak, the lateral support is lost.

Floor joists perpendicular to foundation walls provide good lateral support. Joists parallel to foundation walls need blocking to provide effective lateral support from several joists.

When There Is No Lateral Support

A common building mistake is designing foundation walls to be laterally supported, but incorporating a short wood frame cripple wall or knee wall. This is common on multi-level homes with sunken rooms, houses with stepped footings on sloped lots, etc. The short wood frame wall on top of the foundation creates a weak joint and renders the foundation wall laterally unsupported. These walls may well fail under horizontal loads.

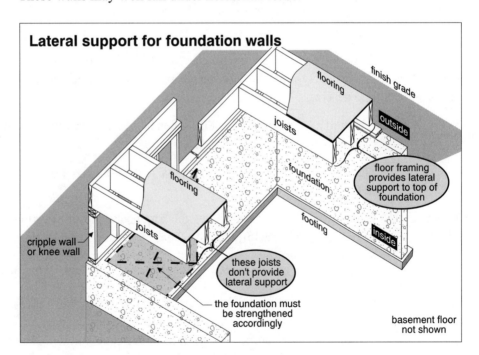

Lateral support for foundation walls

Failure May Be Sudden

Walls may move quickly if there is a heavy rain which saturates the soil, creating substantial pressure against the wall. This may happen not only in particularly heavy rains, but if a downspout becomes disconnected or if gutters are clogged.

Vertical Cracks   If the walls are short, soil pressure may cause a vertical crack and the walls will
Occasionally   kick in at the midpoint. The horizontal forces are abundantly clear, since the direc-
                    tion of movement is into the basement, despite the fact that the cracks are vertical.

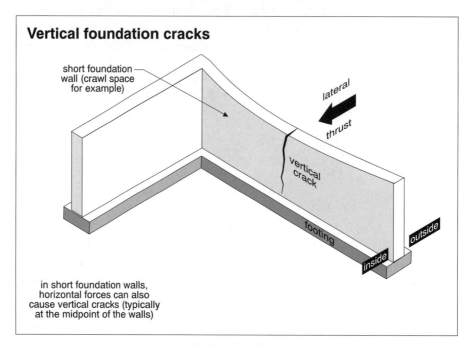

Vertical foundation cracks

short foundation
wall (crawl space
for example)

*lateral
thrust*

*vertical
crack*

footing

inside   *outside*

in short foundation walls,
horizontal forces can also
cause vertical cracks (typically
at the midpoint of the walls)

Verifying   If the movement is significant, you'll be able to see it with the naked eye.
Inward   Cracks will typically be wider on the inside face. A flashlight may be helpful to look
Movement   into the crack.

                A four foot level (mason's level) is often helpful to verify the direction and amount
                of movement. Plumb bobs can also be used.

                Sight along all house walls, both above and below grade, for leaning, bowing, or
                bulging.

Check The   Building codes have rules for how thick foundation walls of various materials must
Height Of   be, given certain backfill heights. There will be one set of rules for foundation
The Backfill walls that are laterally supported, and another set for those that are not. A sample set
                is included in **The Home Reference Book,** check what is accepted in your area.

Careful With Check the height of backfill against the thickness of the wall especially on new
New Houses   construction, where the foundation is too new to display movement. Choose a ref-
                erence point that can be viewed from both inside and out. Basement windows,
                clothes dryer vents, electrical conduits, etc., are areas that you can use to compare
                the height of the foundation wall against the height of the backfill. The foundation
                wall thickness can be easily checked at basement windows.

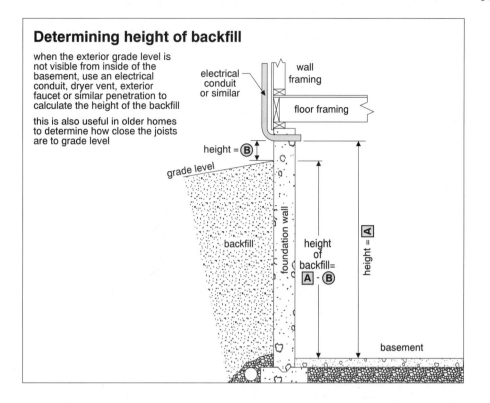

Determining height of backfill

when the exterior grade level is not visible from inside of the basement, use an electrical conduit, dryer vent, exterior faucet or similar penetration to calculate the height of the backfill

this is also useful in older homes to determine how close the joists are to grade level

Driveways Are Potential Problem Areas

We talked about the frost implications of driveways, and the fact that they are not protected by an insulating layer of snow. There are a couple of other driveway issues that make them vulnerable points.

Water Pressure

1. **Driveways are impervious.** If the driveway slope is down toward the house, a large amount of water will be funnelled against the foundation wall. This saturates the soil against the foundation creating a large hydrostatic load. If this saturated soil freezes, the problem is worsened.

Vehicle Loads

2. **Driveways are driven on by vehicles.** Vehicles are heavy, especially trucks. Heavy vehicles on driveways can cause foundation problems. Where the only evidence of horizontal cracking is along one side of a house, it's very often the driveway side. You can point out the possible causes to the client, but don't be definitive, and don't be conclusive about whether the problem is progressive or not, based on one visit.

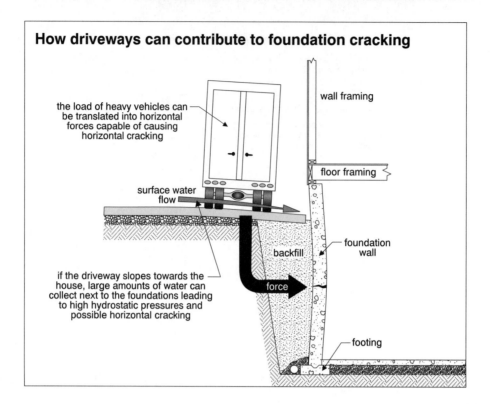

How driveways can contribute to foundation cracking

the load of heavy vehicles can be translated into horizontal forces capable of causing horizontal cracking

wall framing

floor framing

surface water flow

foundation wall

backfill

if the driveway slopes towards the house, large amounts of water can collect next to the foundations leading to high hydrostatic pressures and possible horizontal cracking

force

footing

Expansive Soils   Expansive soils exert tremendous lateral forces on foundations when wet. If the soil can be kept dry, the pressure is greatly reduced. Attention should be paid to controling surface and roof water runoff in areas of expansive soils.

Foundation Irrigation   Where freezing is not an issue, the soils may be kept wet all the time (foundation irrigation) to prevent drying and shrinking of the soil. This is not a great strategy in a basement or crawlspace configuration because keeping the soil wet puts a greater load on foundation walls that have to act as retaining walls.

Tree Roots   Roots can damage foundations by heaving or pushing inward from outside. This damage is usually localized and easy to identify unless the tree has been removed.

Building Settles As Roots Rot   Subsequent settling problems may be experienced as dead roots decay and shrink. Best practice is to remove the roots as well as the tree, although this is rarely done.

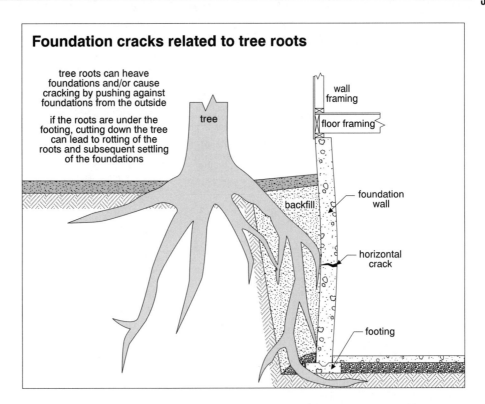

Foundation cracks related to tree roots

tree roots can heave foundations and/or cause cracking by pushing against foundations from the outside

if the roots are under the footing, cutting down the tree can lead to rotting of the roots and subsequent settling of the foundations

tree

wall framing

floor framing

backfill

foundation wall

horizontal crack

footing

Premature Backfilling

Damage during backfilling operations is common on original construction. The damage may be done by heavy equipment or large rocks (more than six inch diameter). Concrete foundation walls are not very strong for the first several days. Forms should not be removed for at least two days after pouring. The longer the forms can be left in place, the better. The foundation walls are not laterally supported until the floor framing is in place. Damage can be done by equipment or backfilling pressure during this vulnerable time.

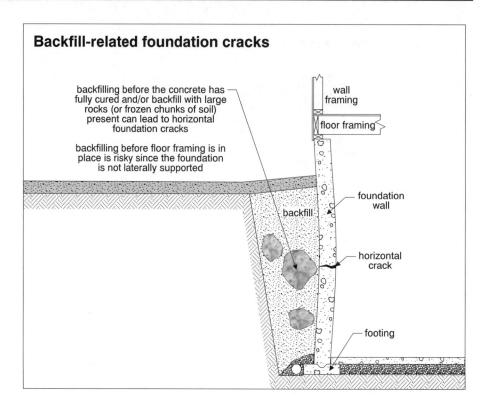

Backfill-related foundation cracks

backfilling before the concrete has fully cured and/or backfill with large rocks (or frozen chunks of soil) present can lead to horizontal foundation cracks

backfilling before floor framing is in place is risky since the foundation is not laterally supported

wall framing

floor framing

foundation wall

backfill

horizontal crack

footing

Impact Damage

Vehicles can also strike and damage the above grade part of foundation. Watch for this along driveways and parking areas, and inside garages. Landscaping work (including adding a swimming pool) with heavy equipment can also cause impact damage in areas away from normal vehicle traffic.

Different Than Soil Pressure

Impact damage often looks like failure of a foundation wall due to lateral soil pressure but is usually more localized. In some cases, there is evidence on the outside of the impact via scraping or crushing of the exterior foundation face. If there is horizontal displacement such as leaning or bowing, the point of maximum deflection will usually be above grade level.

If all foundation walls are similar and exposed to similar forces, you should question why there would be localized failure at one point. If it is a spot where vehicles can access the foundation, consider this possibility.

When The Basement Floor Helps

We said that basement floor slabs are usually not structural elements. However when it comes to resisting horizontal forces from the earth outside foundations, basement floor slabs may help considerably. The basement floor slab is poured on top of the footing and inside the foundation wall. Since the slab is usually continuous, it supports the bottom of the foundation wall.

Basement Floor Holds The Bottom Of Foundations

While good practice dictates that the foundation wall be keyed into the footing, this is often not done and, in some cases, it's not strong enough to stop a foundation from getting pushed inward across the top of a footing. In most cases, the basement floor will stop this.

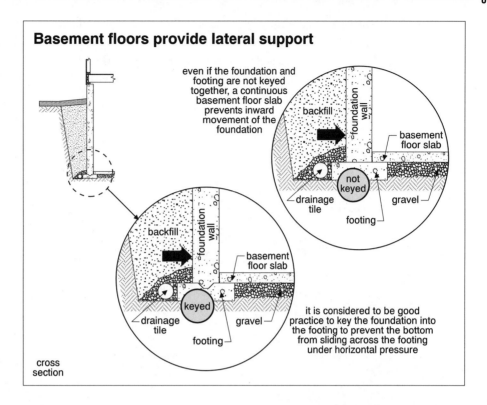

Basement floors provide lateral support

even if the foundation and footing are not keyed together, a continuous basement floor slab prevents inward movement of the foundation

backfill

foundation wall

basement floor slab

not keyed

drainage tile

gravel

footing

backfill

foundation wall

basement floor slab

keyed

drainage tile

gravel

footing

it is considered to be good practice to key the foundation into the footing to prevent the bottom from sliding across the footing under horizontal pressure

cross section

Basement floors that have been removed to allow for interior drainage systems, or are stopped short and filled with an expansion joint are not necessarily a problem, but lack this built-in protection for the bottom of the foundation wall. Again, we would only comment if we saw evidence of failure.

The Possible Corrective Actions

You shouldn't be specifying corrective actions, but should be able to identify solutions when you see them. Where lateral forces have caused cracking, bowing, bulging or leaning of foundation walls, the following steps are sometimes taken:

1. **Buttresses** are added on the inside of the foundation wall.
2. **Pilasters** are added on the inside of the foundation wall.
3. **Wood or steel beams or channels** are added on the inside of the foundation wall, most often spanning from top to bottom.
4. **A separate interior wall** is built against the foundation wall in the basement.
5. **A separate exterior wall** is built against the foundation on the outside (sister wall).
6. **Helical anchor screws** may be turned into the soil outside the house with interior plates holding the foundation wall from moving inward further. These act like the tie–backs in a conventional retaining wall system.
7. **Removal of the water** from the soil outside the foundations is another corrective action.

Buttresses   **Buttresses** are simply large masses placed against walls to resist movement. They may be on the exterior of above-grade walls or on the interior of foundation walls. They are often concrete or filled concrete block. Because the forces are the smallest at the top of the wall, buttresses are often triangular, largest near the floor level and smallest at the top. Buttresses consume basement space and are not a common solution.

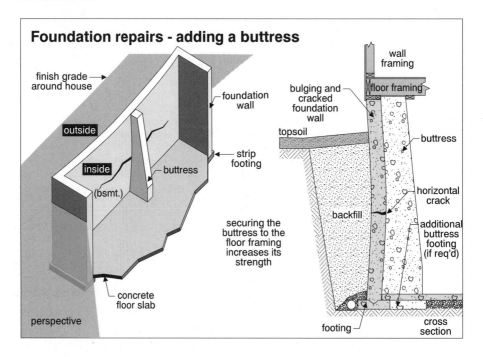

Foundation repairs - adding a buttress

Pilasters   **Pilasters** are a vertical thickening of the wall. They are sometimes part of the original construction, but may also be added. Pilasters act as reinforcing beams for the foundation walls. Pilasters are most often poured concrete or concrete block reinforced with steel.

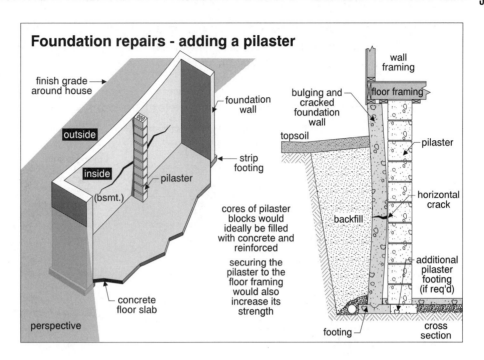

Foundation repairs - adding a pilaster

Wood Or Steel Beams

Other possibilities for reinforcing foundation walls from the inside include steel channels and wood members secured to the basement floor or footing and to the floor framing system at the top. These solutions are typically used on poured concrete walls that tend to act as a single unit. It's more difficult to restrain masonry walls, since the strength of the mortar joints is somewhat unpredictable, and the wall may not act as a single unit.

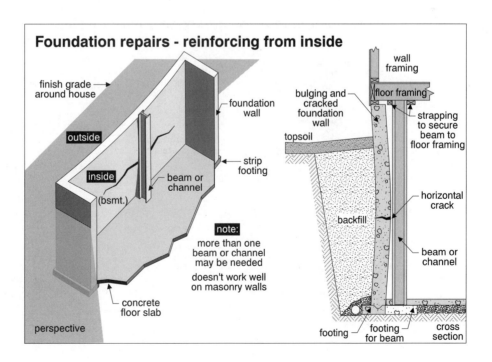

Foundation repairs - reinforcing from inside

Helical Anchors   The screw anchors are a manufactured and patented engineered system that is a variation of anchors for commercial and industrial use. These can be successful if the wall acts as single slab.

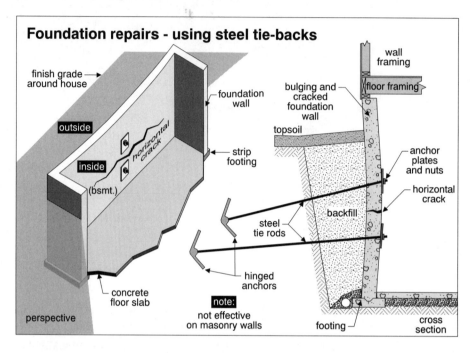

Sister Walls   Where it is unlikely that the wall will act as a unit, sometimes a second wall is built inside the first. This wall is often reinforced, whether or not the first wall was reinforced.

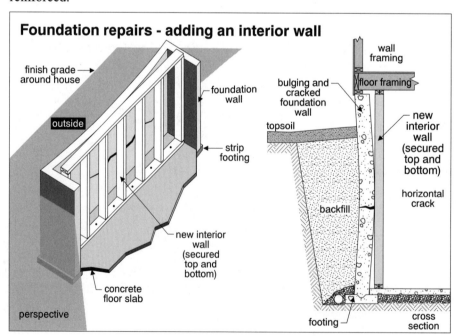

While it is more expensive, the new wall is sometimes added outside the original wall.

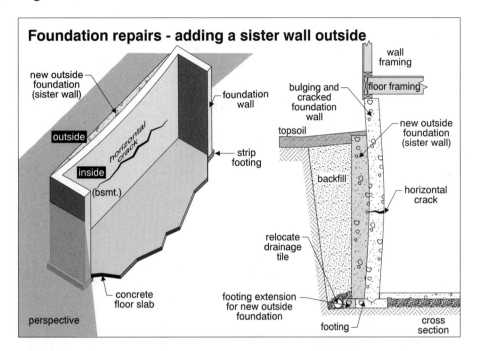

Foundation repairs - adding a sister wall outside

Must Carry House Loads

While it's not normally necessary to push walls back into their original position, care should be taken that support for the superstructure has not been compromised. If it has, additional steps must be taken to adequately transfer the vertical loads to the soil. Wind uplift forces must also be considered. If the foundation wall connection to the wall and floor has been broken, engineering consideration is needed.

Don't Design The Repairs

Again, resolving foundation problems is not for the faint of heart. It is a specialized field and home inspectors should not make conclusive statements. Again, document what's there, make sure your clients are aware of the potential implications, and give them appropriate direction. As we've talked earlier, these directions might include –

1. Do nothing
2. Monitor
3. Engage a specialist to do further investigation
4. Take corrective actions

3.3.2 BOWED, BULGING AND LEANING FOUNDATION WALLS

We discussed these when we looked at cracked foundation walls. These are listed as a separate item here, since they are not always accompanied by cracks. However, the mechanisms, strategies and corrective actions are the same as we discussed earlier.

Structure
MODULE

QUICK QUIZ 7

☑ INSTRUCTIONS

• You should finish reading Study Session 7 before doing this Quiz.

• Write your answers in the spaces provided.

• Check your answers against ours at the end of this Section, after the Final Test.

• If you have trouble with this Quiz, re-read the Session and try the Quiz again.

• If you do well, move on to Study Session 8.

1. Cracks due to horizontal forces rarely result in a structural problem.
True ☐   False ☐

2. List five things that could cause horizontal forces on a foundation.

_____   _____   _____

_____   _____

3. A bow or a bulge in a concrete foundation wall is a result of forces that are applied over a very short period of time.
True ☐   False ☐

4. Often horizontal forces will cause horizontal cracks in a foundation wall. Why might the crack disappear near the edge of the wall?

_____

5. In your own words, give a definition of lateral support as it applies to foundations.

_____

_____

6. Why might a damaged foundation wall start to move suddenly after a heavy rain?

_____

_____

7. The text lists seven possible corrective actions where lateral forces have caused cracking, bowing, bulging or leaning of the foundation wall. Give five.

_____

_____

_____

_____

_____

8. What is the difference between a buttress and a pilaster?

_____

_____

If you had no trouble with the Quiz, you are ready for Study Session 8.

Key Words:

- *Bowing*
- *Bulging*
- *Lateral support*
- *Foundation irrigation*
- *Premature backfilling*

- *Buttress*
- *Pilaster*
- *Helical anchors*
- *Sister walls*

Structure
MODULE

STUDY SESSION 8

1. You should have completed Study Sessions 1 through 7 before starting this Session.

2. By the end of this Session, you should:

- Know the causes of foundation mortar deterioration and spalling
- Know how to identify these conditions
- Know the significance of these conditions

3. This Session may take roughly 45 minutes to complete.

4. There is a Quick Quiz at the end of the Session.

Key Words:
- *Mortar*
- *Rising damp*
- *Spalling*
- *Cinder block*
- *Rot*
- *Insect damage*
- *Fire damage*

3.3.3 MORTAR DETERIORATION

This applies to masonry walls and piers made of stone, concrete block, cinder block, clay tile and brick.

Causes
1. Poor quality mortar.
2. Moisture penetration problems.

Implications
The implications are the same as we've talked about earlier. The ultimate implication is collapse of the structure.

Strategy
Mortar deterioration may be concentrated on the lower part of the wall or pier. This may be where more moisture leaks through a wall, or where **rising damp** (water drawn up through capillary action) is concentrated.

Testing Mortar Strength
Mortar joints can be probed with an awl or screwdriver to test their integrity. With very little practice, you can get a sense of the mortar strength. Most inspectors do not hack away at mortar. Dragging an awl or screwdriver across the joint with medium force will reveal the strength.

Brick Often Looks Bad
Brick foundations are usually three bricks thick (three wythes). The deterioration visible on the inner face of the brick is often alarming. However, this may be far less serious than a similar-looking mortar deterioration problem on a concrete block wall. Concrete block foundation walls are single thickness (wythe). Deteriorating mortar on a concrete block wall is far more likely to cause the wall to lose its strength than a similar amount of deterioration on a brick wall.

Poured Concrete Is Stronger
Because of the mortar joints, masonry foundation walls are generally not as strong as poured concrete walls.

Concrete Blocks Have A Top And A Bottom
The top surface of a concrete block is slightly wider than the bottom surface. This allows more mortar to sit on the top bedding surface when building the wall. The narrow bottom surface sits in the bed of mortar which surrounds the bottom surface of the block above. This helps lock the blocks together and provides more lateral strength.

Blocks are often installed upside down which defeats the purpose. The wall will often work but will be weaker as a result.

3.3.4 SPALLING FOUNDATION MATERIAL

Causes

Spalling is splitting, chipping, crumbling or splintering of masonry or concrete. Spalling may be caused by –

1. Moisture penetration through the foundation wall from the outside (usually over the long term)
2. Low quality concrete, or poor installation practices
3. Masonry not intended for use below grade
4. Freeze/thaw cycles

Strategy

How Much Material Is Lost?

Deteriorating concrete or masonry can be very serious. Look at the thickness of the foundation wall, and the amount of material that has been lost. What percentage of the wall has been compromised? In some cases, you'll recommend a specialist to determine whether the wall is likely to fail.

Floors And Walls Affected?

Consider where the damage has taken place. If there is lots of spalling near the top of the wall, the wood flooring and wall members may be exposed to moisture and may rot.

Loss Of Bearing

Another issue is the loss of bearing surfaces for floors and walls, if the top of the foundation wall is deteriorating.

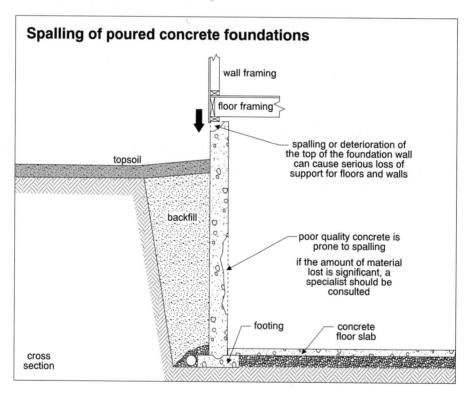

Spalling of poured concrete foundations

- wall framing
- floor framing
- spalling or deterioration of the top of the foundation wall can cause serious loss of support for floors and walls
- topsoil
- backfill
- poor quality concrete is prone to spalling
- if the amount of material lost is significant, a specialist should be consulted
- footing
- concrete floor slab
- cross section

Cinder Block Is Weak

Cinder blocks installed below grade will deteriorate over time if exposed to chronic moisture. Cinder block is weaker and less moisture resistant than concrete block. If you see cinder block foundations, (typically cinder block is made from slag and has a rougher, darker texture than concrete block), watch for evidence of deterioration of the blocks. In some cases, this is not visible on the interior face of the foundation, but the cinder block can be deteriorated on the outer side. There is no way to predict this.

Bad Concrete

Poor quality concrete prone to spalling may be the result of –

- Too much moisture in the mix.
- Excessive movement or vibration when placing the concrete, which causes de-segregation of the aggregate.
- Failure to keep the concrete moist during curing.
- Concrete which freezes before it cures.
- Impurities in the concrete causing poor bonding.
- A poor mix.

These last two problems often crop up where native sand is used to make the concrete on site. The sand at the site may or may not be good sand for concrete.

3.3.5 ROT, INSECT OR FIRE DAMAGE

Rot is the biggest enemy of wood foundations and piers.

Causes

Rot occurs in wood if three conditions are met:

1. The wood must be surrounded with **air** which always contains fungal spores. Wood under water does not rot.
2. The **moisture content** of the wood must be greater than **20%**. Dry wood will not rot.
3. The **temperature** of the wood must be between roughly **40°F** and **115°F**. Room temperature is ideal.

Since foundation walls are almost always going to be surrounded with air between 40°F and 115°F, we have two of the three conditions to support rot. The only thing we can control is the moisture content.

Strategy

Many inspectors use moisture meters (beyond the Standards) to evaluate moisture content in wood. Any moisture content over 20% should be a red flag.

When looking for rot, a carpenter's awl is very helpful. Probing wood (other than that used as a decorative interior finish) is required by the Standards where you suspect rot.

Clues
- Sometimes rot will show up clearly through cracks or checking in the wood and a crumbling surface.
- There may be fungal growth on the wood.
- The smell of the crawlspace or basement area may tell you that the moisture levels are high and that rot is likely.

Wood/Soil Contact
Pay particular attention where the wood is in direct contact with the soil. Moisture contents in excess of 20% are very difficult to avoid where there is wood/soil contact.

Rot
Evaluating the extent of the rot and the amount of weakening of the structure requires considerable experience and expertise. Again, unless you have strong knowledge in this area, or the situation is black and white, call for further investigation.

Stopping Rot
Reducing moisture levels is the best way to control rot. Weakened wood may have to be replaced. Epoxies can be used to restore strength to rotted wood but this expensive process is normally only used on historically significant buildings.

Insect Damage
Insect damage may be found on its own or with rotted wood. You don't have to identify the type or cause of damage, simply that the wood is damaged.

Fire Damage
Fire damage to wood members may be superficial or structural. Several factors affect the significance of the damage, including the depth and location of charring and the size, function and location of the components. Where in doubt, recommend further evaluation by a specialist.

Structure
MODULE

QUICK QUIZ 8

☑ INSTRUCTIONS

- You should finish Study Session 8 before doing this Quiz.

- Write your answers in the spaces provided.

- Check your answers against ours at the end of this Section, after the Final Test.

- If you have trouble with this Quiz, re-read the Session and try the Quiz again.

- If you do well, move on to Study Session 9.

1. Give two causes of mortar deterioration in foundations.

   _____

   _____

2. Which is stronger, a poured concrete wall or concrete block wall of the same dimensions?

   _____

3. In your own words, describe **spalling**.

   _____

4. Give two causes of spalling of foundation masonry.

   _____

   _____

5. How can you tell the difference between a cinder block wall and a concrete block wall?

_____

6. Which foundation would be more likely to be damaged by water; cinder block or concrete block?

_____

7. Which of the following is required by the Standards?

   a. Probing wood to identify rot.
   b. Measuring the wood moisture content with a moisture meter.

If you had no trouble with the Quiz, you are ready for Field Exercise 2.

Key Words:
- *Mortar*
- *Rising damp*
- *Spalling*
- *Cinder block*
- *Rot*
- *Insect damage*
- *Fire damage*

Structure

MODULE

FIELD EXERCISE 2

☑ INSTRUCTIONS

You should have completed everything up to Quick Quiz 8 before doing this Exercise.

This Field Exercise is specific to houses with visible foundations (either a crawlspace or a full basement). If you inspect in an area with only slab on grade homes, then this Field Exercise will not apply.

For this Exercise you will be inspecting the foundation of at least four houses, ideally with unfinished basements or crawlspaces.

Allow 15 to 30 minutes for each house. You'll start your inspection on the exterior and finish on the interior.

For each house, answer as many of these questions as possible:

1. What is the foundation material? _____

2. Are there any cracks visible from the exterior? If so, note their location width and number of planes of movement. (Some inspectors use sketches.)

   _____

3. Are there any other irregularities visible from the exterior?

   _____

4. Are there any cracks visible on the interior of the foundation? If so, note their location, width and number of planes of movement. (Some inspectors use sketches.)

5. Can you see any cause for the cracking? –

   • weak spots in foundation
   • large trees
   • driveways
   • soil moisture levels
   • exterior basement stairwells

6. Is there any evidence of rot, heaving, leaning bowing or bulging?

   _____

7. Is there any mortar deterioration or spalling?

   _____

8. Is the foundation laterally supported or unsupported?

   _____

9. What are your local rules for maximum backfill height on laterally supported and unsupported foundations of different materials?

   _____

10. What is your conclusion? (Is the foundation stable? Are repairs needed?)

    _____

When you have completed this Exercise, you are ready for Study Session 9.

Structure

MODULE

STUDY SESSION 9

1. You should have completed Study Session 1 through 8, and Field Exercises 1 and 2 before starting this Session.

2. By the end of this Session, you should:

- Know the causes of pier movement
- Know the implications of pier movement
- Know how to identify pier movement
- Know the causes and implications of cold joints and honeycombing

3. This Session may take about 45 minutes.

4. This is the last Session in this section. There is a Quiz at the end. After the Quiz you will be ready to try the Final Test.

Key Words:

- *Piers*
- *The 1/3 rule*
- *Pilaster*
- *Buttress*
- *Cold joint*
- *Honeycomb*

3.3.6 PIERS MOVING OR DETERIORATING

Causes   Piers may move because:

Footing   • Footings are – missing
Problems   – undersized
                             – deteriorated

Soil   • Soil under the footings is – disturbed, on original construction, by tree roots or
Problems   when lowering floors or building additions for
                                                  example
                                               – weak (poor bearing capacity)
                                               – expansive
                                               – eroding or slipping
                                               – freezing and heaving then settling

Load   • Loads increase due to – snow and ice
Problems   – building additions (e.g. adding a second floor)

To summarize, differential settlement occurs when the weight of the building exceeds the bearing capacity of the soil under part of the building.

Other Causes   Other causes of pier movement include –

• Poor connection of piers to footings or to the floor assembly
• Eccentric or uneven loading of the pier
• Undersized or overloaded piers
• Deterioration of or damage to the pier itself
• Hollow masonry units installed on their side

Strategy   Piers can be checked for plumb using a mason's level (four foot long spirit level). Look for a gap at the top of the pier. If the pier has settled, it may no longer be carrying the load from the floor or wall system above. Look also for a sag in the floor
The ⅓ Rule   above the pier. Piers out of plumb by more than ⅓ of the pier thickness should be considered unstable.

Look for bowing or buckling of the pier. Is the beam on top of the pier on the center, or off to one side?

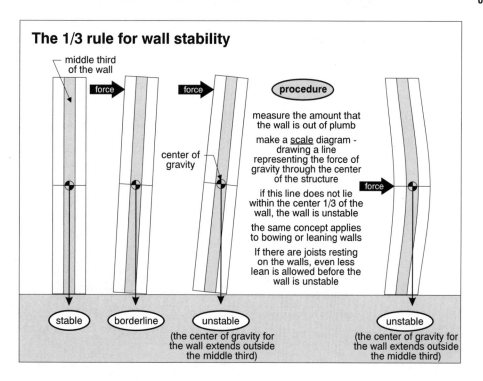

Crushing   Look for crushing at the top of the pier or the underside of the floor framing member above. Is there adequate endbearing for beams? Is the top of the pier wide enough to carry the full width of the beam? Look also for crushing at the bottom of wood piers.

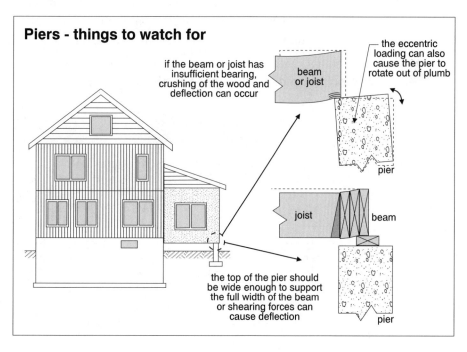

Block Or Brick On Sides   Hollow concrete block, cinder block, clay tile, and cored brick must be installed with the channels vertical. If the channels are horizontal, the pier will not be as strong.

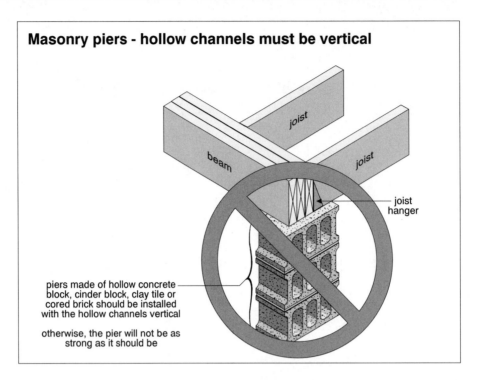

Masonry piers - hollow channels must be vertical

joist

beam

joist

joist hanger

piers made of hollow concrete block, cinder block, clay tile or cored brick should be installed with the hollow channels vertical

otherwise, the pier will not be as strong as it should be

Deteriorating Material

Look at the pier material itself for rot, mortar deterioration, spalling, cracking or delamination.

Check Floor Around Pier

In most cases, you won't be able to see whether there is a footing. If there is a concrete floor at the base of the footing, look for cracking and deflection of the concrete around the pier. If the concrete has dropped in this area, settlement is the problem. If the concrete has heaved, there may be a frost or expansive soil issue.

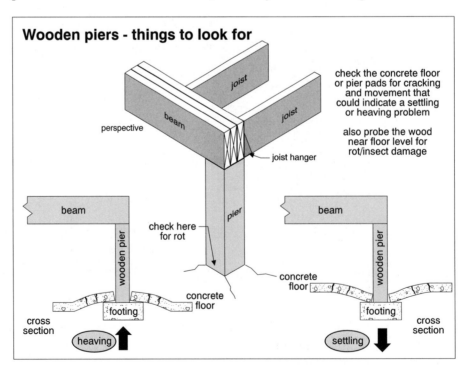

Wooden piers - things to look for

joist

check the concrete floor or pier pads for cracking and movement that could indicate a settling or heaving problem

also probe the wood near floor level for rot/insect damage

perspective

beam

joist

joist hanger

beam

beam

pier

check here for rot

wooden pier

wooden pier

concrete floor

concrete floor

cross section

footing

concrete floor

footing

cross section

heaving

settling

Rising Damp And Rot   Look for evidence of moisture damage around the bottom of the pier which would indicate rising damp. Probe wooden piers, especially near the bottom and near any wood/soil contact.

3.3.7 PILASTERS OR BUTTRESSES PULLING AWAY FROM WALL

Pilasters and buttresses may be an integral part of the wall or may have been added. Where pilasters are integral, separation is rare. Problems are more common where the pilaster or buttress has been retrofit.

Causes   Problems may be the result of –
• poor installation
• too small
• not well secured
• poor location
• wrong material
• footing deteriorating, missing or undersized
• foundation wall is pushing the pilaster away

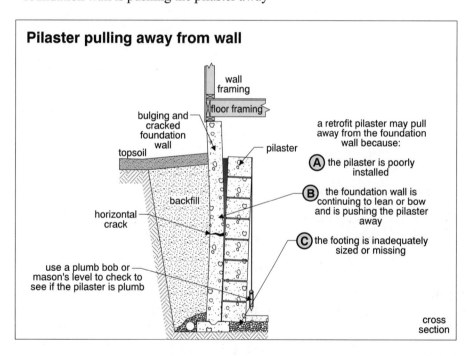

Pilaster pulling away from wall

wall framing

floor framing

bulging and cracked foundation wall

topsoil

pilaster

a retrofit pilaster may pull away from the foundation wall because:

(A) the pilaster is poorly installed

backfill

(B) the foundation wall is continuing to lean or bow and is pushing the pilaster away

horizontal crack

(C) the footing is inadequately sized or missing

use a plumb bob or mason's level to check to see if the pilaster is plumb

cross section

Strategy   Make sure that pilasters and buttresses are plumb. A mason's level is helpful here. Look at the joint between the memebr and wall for gaps or cracking. The pilaster or buttress may move laterally or vertically relative to the wall.

Look At Bottom And Top   Look at any concrete floor around the base for evidence of settlement or heaving. Look also at the top for evidence of lateral slippage, gaps, bumps or crushing in the floor above.

3.3.8 COLD JOINTS

Pouring At
Two Times

Cold joints are the result of pouring a foundation at two separate times. If part of the foundation is poured and starts to cure, when the second part is poured the visible joint between the two is a **cold joint** or **cold pour**. Cold joints are horizontal or diagonal, although closer to being horizontal than vertical. The joint can be ragged and irregular or it can look like a crack, particularly if it's relatively straight.

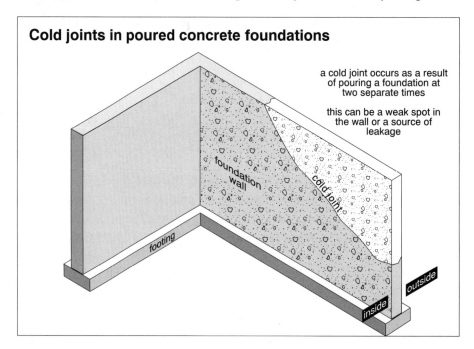

Cold joints in poured concrete foundations

a cold joint occurs as a result of pouring a foundation at two separate times

this can be a weak spot in the wall or a source of leakage

foundation wall

cold joint

footing

inside

outside

Causes

Pouring the foundation in two stages.

Implications

Cold joints may be a –

• Source of leakage
• Weak spot in the wall

The bonding is often less than perfect at the cold joint.

Strategy

While structural failure of the wall at cold joints are rare, this can be a weak spot. The trick is to be able to identify a cold joint, and differentiate it from a crack. This requires a little bit of experience and a close look. There are small voids in the

Identification

concrete at cold joints. This is not true of cracks. Cold joints are not usually as straight as cracks, although cracking may develop along the cold joint. Cold joint patterns are usually different than crack patterns. Cold joints are never vertical and and not necessarily at weak points in the wall.

Leaks

Watch for leakage through cold joints although this is not a structural problem.

3.3.9 HONEYCOMBING

Defined

Honeycombing is large voids or bubbles in poured concrete walls.

Honeycombing shows up as voids in the face of the concrete, often up to one inch in diameter. Very often, the concrete appears to be missing its cement. Large pieces of aggregate are often surrounded by air.

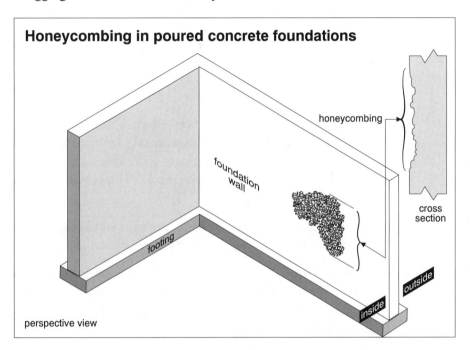

Honeycombing in poured concrete foundations

honeycombing

foundation wall

cross section

footing

inside

outside

perspective view

Causes

Honeycombing is caused by insufficient consolidation (compaction or rodding) of the concrete which is usually done with puddling sticks (tamping rods) or vibrators.

Implications

Honeycombing is a weakness in the wall with respect to both moisture penetration and strength. Cracking or bowing of a wall is more likely where there are large sections of honeycombing in the wall. It's also common to find evidence of leakage in a foundation wall where there is honeycombing.

Strategy

Signs of leakage include –

Identification of Leakage

• Moisture on the wall or floor
• Streaking or staining running down the wall
• Efflorescence (salt deposits on the wall left by evaporating moisture)
• Rusting of nails or other metal components in or on the wall
• Rusting of metal feet of appliances on the floor, rot on wood trim
• Mold, mildew, deterioration of cardboard or other paper products against walls or on the floor
• Lifted or loose floor tiles
• Crumbling drywall
• Discolored paneling

Keep Water Away   There are, of course, several conditions that may result in leakage. Houses are not boats, and foundation walls are not hulls. If water collects outside a foundation wall, it will find its way through. The best moisture control strategy is to keep the water away from the outside of the house with good gutters and grading, for example.

3.3.10 PRIOR REPAIRS

Cause   Prior repairs are the result of past problems.

Strategy   Try to figure out why the problem occurred in the first place. Is there a natural weak spot in the foundation at this point? Is there a load concentration point outside or above?

Look at whether the repair has been effective. Has the repair itself cracked? This suggests ongoing movement. Is there leakage through the crack? This may only be a nuisance issue, but should be reported. In some cases, walls are stronger where they have been patched than anywhere else. This is true, for example, where epoxy patching is well done.

If the forces that caused the initial problem still exist, a crack will often open nearby. Check around repairs for evidence of new cracks.

Have Walls Been Repaired?   Look for evidence of re-supporting. Have buttresses or pilasters been added? Are there plates on the foundation wall that indicate that reinforcing has been done, perhaps attached to anchors going out into the soil? Have wood or steel channels been installed against the wall to stop further movement? Have new walls been added, inside or out?

Lowered Floors   Has the basement floor been lowered – is there a bench footing; has the wall been underpinned? While these are not repairs, they are disruptive structural activities undertaken after original construction. They may be thought of as repairs.

The Tough Question   Where foundation walls have been reinforced, you are likely to be asked whether the repairs have been successful. The only yardstick you can use is whether the wall shows evidence of movement since the repairs have been made. Without knowing exactly when the repairs were made, it will be difficult to answer this question, even if you don't see subsequent movement.

Don't Guess   In many cases, it will be tough to look at the cracks in the foundation walls and assure the client that they occurred before the reinforcement was done, and that the cracks have not gotten any larger since reinforcing. Again, without special knowledge, recommend continued monitoring at the least.

Drawings   In some cases, there are drawings, specifications and permits that document and support the work that has been done. While these increase the chances of the work having been successfully, they are no guarantee.

3.3.11 FOUNDATION WALLS THAT ARE TOO SHORT

Cause

Foundations that are too short are usually a result of –
- An original construction mistake
- Lot regrading
- Adding a planter or garden against the house

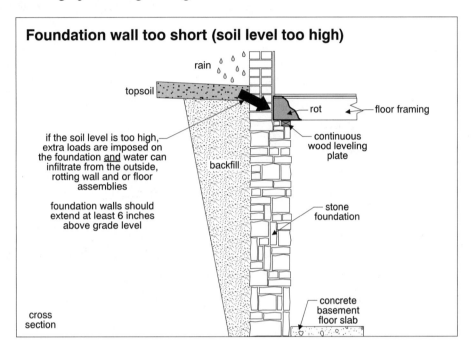

Foundation wall too short (soil level too high)

rain

topsoil

if the soil level is too high, extra loads are imposed on the foundation <u>and</u> water can infiltrate from the outside, rotting wall and or floor assemblies

foundation walls should extend at least 6 inches above grade level

backfill

rot — floor framing

continuous wood leveling plate

stone foundation

concrete basement floor slab

cross section

Implications

The implications include not only the extra soil load imposed by a taller than anticipated backfill height, but also rot to floor and wall assemblies that rest on the foundation.

Strategy

Look for foundation walls that extend at least six inches above grade, and look for wood members that sit on top of the foundation. If the framing is buried in the top of the foundation, ensure that the foundation is high enough that the wood members are not below grade.

Concealed Rot At Joist And Beam Ends

While people may get away with this in dry soil environments, it is risky where there is moisture in the soil. Soil moisture will find its way through foundation walls over time. Concealed rot at the end of joists can go unnoticed for some time and lead to structural failure without much warning. Probe these members for evidence of rot.

3.3.12 FOUNDATION WALLS THAT ARE TOO THIN

Lateral Support

The foundation walls may be too thin for the height of backfill. However, before you make this determination, decide whether the walls are laterally supported. The floor system at the top of a foundation wall may or may not provide this support as we've discussed.

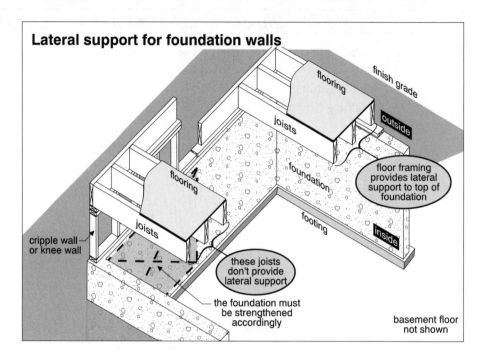

Lateral support for foundation walls

Labels in figure: flooring · finish grade · joists · outside · flooring · foundation · floor framing provides lateral support to top of foundation · joists · footing · inside · cripple wall or knee wall · these joists don't provide lateral support · the foundation must be strengthened accordingly · basement floor not shown

Walls May Be Reinforced	You also have to be careful because walls that look too thin may be reinforced with steel. These are stronger than they appear.
Causes	Thin foundation walls may be the result of

• An original construction mistake
• A change in the exterior grade level
• Framing changes within the house that remove lateral support

Interior Stairs	Adding or relocating an interior basement stairwell parallel to a foundation wall, for example, can remove the lateral support for the foundation by removing floor joists.
Strategy	Look at the thickness of the foundation wall, determine whether it's laterally supported, and evaluate the height of soil that it is holding back. Evaluate the age of the building. If there has been no movement and no obvious changes in either the structure of the building or the soil conditions outside, even a marginally undersized foundation wall may be performing adequately.
If It's Not Broke, Don't Fix It	Remember, we're doing a performance based inspection. If the wall is working, and has been doing so for some time, even though the construction practice is less than ideal, tell your client exactly that. Don't recommend repairs if there is no visible distress on homes that are more than 20 years old.
Unless It's New	If the building or wall is new, however, you will not be able to use the test of time in your determination, and will have to call out the apparently undersized foundation wall for further investigation. Be careful not to be conclusive, remembering that you can't see concealed reinforcement.

Summary

*Not As Easy
As It First
Seems*

At first glance, the examination of foundations and footings seem simple, since you are looking for no movement in the system, and you can't see a great deal. However, the difficult part of a footing and foundation inspection is to evaluate the very common situation where the conditions are not perfect. It's difficult to know the performance implications of cracks, spalling, leaning, mortar deterioration, etc., without considerable experience and expertise. It's often impossible based on a one-time visit, no matter how much you know.

This is an area where under-stating a problem can be catastrophic. On the other hand, over-stating problems is a serious disservice to your client and will make enemies of all the people involved in the transaction.

*To Call Or
Not To Call
The Expert*

Some home inspectors develop reputations for calling in experts at every turn. Generally speaking, these inspectors are not seen to be helpful, and slow down the real estate transaction while increasing the costs of home buying for their clients. You will need to walk a fine line between providing good value for your clients while not crossing the line into the world of structural engineering.

*You're A
General
Practitioner*

A home inspector is like a doctor who is a general practitioner. You wouldn't expect your family physician to perform reconstructive bone surgery, brain surgery or heart surgery. Family doctors look at your overall condition. Where they suspect or identify problems, they may direct you to a specialist for further analysis and corrective action. That's exactly what good home inspectors do, when they can't make the calls. The trick is to know your business well enough to understand when you can make the call, and when you shouldn't.

*Experts
Aren't Magic*

Do not be defensive about not being the expert in every field. Also, don't give the experts credit for being able to answer all the questions. In many cases, structural experts will inspect a house and not be able to provide definitive answers.

*Precautionary
Repairs*

In some cases, they may recommend and design repairs that may not be necessary because they can't risk saying something is sound when they are not sure. By recommending corrective action, they can be sure that the system is stable.

*Let The
Expert Make
The Call*

If it's a tough call for the expert, you don't want to make the call. Experts are in a much better position to defend their recommendations to take corrective action because of their knowledge and experience. If you, as the general practitioner, recommend expensive corrective action, and a specialist subsequently proves that it's not necessary, you do considerable damage to your reputation. It's not easy, is it?

Inspecting to the Standards

Accessible	We have to inspect house components that are **readily accessible**. That means we don't have to move furniture, lift carpets or ceiling tiles, dismantle components, damage things or do something dangerous. The exception is covers that would normally be **removed by homeowners during routine maintenance**. The furnace fan cover is a good example because homeowners remove this to change the furnace filter. Many inspectors use tools as the threshold. If tools are required to open or dismantle the component, it is considered **not readily accessible**.
Installed	We only have to inspect things that are **installed** in homes. This means we don't have to inspect window air conditioners or portable heaters, for example.
Deficiencies	We have to report on systems that are **significantly deficient**. This means they are unsafe or not performing their intended function.
End Of Life	We are required to report on any system or component that in our professional opinion is **near the end of its service life**. This is tricky since we don't know whether inspectors will be held accountable for failed components on the basis that we should have known the component was near the end of its life. With the wisdom of hindsight, it may be hard to argue that the component could not have been expected to fail, when in fact, it did. Time will tell. The situation is also tricky because it includes not only **systems** but individual **components** as well. For many systems there are broadly accepted life expectancy ranges, but these aren't available for some individual components.
Remaining Life	We are not required to determine the **remaining life** of systems or components. This is related to, but different than, the **end of service life** issue. If the item is new or in the middle part of its life, we don't have to predict service life, even though the same broadly accepted life expectancy ranges would apply. It's only when the item is near the end, in your opinion, that you have to report it.
Reporting Implications	We have to tell people in writing the **implications** of conditions or problems unless they are self-evident. A cracked heat exchanger on a furnace has a very different implication for a homeowner than a cracked windowpane, for example.
Tell Client What To Do	We have to tell the client in the report what to do about any conditions we found. We might recommend they repair, replace, service or clean the component. We might advise them to have a specialist further investigate the condition. It's all right to tell the client to monitor a situation, but you can't tell them that their roof shingles are curled and leave it at that.
What We Left Out	We have to report anything that we would usually inspect but didn't. We also have to include in our report why we didn't inspect it. The reasons may be that the component was inaccessible, unsafe to inspect or was shut down. It may also be that the occupant or the client asked you not to inspect it.

Structure

MODULE

QUICK QUIZ 9

☑ INSTRUCTIONS

• You should finish reading Study Session 9 before doing this Quiz.

• Write your answers in the spaces provided.

• Check your answers against ours at the end of this Section, after the Final Test.

• If you have trouble with this Quiz, re–read the Session and try the Quiz again.

• If you do well, you are ready for the Final Test at the end of the section.

1. List four causes of pier movement or settling.

    _____

    _____

    _____

    _____

2. Give two causes of pilasters pulling away from the wall.

    _____

3. In your own words describe a cold joint as it relates to a concrete foundation.

    _____

    _____

4. What is honeycombing and what might it be caused by?

_____

_____

5. The foundation should extend far enough out of the ground that the wood members are not below grade. Explain why.

_____

_____

If you have no trouble with the Quiz, you are ready to move on. Watch the Foundations Section of the Video again. Then look at 5.0 TOOLS, 6.0 INSPECTION PROCEDURE and 7.0 INSPECTION CHECKLIST, before going to the FINAL TEST.

Key Words:

- **Piers**
- **The 1/3 rule**
- **Pilaster**
- **Buttress**
- **Cold joint**
- **Honeycomb**

► 4.0 INSPECTION TOOLS

1. **Flashlight**

   To examine dark area, such as crawlspaces.

2. **Screwdriver/Awl**

   To probe suspect surfaces.

3. **Moisture Meter**

   To identify high moisture content in building materials.

4. **Tape Measure**

   To evaluate foundation height and thickness against grade height, for example.

5. **Plumb Bob**

   Is used to quantify leaning or bowing wall conditions.

6. **Mason's Level**

   To help quantify out-of-plumb situations.

► 5.0 INSPECTION CHECKLIST

Location Legend   N = North   S = South   E = East   W= West
B = Basement   1 = 1st story   2 = 2nd story   3 = 3rd story

LOCATION		LOCATION	
	FOUNDATION WALLS		**PIERS**
	• Cracks - shrinkage		• Leaning
	- settlement		• Mortar - loose
	- heaving		- missing
	- lateral thrust		• Concrete or masonry - spalling
	• Bowed		- crushed
	• Bulging		• Hollow masonry units on sides
	• Leaning		• Soil stability suspect
	• Mortar - loose		• Missing
	- missing		• Rot, insect or fire damage
	• Concrete or masonry - spalling		• Cracking
	- crushed		• Not well secured
	• Hollow masonry units on sides		
	• Soil stability suspect		**FOUNDATIONS – GENERAL**
	• Missing		• Prior repairs - cracks sealed
	• Damaged		- rods, cables, channels
	• Cold joints		- mud jacking
	• Honeycombing		- anchors
	• Pilasters moving		- sister walls
	• Buttresses moving		
	• Too short		
	• Too thin		
	• Laterally unsupported		
	• Basement lowered (vulnerable)		
	• Beam punching through foundations		
	• Brick overhang excessive		
	• Tree roots (vulnerable)		
	• Rot, insect or fire damage		

► ANSWERS TO QUICK QUIZZES

Answers to Quick Quiz 1

1. Foundation and Framing

2. Foundation, floor structure, wall structure, ceiling structure, roof structure.

3. Probing is not required where it would damage any finished surface or where no deterioration is visible.

4. You are not required to enter crawl spaces which, in your opinion, will be dangerous to you or other people, or will damage the property. You are also not required to enter crawl spaces which are not readily accessible.

5. You don't have to enter attics when it is dangerous to you or others, when it may damage the property, or when the attic is not accessible. We do not enter attics if the insulation covers the ceiling joists or bottom truss chords.

6. Yes.

7. No, because it's usually not visible.

8. No, you are not required to do a design review. Nor are you required to determine the strength, adequacy, effectiveness or efficiency of any system. You are also not required to perform any engineering services.

Answers to Quick Quiz 2

1. Footings transfer the live and dead loads of the building to the soil over a large enough area so that neither the soil nor the building will move. In areas where frost occurs, footings prevent frost from moving the building. Foundations transfer loads from the building to the footings. Foundations may also act as retaining walls, resisting lateral soil pressure, for example.

2. Common foundation configurations include basements, crawl spaces, and slab-on-grade. Common foundation types include spread footings, pad footings, piles, and piers.

3. A strip footing or spread footing is used under a foundation wall. A pad footing is used under a column. Pad footings distribute concentrated loads. Strip footings handle more evenly distributed loads.

4. A structural review includes an analysis of the design. A home inspection is a field review based on the test of time and evidence of performance or non-performance of the system. A full structural review would typically include reviewing calculations or checking codes to ensure proper sizing and arrangement of components.

5. Foundation materials include concrete, concrete block, cinder block, brick, clay tile, stone and wood.

6. False. If the building is not heated, the frost line will be lowered. If the depth of frost is two feet, for example, it may be expected to be two feet below the basement floor if the home is not heated.

7. Your client has to understand the limitations of your inspection. Crawl spaces can be troublesome. If you couldn't get a good look, your client should understand that there is a greater risk of unforeseen problems.

8. Live loads, such as people, wind and snow, vary. Dead loads, such as the building materials, are relatively fixed.

9. A pilaster is a thickening of a foundation wall to accommodate the concentrated load of a beam or column. A pier is a stand-alone structural member that can be thought of as a column sunk into the ground.

10. No.

Answers to Quick Quiz 3

1. Shrinkage, differential settling, heaving, horizontal forces.

2. In uniform settlement, the entire house moves and no cracking develops. With differential settlement, one part of the house moves relative to another. This typically results in cracking.

3. Shrinkage cracks are typically caused by natural curing of concrete.

4. Shrinkage cracks are rarely more than $1/8$ inch wide and typically do not involve displacement of the concrete on either side of the crack. Shrinkage cracks usually show up within the first year of the life of a home. Shrinkage cracks do not extend through the footings or up into the structure above. Shrinkage cracks may occur at stress concentration points such as window openings. The implications of shrinkage cracks may be leakage, but not structural problems.

5. Differential movement may be caused by

    • footings that are missing, undersized or deteriorated:
    • soil below the building that is disturbed, weak, expansive, eroding, or heaving due to frost;
    • increased loads due to snow and ice
    • building additions.

Answers to Quick Quiz 4

1. No.

2. A cut and fill lot is a side-hill lot where some of the hill is cut away to allow part of the house to fit into the hillside. The excavated material is often used to fill in the lower part of the slope and create a level pad for the rest of the home. Part of the house sits in the cut area and part of the home sits on the filled area. The filled area is disturbed soil and is more likely to settle.

3. Look for structural problems in other homes in the neighborhood. Check the general topography. Houses on side-hill lots may be subject to cut and fill type settlement problems. Houses near the bottom of slopes may experience flooding problems. The general age of the neighborhood is useful information. Older neighborhoods provide a more reliable test of time. You also may know about specific problems such as expansive or weak soils, high water tables, underground streams or reclaimed land.

4. Cracks in more than one plane.

5. Clues that the crack may indicate active movement include:

   • Opened patches
   • Cracks with no paint in the cracks (if paint is in the crack and the paint is old, the crack existed before the paint was applied).
   • A lack of dirt and debris in the crack (old cracks are often largely filled with dirt and debris)
   • Sharp corners on cracks (old cracks are often worn and rounded)

6. Underpinning is re-supporting footings from below. This can include new foundations and footings, helical anchors, or piles. Underpinning is used in situations where differential settlement has to be stopped. Before underpinning, there should be some confidence that the soil below the building can support the underpinnings.

Answers to Quick Quiz 5

1. A step footing is typically used on a house built on a sloping lot. Cracking is common at the steps in the foundation. They may be diagonal, vertical or horizontal cracks.

2. Clues that a basement floor has been lowered include:

   • Curbs around the perimeter indicating bench footings
   • The foundation wall material changes part way down, indicating underpinning
   • Unusually high basement ceilings
   • New or extended basement stairs
   • Furnaces or other equipment on raised pads on the floor
   • Utility lines entering or leaving the house above basement floor level
   • Sump pumps or sewage ejector pumps
   • Interior foundation drains
   • The basement floor is different from other houses in the area

3. Lowering a basement floor may undermine the original footings. The original footing may settle down onto the new foundation and footing system that shrinks while it cures. Flooding and seepage problems are common in lowered basements.

4. Cracks between the original house and additions are common where the houses are attached because the original house has settled before the addition is added. As the addition settles, it moves relative to the original house, resulting in a crack.

5. Loads from large areas are concentrated on a small point. This could be the end of a beam, bottom of a chimney or a column, for example.

Answers to Quick Quiz 6

1. Ad-freezing acts on the sides of the foundation. Frost in the soil bonds to the foundation wall and lifts the wall as the ground heaves.

2. Frost heave may be the result of footings that are too shallow, saturated soils, increasing the frost depth by insulating basements, or leaving the house unheated during freezing weather.

3. • To differentiate between settlement and heaving, check whether cracks are opening, crushing, or sliding type cracks.
   • If sidewalks, driveways and patios slope down toward the house, settlement is more likely. If they slope up towards the house, heaving is more likely
   • If there is hump in the central part of the house but the columns are not cracked or displaced, the house perimeter is probably settling. If central columns show lots of cracks in the floor area and the floor slopes up toward the column, heaving is more likely.
   • Are overhead electric wires at a different angle than neighboring houses? Is the house higher or lower?
   • Check adjacent houses for similar evidence and neighborhood trends.
   • Look at the soil line against the building. If the front door sill is below grade level, settling is more likely. If you can see a dirt line six inches above the existing grade, heaving is more likely.

4. False.

5. Adding an exterior basement stairwell can allow the frost depth to get below the original house footings. This can lead to frost heave of the house in the area of the stairwell.

6. True.

7. Insulating basements, leaving houses unheated or changing the exterior grade height can lead to frost heaving. Adding moisture to the soil can also create ad-freezing problems.

8. False, if the water table is high, the drainage tile around the house may not handle the water.

Answers to Quick Quiz 7

1. False.

2. Horizontal forces are typically due to:

    • Frost pressure
    • Hydrostatic pressure
    • Vehicle loads adjacent to the building
    • Expansive soils
    • Tree roots
    • Impact damage

3. False.

4. The perpendicular wall reinforces the cracked wall near the end, preventing it from moving.

5. Lateral support is usually a floor system secured to the top of a foundation wall, preventing it from tipping inward.

6. Increase in hydrostatic pressure, or swelling of expansive soils.

7. Corrective actions include:

    • Buttresses
    • Pilasters
    • Wood or steel beams or channels
    • Separate interior walls
    • Separate exterior walls
    • Helical anchors
    • Removal of water from the soil

8. A buttress is a large structural mass placed against a wall to resist horizontal movement. It can be above or below grade. A pilaster is a vertical thickening of the wall. It may act as a reinforcing beam for the foundation wall and is often designed to carry concentrated vertical loads.

Answers to Quick Quiz 8

1. Mortar may deteriorate due to poor quality mortar or moisture problems.

2. A poured concrete wall.

3. Spalling is splitting, chipping, crumbling or splintering or masonry or concrete.

4. Spalling may be caused by moisture penetration, low quality concrete, poor installation, masonry not intended for use below grade, or freeze/thaw cycles.

5. Cinder block has a rougher, darker texture than concrete block and is made from rock slag.

6. Cinder block.

7. A

Answers to Quick Quiz 9

1. Causes of pier movement include:

    • Poor connection of piers to footings or floor assemblies
    • Uneven loading of the pier
    • Undersized or overloaded piers
    • Deterioration of, or damage to, the pier
    • Hollow masonry units installed on their side

2. Pilasters may pull away from walls due to:

    • Poor installation, footing deteriorating, missing or undersized
    • Foundation wall pushing the pilaster away

3. A cold joint is formed when a foundation is poured at two separate times. The first part of the foundation has started to cure when the second part is poured. At the intersection, a cold joint is created.

4. Honeycombing is a series of large voids or bubbles in poured concrete. This is typically cause by insufficient consolidation of the concrete before it is cured.

5. Wood members are prone to rot if they are at or below grade level.

2

FLOORS

Structure

M O D U L E

► TABLE OF CONTENTS

FIELD EXERCISE 2

► 1.0 OBJECTIVES

During this Section you will learn –
• How to inspect floor systems, and their components
• About the various types of systems commonly found
• About the various materials used for columns, beams, floor joists and subfloors
• The common conditions found with floor structures
• To identify these conditions
• The causes and implications of these conditions

Not The
Last Word
This program is not an in-depth Structure course and you should not assume that you have all the knowledge of a professional engineer, architect, designer, carpenter, mason, etc. after studying this material. This program does not qualify you to design or build homes. There are many places to go to learn more and we encourage you to continue expanding your knowledge.

Structure
M O D U L E

STUDY SESSION 1

1. The first Session covers the Scope of the inspection as set out in the ASHI® Standards of Practice. This Session also includes some introductory comments about floors and a discussion on sills.

2. At the end of this Session you should be able to:

   • Understand what part of the ASHI® Standards apply to floors.
   • Understand the components of floor systems.
   • Understand the function of floor systems.
   • Understand the problems with wood-soil and wood-concrete contact.
   • Understand the function of sills and common sill problems.

3. To give you a general overview on Floor Structures, you should read pages 23 to 38 of the Structure Section of **The Home Reference Book**. The Exercises and Quizzes assume that you have read it. If you have not read these pages, read them now.

4. This Session may take you roughly 45 minutes to complete.

5. Quick Quiz 1 will help you make sure you have understood and remembered the material.

Key Words:

- *Sills*
- *Columns*
- *Beams*
- *Joists*
- *Subfloors*
- *Probing*
- *Bouncing*
- *Measuring*
- *Strength*
- *Stiffness*
- *Bending*
- *Wood/concrete contact*
- *Wood/soil contact*
- *Nailing practices*
- *Compression*
- *Tension*
- *Shear*
- *Sill gasket*
- *Mud sill*
- *Anchor bolts*
- *Rot*
- *Insect damage*
- *Sill crushing*

► 2.0 SCOPE AND INTRODUCTION

2.1 SCOPE

The following is the Structure Section of the ASHI® Standards of Practice, effective January 2000. We have not repeated the Purpose and Scope, General Limitations and Exclusions, and Glossary, which are included in the Footings and Foundations Section

3.0 STRUCTURAL SYSTEM

3.1 The *inspector* shall:

A. *inspect:*
1. the *structural components* including foundation and framing.
2. by probing a *representative number* of structural components where deterioration is suspected or where clear indications of possible deterioration exist. Probing is NOT required when probing would damage any finished surface or where no deterioration is visible.

B. *describe:*
1. the foundation and *report* the methods used to *inspect* the *under-floor crawl space*
2. the floor structure.
3. the wall structure.
4. the ceiling structure.
5. the roof structure and *report* the methods used to *inspect* the attic.

3.2 The *inspector* is NOT required to:

A. provide any *engineering service* or *architectural service*.
B. offer an opinion as to the adequacy of any *structural system* or *component*.

► NOTES ON THE STANDARDS

Components   Our inspection of the floor structure includes the sills, columns, beams, joists and subfloors.

Looking, Probing Bouncing, And Measuring   The inspection is performed from above and below the floor itself. It includes looking at the components, probing exposed wood members where damage is suspected (unless they are part of a decorative finish) and bouncing on the floors to get a sense of their stiffness. In some cases a measuring tape is helpful to verify member sizes or spans. Spirit levels can be used to qualify sagging or sloping floors.

Judgment Needed   There are many conditions that may affect performance. It is common to find minor deflection and/or springiness and good judgment and experience are needed to determine whether the situation is typical or not. Serious problems are rare but can be costly to correct. Structural problems are also life safety hazards in many cases.

Concealed   As with all other components, it's common to find much of the floor system concealed by finishes or other access restrictions. Let your client know if your inspection was limited by these factors.

2.2 INTRODUCTION

Materials   Most suspended floors are wood and most floors resting on the earth are concrete slabs. While there are other systems, we'll restrict our discussion to these.

Function   Floors transfer both live and dead loads to the foundations, footings and ultimately to the soil below the house. Floor systems also provide lateral support for foundation walls. In houses with basements, the concrete basement floor provides lateral support for the bottom of the foundation wall and the wood frame first floor typically supports the top of the foundation wall.

Vertical And Horizontal Loads   Floor systems see both vertical and horizontal loads, although most people think of the vertical loads when they think of floors.

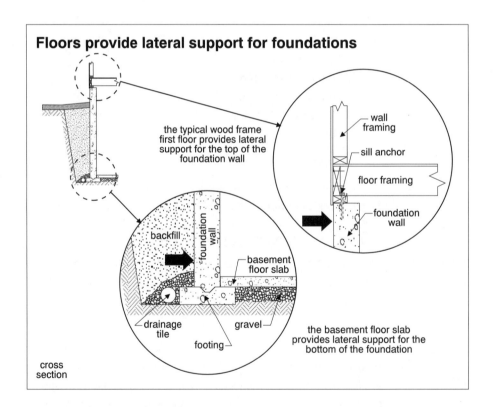

Floors provide lateral support for foundations

the typical wood frame first floor provides lateral support for the top of the foundation wall

wall framing

sill anchor

floor framing

foundation wall

backfill

foundation wall

basement floor slab

drainage tile

gravel

footing

the basement floor slab provides lateral support for the bottom of the foundation

cross section

To perform their functions, floors must have **strength** and **stiffness.**

Strength And Stiffness   Contrary to common understanding, strength refers to how much load can be applied before something breaks. Stiffness refers to how much bending or **deflection** takes place with a given load.

Strength   Floor systems must be strong enough to carry their loads. If the loads are excessive, the wood or concrete will break and the floors will collapse.

Stiffness

*1/360th
Of Length*

Floors also have to be stiff. This means that they have to limit the deflection that takes place when structural members respond to live loads. There will always be some deflection, but if the deflection is too great, damage to the interior finish will result. In some jurisdictions, the maximum allowable deflection is 1/360th of the length of the joist. This number is not magic, but comes from the amount of deflection that plaster and drywall will tolerate without cracking. Check what numbers are used in your area.

Generally speaking, floors with ceilings below use this limiting factor. In some cases, the allowed deflection is either 1/360th of the length or one half inch, whichever is less.

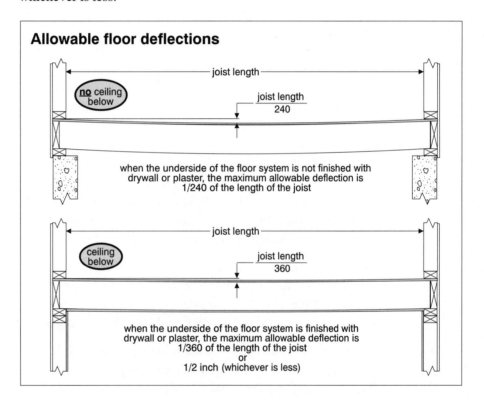

Allowable floor deflections

joist length

no ceiling below

joist length
240

when the underside of the floor system is not finished with drywall or plaster, the maximum allowable deflection is 1/240 of the length of the joist

joist length

ceiling below

joist length
360

when the underside of the floor system is finished with drywall or plaster, the maximum allowable deflection is 1/360 of the length of the joist
or
1/2 inch (whichever is less)

*1/240th
Of Length*

Where a plaster or drywall ceiling will not be attached on the underside (for example, the floor over a crawlspace), the maximum deflection may be allowed to be 1/240th of the length.

*Limited By
Bending*

Floor systems in houses are designed with maximum bending, not strength, as the restricting factor. As a result, floors are usually much stronger than they need to be. It's rare for floor systems to fail catastrophically, unless they have been severely damaged by rot, insects or careless carpentry work.

*Large Loads
Transferred
Through
Center Of
House*

Many think that the perimeter foundation walls have a large vertical load to carry because they are below the outside walls. A typical house with wood siding and a central bearing beam actually has a greater percentage of its weight on the beams and posts than it does on the outside walls! That's because the foundation wall only sees floor loads from one side of the wall (the inside, of course). A beam running down the middle of the house sees floor loads from both sides.

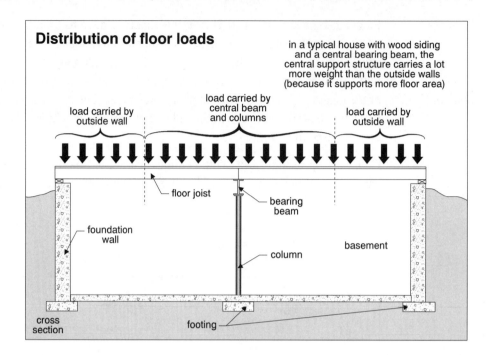

Distribution of floor loads

in a typical house with wood siding and a central bearing beam, the central support structure carries a lot more weight than the outside walls (because it supports more floor area)

load carried by outside wall

load carried by central beam and columns

load carried by outside wall

floor joist

bearing beam

foundation wall

column

basement

cross section

footing

Many people skimp on footings, columns and beams since they mistakenly assume the loads will be lighter for these interior members. Good design of beams and columns or interior bearing walls is critical to avoid sloping floors. The amount of settlement through the middle section of the house should be similar to that around the perimeter. If the settlement is greater or less in either area, floors will be uneven.

Avoid Wood/ Concrete Contact

In areas at or below grade the best practice is to avoid direct contact of wood with concrete. Polyethylene separators or sill gaskets can be used. Alternatively the wood can be pressure treated. We want to avoid moisture in the concrete being wicked into the wood, causing rot. This applies to beams, columns, joists and sills.

Joist/Beam Pockets

Where beams or joists go into pockets in foundation walls, it's common to keep the sides, top and ends of the wood half an inch away from the concrete to allow air circulation and keep the wood dry. Where the wood has to be embedded, it should be pressure treated and/or field treated with a wood preservative to prevent rot.

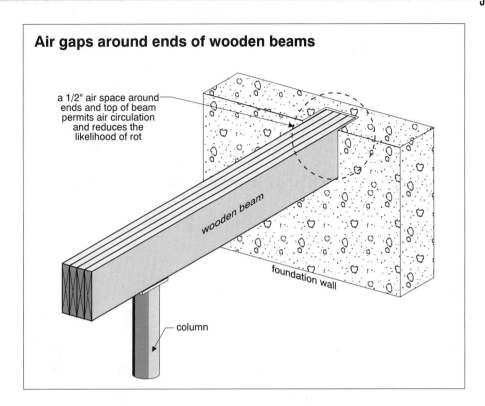

Air gaps around ends of wooden beams

a 1/2" air space around ends and top of beam permits air circulation and reduces the likelihood of rot

wooden beam

foundation wall

column

Nailing

Appropriate nailing is required to achieve a solid structure. Carpentry books or building codes tell you

1. how long nails should be,
2. how many should be used, and
3. what type should be used for any given connection.

We'll mention a few good nailing practices, although most nailing is not visible to the home inspector.

Good Practice

1. Each nail should have half its length go through into the second piece of material.
2. Nails should not split the wood that they are driven through, and must be kept away from edges to avoid this.
3. When several nails are driven in along the length of a piece of wood, it's good practice to stagger the nails, so the nails don't split the wood along a single grain line.

Good In Shear, But Lousy In Tension

Nails hold well when the forces are pushing the nailed pieces together or trying to make one piece slide against the other. Nails are not good in tension, where the forces want to pull the wood apart. This tends to pull the nails straight out.

Components   We'll look at the five components of wood flooring systems:
- Sills
- Columns
- Beams
- Joists
- Subflooring

We'll finish this section with a look at concrete floor systems.

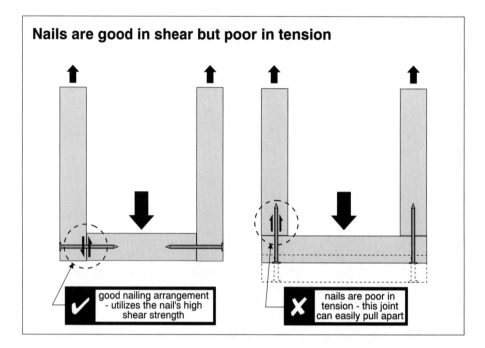

Nails are good in shear but poor in tension

good nailing arrangement - utilizes the nail's high shear strength

nails are poor in tension - this joint can easily pull apart

► 3.0 SILLS

Function   A wood sill is typically used to connect the top of the foundation to the wood floor system above. In balloon framing, the sills also connect the wall system to the foundation.

Loads   Sills see primarily compressive loads, but may experience tension (uplift) or shear (lateral) forces due to wind.

Material   Sills might be two by four or two by six or even two by eight lumber, typically the same species and grade as the rest of the lumber. Sills in some areas have to be pressure treated lumber, redwood, cedar or other rot and insect resistant wood.

Sill Gasket   Sills are often separated from the foundation wall by a sill gasket. The **sill gasket** is a compressible material designed to –

- Stop air leakage through any gaps between the foundation wall and sill
- Separate the sill from the concrete

The sill should have full bearing on the foundation along its entire length.

*Inside Or
Outside Of
Foundation*

Sills may be mounted flush with the inside or outside foundation wall face, depending on the wall construction. If the walls are to be wood frame, with masonry veneer, the sills go on the inside part of the foundation, leaving room for the masonry units to rest directly on the foundation. We don't want the masonry resting on the wood. If the walls are to have a siding material, the sills are typically flush with the outside face.

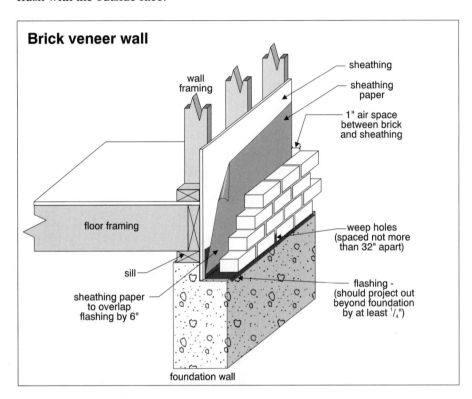

Brick veneer wall

wall framing

sheathing

sheathing paper

1" air space between brick and sheathing

floor framing

weep holes (spaced not more than 32" apart)

sill

flashing - (should project out beyond foundation by at least $^1/_4$")

sheathing paper to overlap flashing by 6"

foundation wall

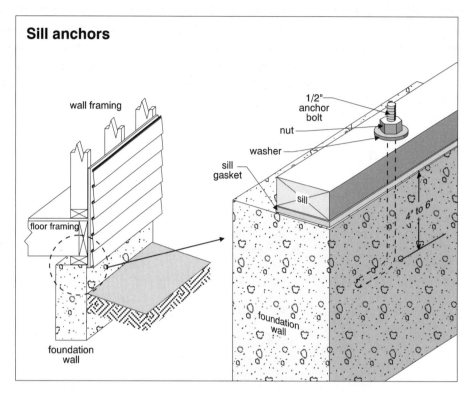

Sill anchors

Sills may also be embedded in the concrete foundation as it is poured. There are different approaches, but the function is the same. In some climates, embedding the sills in concrete is an invitation to sill rot.

Should Be Above Grade

We have talked about foundation walls and how they should extend at least six inches above finished grade level. Sills should also be well above grade level. Sills are often at or below grade on older homes, as a result of

• Poor construction initially
• Changes to grade level
• Building settlement

Implications of Rot

This is a recipe for problems. Rotted sills are easily crushed by the weight of the house, and will lead to differential settlement of the floors and walls above. Rotted sills also often mean rotted joists and studs. Rotted sills mean the house frame is not well anchored to the foundation.

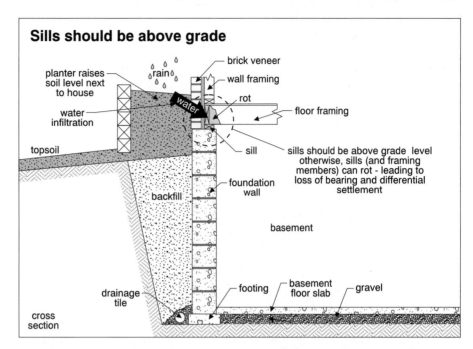

Sills should be above grade

planter raises soil level next to house

rain

brick veneer

wall framing

water infiltration

rot

floor framing

topsoil

sill

sills should be above grade level otherwise, sills (and framing members) can rot - leading to loss of bearing and differential settlement

foundation wall

backfill

basement

drainage tile

footing

basement floor slab

gravel

cross section

A Mud Sill Is Not A Sill

Some old houses and cottages were built with **mud sills**. These are really beams laid directly on the ground. Houses with mud sills typically have no foundations. The top-soil was merely scraped off, and wood members (often eight by eight or six by eight) were laid directly on the ground. Floors and wall systems were built on top of these.

Rot And Frost Problems

The wood/soil contact often resulted in rot attacking the mud sills. The absence of frost footings often causes these buildings to move dramatically during cold winter months. However, where soils are dry and frost heave does not occur, mud sills may still be serviceable on older structures.

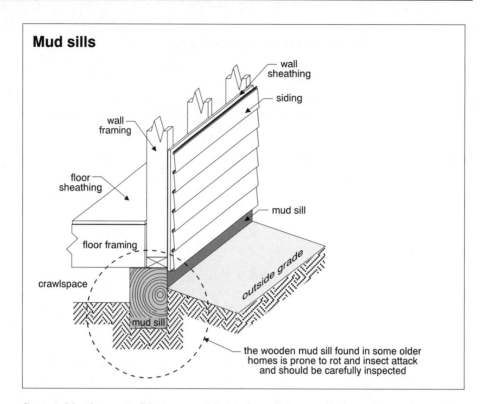

Mud sills

wall sheathing

siding

wall framing

floor sheathing

mud sill

floor framing

crawlspace

outside grade

mud sill

the wooden mud sill found in some older homes is prone to rot and insect attack and should be carefully inspected

The Evolution Of The Mud Sill

Some older houses with stone and brick foundation walls have large six by six or eight by eight sills at the top of the foundation. Floor and wall systems were built on top of these sills. While there is no reason for making the sills this large (and there are some good reasons not to do it), as long as these sills are not rotted or attacked by insects, they may perform satisfactorily.

Watch For Large Sill Beams

Watch for sills crushing as a result of rot and/or insect attack. Also watch for buildings that have settled as a result of wood shrinkage across the grain (which is considerable). Tall wood sills add more horizontal wood to the structure than is desirable, since there is so much shrinkage across the grain.

Framing Shrinkage

It's not unusual to have 4% shrinkage across the grain as wood dries out from 19% moisture content, common in framing lumber, to about 5%. Every horizontal piece of wood in the structure can shrink this amount, resulting in the building getting considerably shorter after it is built. A two by ten, for example, for example, will shrink about $^3/_8$ of an inch as a result of this drying process. If the wood frame structure shrinks, and there is brick veneer on the exterior, problems can be experienced because the brick veneer will not shrink and, in fact, will expand slightly.

Securing Sills To Foundations

In modern construction, $^1/_2$ inch diameter bolts anchored into the foundation wall hold the sill plates down. While some say the **anchor bolts** should be buried 4 inches minimum into the foundation, others say 6 or even 7 inches. Where the foundation walls are concrete or cinder block, some say that the bolts have to be long enough to go down into the second block. This means that the bolts have to be well over 8 inches long. In most cases, you won't see how this was done and won't know how well or how deeply the bolts are anchored into the foundation.

Anchor Bolt Spacing

You can, however, see how many bolts have been provided. Some building authorities call for bolts every 8 feet. Others call for bolts every 6 feet and bolts within 12 inches of each corner. In seismic (earthquake) prone areas, bolts are required every 4ft. What does your area call for?

Nuts And Bolts

Check whether the bolts go through the center of the sills. Sometimes the bolts miss the sills altogether. You can also see whether washers and nuts have been provided and tightened down.

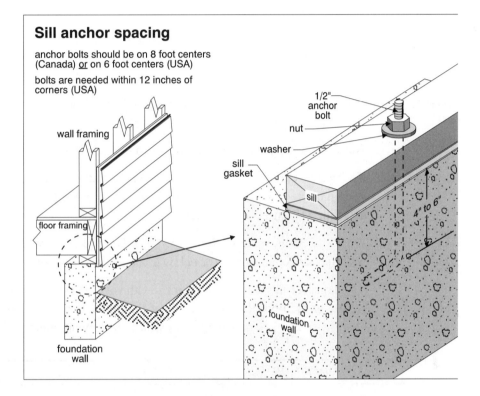

Sill anchor spacing

anchor bolts should be on 8 foot centers (Canada) or on 6 foot centers (USA)

bolts are needed within 12 inches of corners (USA)

wall framing

floor framing

foundation wall

1/2" anchor bolt

nut

washer

sill gasket

sill

4" to 6"

foundation wall

Wind Uplift During Construction

Buildings are most vulnerable to wind uplift during the construction phase, when framing is complete with wall and roof sheathing, but no windows are in. A house can act very much like a box kite in a strong wind, and be lifted off its foundations, or flipped over by the wind.

Let's look at some of the common sill problems.

3.1 CONDITIONS

Common sill problems include –
1. Sills below grade
2. Rot or insect damage
3. Gaps between the sill and foundation
4. Crushed sills
5. Not properly anchored
6. Missing

3.1.1 SILLS BELOW GRADE

We discussed sills in conjunction with foundation height. When sills are below grade, there is a danger of rot and insect infestation. Even if there is no evidence of dampness or rot, this is a dangerous condition. There could be rot you can't see.

Causes

Causes of sills below grade include –
• an original construction mistake
• changes in exterior landscaping
• building settlement

Implications

• rot
• insect damage
• building settlement

Strategy

Check the height of a basement window. If the grade level is at or above the top of the foundation, be suspicious.

Siding

Watch for siding material extending down to grade level.

Concrete Curb

If a concrete curb projects out from the plane of the wall, you may be looking at an attempt to prevent water infiltration over the top of the original foundation. This may hide a sill that is below grade.

Basement Stairs

Where basement walkouts have been converted to finished basement stairs, the wall studs are often close to or below grade level. Watch out for these.

If you suspect sills are too low confirm with your tape measure. Measure from the bottom of the floor joists or the top of the foundation to something that can be identified outside (such as a window sill, dryer vent, electrical conduit, etc.).

3.1.2 ROT OR INSECT DAMAGE

Causes

Rot or insect damage results from –
1. **Moisture** due to
    • foundation walls that are too short
    • leaks in wall or roof systems (including faulty flashings at the base of brick veneer walls)
    • water leaking from plumbing or heating systems within the house
    • condensation

2. **Attack by termites, carpenter ants**, etc.

Implications

The implications of this and the other problems in this section include –

• differential settlement
• sloped floors
• sagging floors
• shifting or overturning due to wind or earthquake
• partial collapse
• total collapse of the structure

Strategy	Look at and probe wood sills with an awl or screwdriver. Pay particular attention to areas that may be close to a water source. If the grade is high in one area, pay particular attention to it.
More Insulation	In some cases, insulation must be temporarily removed to check the sills. This can be done easily with an awl or screwdriver.
	Learn what types of insect damage are found in your area. While you don't have to look for insects according to the Standards, you do have to identify damaged wood.
Crawlspaces Need Soil Clearance	Watch for crawlspaces that are shallow. The earth in sub-grade areas should be at 18 inches below floor joists and 12 inches below beams. Where earth is closer, there is a greater risk, rot and insect damage to sills as well as joists and beams.
Crawl Space Ventilation	The risk of rot to sills, joists and beams is also increased where earth-floor crawlspace ventilation is less than 1 sq. ft. of venting for every 150 to 1,500 ft. sq. of floor area. Check your local requirements for venting. These vary with climate and type of floor surface.
Access	These should always be access into under floor spaces. While authorities may specify 20 by 28 inches, 18 by 24 inches, or something different, use common sense to determine whether the access is large enough to get through.

3.1.3 GAPS UNDER SILLS

Causes	The most common cause of gaps under sills is an uneven foundation wall top.
Implications	Slight differential settlement and excess heat loss are the typical implications.
Strategy	Look for a continuous and level bearing surface under sills. Where foundation walls have an uneven top, a bed of mortar is sometimes used to provide a level surface for the sills. Sill gasket material, which is typically about $\frac{1}{4}$ inch thick, should not be expected to take up significant gaps. This gasket material has no structural strength.
	Floor systems built on sills spanning gaps may not deflect until the floor is loaded with furniture and people. Where unusual floor deflection is noted with no apparent cause, it may be a result of sills being pushed down onto the uneven foundation surface by the live loads.

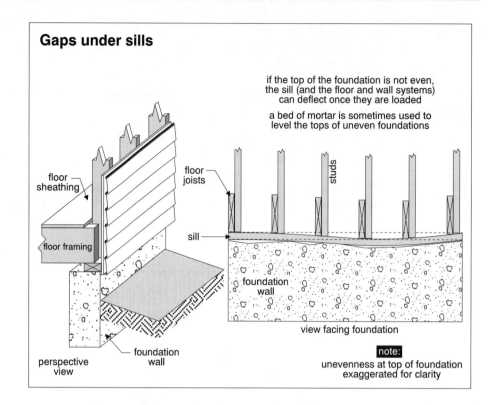

Gaps under sills

if the top of the foundation is not even, the sill (and the floor and wall systems) can deflect once they are loaded

a bed of mortar is sometimes used to level the tops of uneven foundations

floor sheathing

floor joists

studs

floor framing

sill

foundation wall

view facing foundation

perspective view

foundation wall

note:
unevenness at top of foundation exaggerated for clarity

3.1.4 CRUSHED SILLS

Causes   Sills may be crushed because –

1. they have been weakened by rot or insect damage
2. they see concentrated loads from inadequate end bearing of joists and beams
3. of concentrated loads from columns with missing or poorly installed bearing plates resting on sills.

Steel structural members, including beams and columns, should not bear on wood. This rule is sometimes broken without problems, but there is a risk.

Strategy   Look for crushing of the sills as you go around the foundation perimeter.

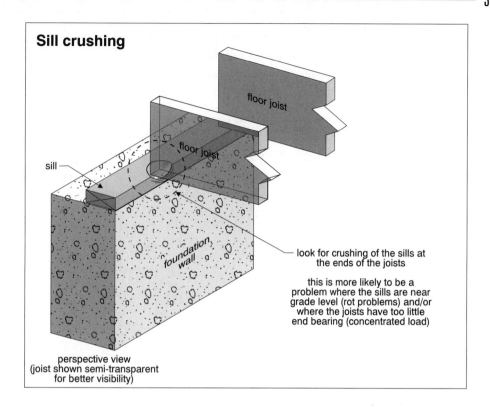

Sill crushing

floor joist

floor joist

sill

look for crushing of the sills at
the ends of the joists

this is more likely to be a
problem where the sills are near
grade level (rot problems) and/or
where the joists have too little
end bearing (concentrated load)

foundation wall

perspective view
(joist shown semi-transparent
for better visibility)

Probe for rot and insect damage. Check that there is roughly $1\frac{1}{2}$ inch end bearing for joists and $3\frac{1}{2}$ inch end bearing for beams.

3.1.5 POORLY ANCHORED

Causes

Sills may not be well anchored because –

1. anchor bolts are missing
2. there aren't enough anchor bolts
3. the anchor bolts are not well secured to the foundation
4. the anchor bolts are not centered in the sills
5. the sill is split where the bolt penetrates
6. nuts and or washers are missing (sometimes because the bolts are too short)
7. nuts are not tightened down.

Strategy

Look for anchor bolts at the appropriate spacings. Make sure the sills aren't damaged where the bolts go through. While it is poor practice, sometimes sill plates are set on top of the bolts and hammered until the bolts puncture through the wood. Holes should be drilled in the sills and the sills then slipped over the bolts. In some cases, the sill and bolt are in place, but the bolt misses the sill altogether, or only catches the very edge.

3.1.6 MISSING

Causes   Missing sills may be a result of –
- Original construction mistakes
- Amateurish remodeling

Strategy   All modern construction should have sills. Older houses, particularly solid masonry houses, may not have sills. Joists may bear directly on masonry. This is less desirable, but if time has proven the installation acceptable, you should not criticize. Probe the joists carefully where they enter pockets in the foundation walls. Rot is common here, particularly if the joists are at or near grade level.

Structure
MODULE

QUICK QUIZ 1

☑ INSTRUCTIONS

• You should finish reading Study Session 1 before doing this Quiz.

• Write your answers in the spaces provided.

• Check your answers against ours at the end of this Section.

• If you have trouble with the Quiz, re-read the Session and try the Quiz again.

• If you do well, move on to Session 2.

1. List five general structural components that must be inspected according to the Standards.

    _____

    _____

2. List five structural components of floors, as defined in this Module.

    _____

    _____

3. All of these may be floor functions except:

    a. transferring live and dead loads to the foundation
    b. providing lateral support for foundation walls
    c. carrying the weight of masonry chimneys

4. Floors will bend a little before they break.
    True ☐   False ☐

5. Vertical loads on beams and columns running through the center of the house can be greater than the vertical loads through foundations.
   True ☐   False ☐

6. Why is wood contact with concrete near or below grade level discouraged?

   _____

   _____

   _____

7. What is the main function of sills?

   _____

   _____

8. Why are rotted sills a problem?(3 answers)

   _____

   _____

   _____

9. How are sills anchored to foundations?

   _____

   _____

   _____

10. List five common sill problems.

   _____

   _____

   _____

If you had no trouble with the Quiz, you are ready for Study Session 2!

Key Words:

- *Sills*
- *Columns*
- *Beams*
- *Joists*
- *Subfloors*
- *Probing*
- *Bouncing*
- *Measuring*
- *Strength*
- *Stiffness*
- *Bending*
- *Wood/concrete contact*
- *Wood/soil contact*
- *Nailing practices*
- *Compression*
- *Tension*
- *Shear*
- *Sill gasket*
- *Mud sill*
- *Anchor bolts*
- *Rot*
- *Insect damage*
- *Sill crushing*

Structure
MODULE

STUDY SESSION 2

1. You should have completed Study Session 1 and Quick Quiz 1 before starting this Session.

2. By the end of this Session, you should be able to –

- List five materials columns may be made of.
- List 13 common problems with columns.
- List two implications of column problems.
- Describe in one sentence each how looking, probing, measuring and kicking can help identify column problems .

3. This Session may take roughly 45 minutes to complete.

4. At the end, there is Quick Quiz 2.

Keywords:

- *Pilasters*
- *Collapse*
- *Weak link in chain*
- *Missing*
- *Settled*
- *Crushed*
- *Leaning*
- *Buckled*
- *Rust*
- *Poorly secured*
- *Mortar deterioration*
- *Spalling*
- *Mechanical damage*
- *Rot or insect damage*
- *Heaved*
- *Prior repairs*
- *⅓ rule*
- *Slip sheet*
- *Rising damp*

► 4.0 COLUMNS

Function Columns are designed to transfer loads from beams down through footings to the soil. They are located inside the perimeter of the foundation wall, typically, and may or may not be visible during an inspection. Columns are often concealed within interior wall systems. Columns built into perimeter walls are called **pilasters.**

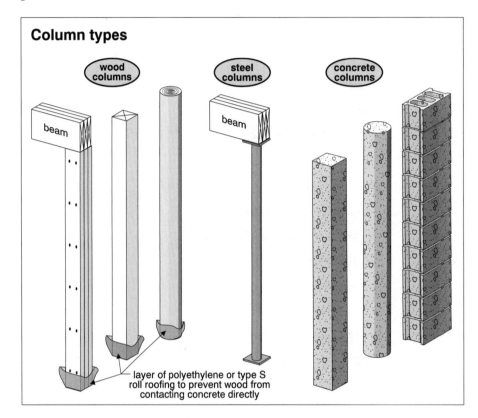

Column types

wood columns

steel columns

concrete columns

beam

beam

layer of polyethylene or type S roll roofing to prevent wood from contacting concrete directly

Materials Columns may be concrete, concrete block, brick, steel or wood, typically. They can be a combination of these.

Loads Columns must be rigid and strong enough to resist crushing and buckling. Columns see mostly compressive loads. They must be durable and well secured to withstand impact loads and mechanical damage.

Implications The implications of column failure may be minor sagging or complete collapse of the structure. Columns are a very important part of the structure.

One Weak Any assembly is only as strong as its weakest link. A wonderful job with joists
Link Ruins and beams, for example, can be undone by a single poor connection between
The Chain a beam and a column or a column and a footing. Think of structures as a chain of components and be on the lookout for a weak link.

4.1 CONDITIONS

The common problems that we find with columns include –

1. missing
2. settled
3. crushed
4. leaning
5. buckling
6. rust
7. poorly secured at the top or bottom
8. mortar deterioration
9. spalling concrete or brick
10. mechanical damage
11. rot or insect damage
12. heaved
13. prior repairs

4.1.1 MISSING

Causes   Missing columns are unusual on original construction. They are most often caused by homeowners trying to make more clear space available in a room. Depending on the house configuration, the results can be catastrophic failure or sagging.

4.1.2 SETTLED COLUMNS

Causes   Columns may settle for the same reason that foundations do. There may be –

1. no footing
2. an undersized footing
3. poor soil conditions under the footing
4. a larger than intended load on the column

Floors around the column may or may not setlle with the column.

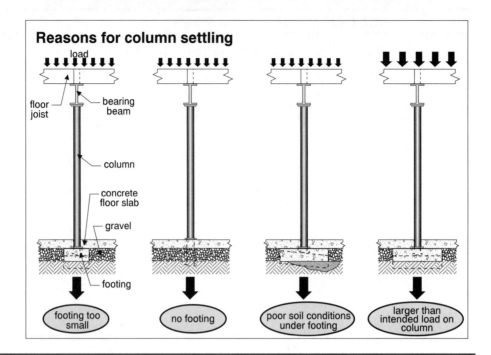

Reasons for column settling

load

floor joist
bearing beam
column
concrete floor slab
gravel
footing

footing too small

no footing

poor soil conditions under footing

larger than intended load on column

4.1.3 CRUSHED

Causes

While it is rare for an entire column to be crushed, it is quite common for shims at the top of a column to be crushed, particularly if they are cedar (not a strong wood). Concrete can also be crushed, especially if there is a point load. Wood columns may also be crushed at the top or bottom. If crushed at the bottom, there is often rot involved. The rot weakens the wood, making it susceptible to crushing.

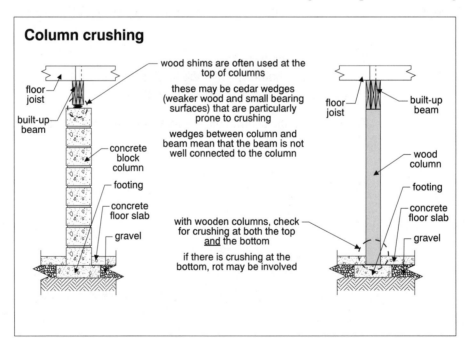

Column crushing

floor joist
built-up beam
concrete block column
footing
concrete floor slab
gravel

wood shims are often used at the top of columns

these may be cedar wedges (weaker wood and small bearing surfaces) that are particularly prone to crushing

wedges between column and beam mean that the beam is not well connected to the column

with wooden columns, check for crushing at both the top and the bottom

if there is crushing at the bottom, rot may be involved

floor joist
built-up beam
wood column
footing
concrete floor slab
gravel

4.1.4 LEANING COLUMNS

Causes   Columns may lean because –

1. the entire building is racking
2. of an impact
3. beams are not laterally supported and are twisting
4. the column is not adequately secured to the beam above
5. the column is not well secured to the footing below

Strategy   Leaning columns may be catastrophic. Columns cannot lean out of plumb very far without becoming unstable. Generally speaking, if the distance the column is out of plumb exceeds 1/3rd of the column width (in the smallest dimension) the column is unstable. A plumb bob can be used to measure the lean.

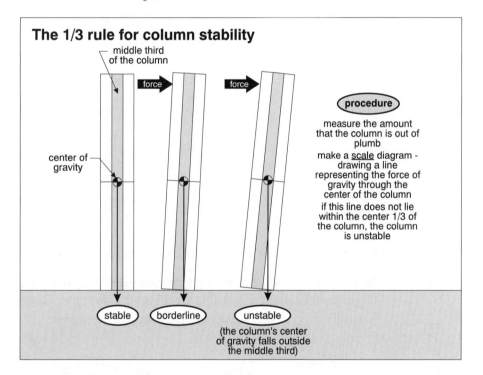

The 1/3 rule for column stability

middle third of the column

force

force

procedure

measure the amount that the column is out of plumb

make a scale diagram - drawing a line representing the force of gravity through the center of the column

if this line does not lie within the center 1/3 of the column, the column is unstable

center of gravity

stable   borderline   unstable

(the column's center of gravity falls outside the middle third)

4.1.5 BUCKLING

Columns may buckle if they are too slender. This is a function of their height and loading. Steel columns (lally columns) are typically 3 inches or more in diameter with a wall thickness of about $^3/_{16}$ of an inch. Standard top and bottom bearing plates are four inches by four inches by $^1/_4$ inch thick. Larger top bearing plates may be required to support wood beams.

Rough Rules   Built-up wood columns should be bolted together with 2 bolts every 16 inches,
For Wood   typically, or nailed together with 2 nails every 12 inches. The bottom of wood
Columns   columns should not directly contact concrete. Round wood columns should be 7$^1/_4$ inch diameter, minimum, typically. Square solid wood columns should be 6 inches by 6 inches minimum.

Masonry And Concrete Columns

Hollow masonry columns should be at least 12 by 12 inches or 10 by 16 inches. Round concrete columns should be 9 inch diameter, minimum, and square concrete columns should be 8 inches by 8 inches, minimum.

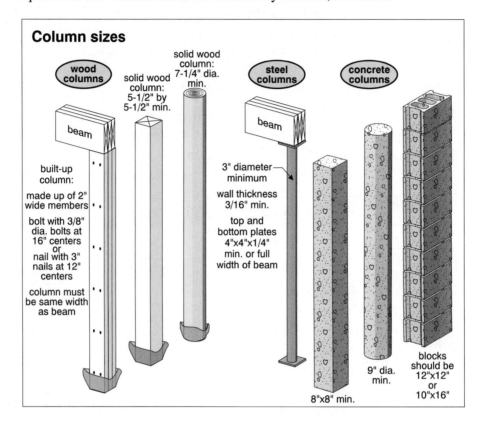

Column sizes

wood columns

solid wood column: 5-1/2" by 5-1/2" min.

solid wood column: 7-1/4" dia. min.

steel columns

concrete columns

beam

built-up column:

made up of 2" wide members

bolt with 3/8" dia. bolts at 16" centers or nail with 3" nails at 12" centers

column must be same width as beam

beam

3" diameter minimum

wall thickness 3/16" min.

top and bottom plates 4"x4"x1/4" min. or full width of beam

8"x8" min.

9" dia. min.

blocks should be 12"x12" or 10"x16"

Multi-story houses or large concentrated loads require larger columns.

Strategy

In some cases, a mason's level is helpful to determine whether a column is buckling, although usually it is visible. Reinforcing wood columns to prevent buckling is usually easy, as long as the movement has not been great.

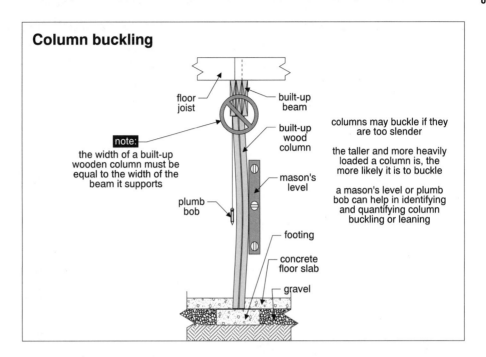

Column buckling

floor joist

built-up beam

built-up wood column

note:
the width of a built-up wooden column must be equal to the width of the beam it supports

mason's level

plumb bob

footing

concrete floor slab

gravel

columns may buckle if they are too slender

the taller and more heavily loaded a column is, the more likely it is to buckle

a mason's level or plumb bob can help in identifying and quantifying column buckling or leaning

---

4.1.6 RUST

Cause

Rust is caused by moisture and is most commonly found near the base of columns. The moisture may be from condensation, leakage of outside water through the foundation walls, leakage from plumbing or heating systems inside the house, etc.

One Rusted Column

One of the famous home inspector stories involves a single badly rusted steel column in a basement, but two other columns in the basement showed no rust. The rust was near the base, and there was no evidence of plumbing, heating, or foundation wall leakage. The story says the column was rusted because a dog tied to this column daily relieved himself against the column. The urine rusted the column.

Strategy

When looking at metal columns, watch for rust at the bottom. A kick at the bottom of the column should not result in any movement.

4.1.7 POORLY SECURED AT THE TOP OR BOTTOM

Problems More Common At Top

Columns must be well secured to footings and to beams above. Securement at the bottom is not usually difficult, since the footing is usually poured below the basement floor. The basement floor is poured around the column, locking it in its proper position on the footing. The exception is when the column is added after original construction. If so, it may be sitting on top of the concrete floor. This raises two questions:

1. Is there a footing?
2. How is the column secured to the floor?

Securing the top of the column to the beam is a much more common problem area.

Causes

Poor connections are usually an original installation issue.

Strategy   Look at the beam/column intersection, after checking that the base of the column is surrounded by the concrete floor. Incidentally, it's good practice to use a plastic or building paper slip sheet between the column and the floor slab to prevent floor slab movement of the slab affecting the column.

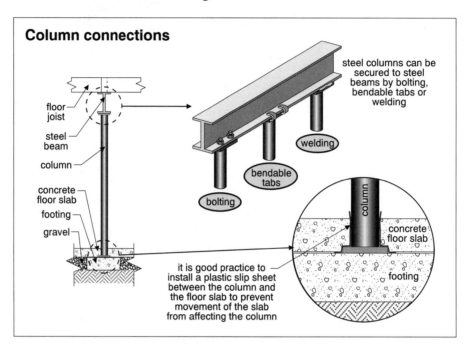

Column connections

Is Top Plate Wide Enough?   Make sure the top of the column bearing plate is the full width of the beam. For example, a 4 inch by 4 inch steel plate is not wide enough to support a built–up beam made of four members. A built-up beam made of four two by eights, for example, will be 6 inches wide. The bearing plate needs to be the full width of the beam in order to transfer the loads effectively.

Is Beam Secured To Column?   Next, make sure that the beam is not merely resting on the column. If it is a wood beam and the bearing plate is steel, it is common for holes in the bearing plate to be provided, and nails or screws may be used to secure the bearing plate to the beam.

Steel To Steel   Steel columns may be secured to steel beams by bolting, welding or bendable metal tabs.

In some cases, the method of securing the column to the beam is not visible.

In hurricane or earthquake areas, additional securement may be necessary. Special straps are used to accomplish this.

Differential movement between the beam and the column can result in catastrophic failure. The loads transferred from beams to columns are significant, and the transfer must be completed effectively. Watch for evidence of movement of the top and bottom of columns.

4.1.8 MORTAR DETERIORATION

Causes   Common causes for mortar deterioration include

1. poor quality mortar and/or installation, and
2. moisture penetration problems.

The moisture problems may be the result of foundation wall leakage and flooding of a basement floor, or rising damp (water wicking up into masonry by capillary action).

Strategy   Probe suspect mortar with a screwdriver or awl to make sure it is not completely disintegrated. A masonry column has to act as a unit. Repairs are usually not expensive, but are important. Mortar is more important in resisting lateral shear forces than vertical compressive forces. Masonry columns with weak mortar are easily dislodged by impact.

4.1.9 SPALLING CONCRETE OR BRICK

Causes   These conditions are caused by moisture, again as a result of leakage from outside or **rising damp** (moisture wicking up into the column from soil or water on the floor).

The implications are similar to what we talked about in concrete and brick foundation spalling. The problem is less likely to arise on interior columns than on perimeter foundation walls, because spalling is often a result of freeze/thaw action. Unless the house has been left unheated, columns are rarely susceptible to freezing temperatures. Spalling is usually concentrated near the column base, and is often a surface problem only. However, if more than about 10% of the column cross sectional area is missing or weakened, further investigation is needed.

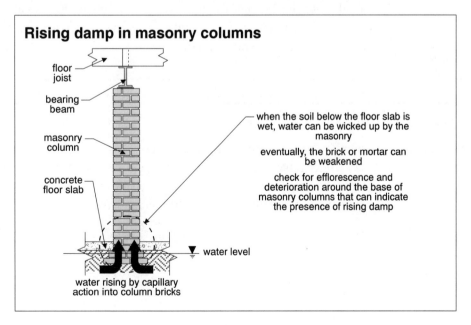

Rising damp in masonry columns

floor joist

bearing beam

masonry column

concrete floor slab

when the soil below the floor slab is wet, water can be wicked up by the masonry

eventually, the brick or mortar can be weakened

check for efflorescence and deterioration around the base of masonry columns that can indicate the presence of rising damp

water level

water rising by capillary action into column bricks

4.1.10 MECHANICAL DAMAGE

This can result from impact as a result of hammers being used to nail things into columns, for example, or careless work nearby. Mechanical damage includes cutting wood with saws, or cutting steel with torches.

Strategy   Mechanical damage is usually fairly obvious, but concealed columns can't be inspected.

4.1.11 ROT OR INSECT DAMAGE

Causes   This is normally the result of wood/soil contact and failure to protect against termite infestation, for example.

Strategy   Probe the wood close to the basement floor and look for discoloration, checking, mold, mildew and crushing. Watch for wood columns that go through the floor.

4.1.12 HEAVED

Occasionally, columns will have heaved and may be hanging from the beam, not touching the floor. (In some cases, this will look like heaving but, in fact, is a result of the bottom of the columns rusting or rotting away.)

Cause   Where heaving has taken place, the cause will usually be –
• expansive soils
• tree roots
• frost

Strategy   The footing and basement floor may heave, pushing the entire house up. When the footing settles back down, the column may not come with it, or may not come down straight. Beam/column or footing/column connections may break. In some cases, part of the basement floor will get stuck between the column and the footing. This is an unstable and dangerous condition.

4.1.13 PRIOR REPAIRS

Cause   This is a result of prior damage.

Strategy   Some repairs are substantial and make columns stronger than they were to begin with. Other repairs are superficial only and do not address the problem. Try to identify the cause of the damage that led to the repair. Where columns have been repaired, try to determine whether the column will be as strong as it was originally.

Structure
M O D U L E

QUICK QUIZ 2

☑ INSTRUCTIONS

- You should finish reading Study Session 2 before doing this Quiz.

- Write your answers in the spaces provided.

- Check your answers against ours at the end of this Section.

- If you have trouble with this Quiz, re-read the Session and try the Quiz again.

- If you do well, move on to Session 2.

1. Columns transfer live and dead loads:

    a. from joists to footings
    b. from beams to footings
    c. from joists to soil directly
    d. from subfloors to joists
    e. from subfloors to footings

2. List five common column materials.

    _____

    _____

3. List 12 common column problems.

    _____   _____   _____

    _____   _____   _____

    _____   _____   _____

    _____   _____   _____

4. Why would columns settle?(Give three reasons)

    _____ _____ _____

5. Which column materials are susceptible to crushing?

    _____

6. How wide should the top of a column be, relative to the width of the beam above?

    _____

7. How may steel columns be fastened to steel beams? (three answers)

    _____ _____ _____

8. What tool, in addition to your eyes, is commonly used to inspect columns?

    _____

9. Name three common causes of heaving columns.

    _____ _____ _____

10. Columns are most likely to rot at the –

    • top
    • middle
    • bottom

If you had no trouble with the Quiz, you are ready for Study Session 3.

Key Words:

- *Sills*
- *Columns*
- *Beams*
- *Joists*
- *Subfloors*
- *Probing*
- *Bouncing*
- *Measuring*
- *Strength*
- *Stiffness*
- *Bending*
- *Wood/concrete contact*
- *Wood/soil contact*
- *Nailing practices*
- *Compression*
- *Tension*
- *Shear*
- *Sill gasket*
- *Mud sill*
- *Anchor bolts*
- *Rot*
- *Insect damage*
- *Sill crushing*

Structure
MODULE

STUDY SESSION 3

1. You should have completed Study Sessions 1 and 2 before starting this Session.

2. By the end of this Session you should be able to –

- Identify two common beam materials.
- List three types of engineered wood.
- Describe in one sentence the function of beams.
- List 14 common beam problems.

3. This Session may take you about 45 minutes to complete.

4. Quick Quiz 3 is at the end of this Session.

Keywords:

- *Beams*
- *Sag*
- *Girders*
- *Poor bearing*
- *Built-up*
- *Rotated or twisted*
- *Glulams*
- *Split or damaged*
- *LVL*
- *Notches and holes*
- *Parallel strand*
- *Poor connections to joists*
- *Engineered wood*
- *Concentrated loads*
- *Lateral support*
- *Missing sections*
- *End bearing*
- *Prior repairs*
- *Continuous span*
- *Shims*
- *Simple span*
- *Ribbon boards*
- *Rust*
- *Rot or insect damage*
- *Checking*
- *Joist hangers*
- *Poor connections of built-up beam components*
- *Ledger boards*

► 5.0 BEAMS

Function Beams (girders) are large horizontal members that carry the floor loads from the floors, walls and/or roofs to the columns or foundation walls. Floor joists rest directly on beams. Walls and columns often sit on floors, so they may rest indirectly on beams.

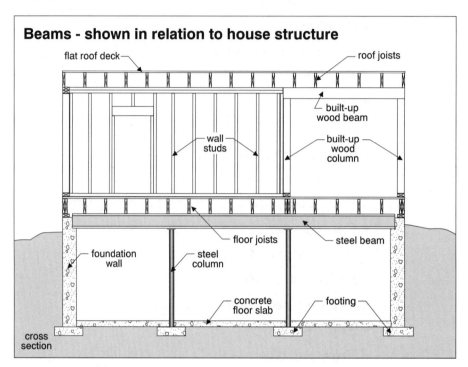

Beams - shown in relation to house structure

Materials Beams are traditionally wood or steel. Wood beams might be solid, built-up, **laminated (glulams)**, **laminated veneer lumber** (LVL – think of it as overgrown plywood), **laminated strand lumber** (LSL) or **parallel strand lumber** (PSL). These last four are known as **engineered wood** products.

Loads On Beams Beams see primarily vertical loads from the weight of floor systems and the live loads above. Lateral loads or tension (uplift) forces may be induced by wind. Beams might fail in bending or shear. Bending is, of course, a combination of compression (felt by the top part of the beam) and tension (felt by the bottom part of the beam).

Notching Worse In Bottom Wood is fairly good in both tension and compression, but it is slightly better in compression. A notch cut in the bottom edge of a beam is more likely to result in failure than one cut in the top edge, although as a general rule, notches and holes should not be cut in beams.

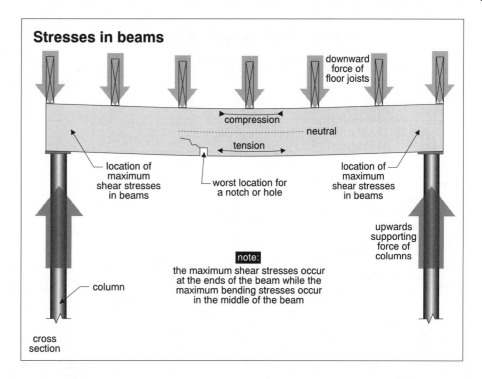

Stresses in beams

downward force of floor joists

compression

neutral

tension

location of maximum shear stresses in beams

worst location for a notch or hole

location of maximum shear stresses in beams

upwards supporting force of columns

column

note:
the maximum shear stresses occur at the ends of the beam while the maximum bending stresses occur in the middle of the beam

cross section

Load
Transfer

Beams transfer their loads vertically to columns or foundations. Beams may receive their loads on a vertical or horizontal face. Joists may rest on top of beams or be fastened to the sides of beams. Joists may also be supported on the bottom flange of a steel beam.

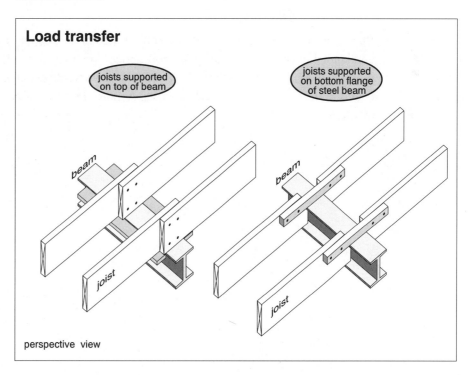

Load transfer

joists supported on top of beam

joists supported on bottom flange of steel beam

beam

joist

beam

joist

perspective view

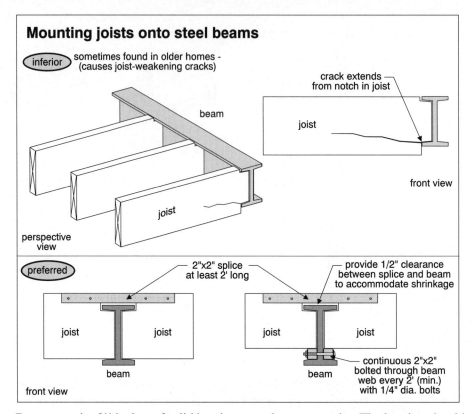

Mounting joists onto steel beams

inferior — sometimes found in older homes - (causes joist-weakening cracks)

beam

joist

perspective view

crack extends from notch in joist

joist

front view

preferred

2"x2" splice at least 2' long

provide 1/2" clearance between splice and beam to accommodate shrinkage

joist   joist

joist   joist

beam

beam

continuous 2"x2" bolted through beam web every 2' (min.) with 1/4" dia. bolts

front view

Bearing

Beams require 3½ inches of solid bearing at each support point. The bearing should be the full width of the beam to avoid crushing or rotation. The end bearing should be level and continuous.

Continuous Beams Are Stiffer Than Simply Supported

Beams are important fundamental structural members. Beams or joists that are continuous over an intermediate support deflect less than individual beams that run from one support to another. Many builders take advantage of this by using long beams with several intermediate supports. A more rigid floor system is achieved this way.

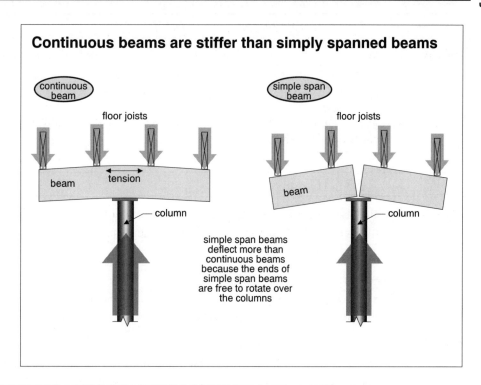

Continuous beams are stiffer than simply spanned beams

continuous beam

simple span beam

floor joists

floor joists

beam

tension

column

beam

column

simple span beams deflect more than continuous beams because the ends of simple span beams are free to rotate over the columns

5.1 CONDITIONS

Commonly found beam problems include –

1. rust
2. rot or insect damage
3. sag
4. poor bearing
5. rotated or twisted beams
6. split or damaged
7. notches or holes
8. poor connections of built-up components
9. weak connections to columns
10. weak connections to joists
11. inadequate lateral support
12. concentrated loads
13. missing beam sections
14. prior repairs

5.1.1 RUST

Causes Steel beams can rust, although this is not a common problem. High moisture levels often combined with incomplete shop priming paint are the causes.

Strategy If rust is experienced, it is most likely to be where the beam rests in a pocket in an exterior foundation wall. Check this area closely.

5.1.2 ROT OR INSECT DAMAGE

Strategy   We've talked about looking for these in various spots. Again, rot is most likely where the beam rests on the foundation wall near the building exterior. Probe with a screwdriver or awl wherever beams are exposed.

Soil Clearance   We've also discussed the need for beams to be at least 12 inches above the soil in earth-floor crawlspaces.

5.1.3 SAG

Causes   Beams may sag because they are overspanned for their size. Another way to look at this is to say that they are undersized for their span.

This may be –
• an original construction mistake
• the result of construction activities in the house (such as adding another floor)
• the result of removing intermediate supports (columns.)

Strategy   Sight along the underside of beams between supports to look for sag. In some cases, a mason's level is necessary, although if you can't see the sag with your naked eye, it's probably not serious enough to worry about.

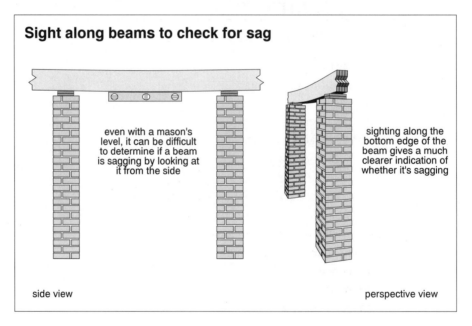

Sight along beams to check for sag

even with a mason's level, it can be difficult to determine if a beam is sagging by looking at it from the side

sighting along the bottom edge of the beam gives a much clearer indication of whether it's sagging

side view   perspective view

5.1.4 INADEQUATE BEARING

Steel or wood beams should rest on flat, full width bearing surfaces.

Causes

Where bearing is inadequate, it may be the result of –

1. an original construction mistake
2. deterioration of the foundation material or column
3. settlement of the foundation or column
4. sagging of the beam
5. loss, movement or crushing of shims between the bottom of the beam and the foundation or column

Strategy

Steel beams should only be supported with steel shims. Steel shims should be welded to the beam so they will not move. Watch for shims that have slid out from their position. Watch also for wood shims under steel beams. They often crush and creep. Shims will often move because the top surface of the foundation wall is not level.

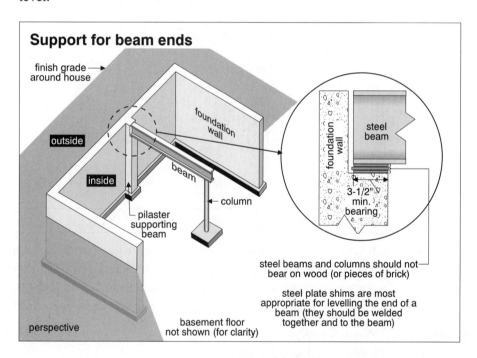

Support for beam ends

finish grade around house

outside

inside

foundation wall

beam

column

pilaster supporting beam

perspective

basement floor not shown (for clarity)

foundation wall

steel beam

3-1/2" min. bearing

steel beams and columns should not bear on wood (or pieces of brick)

steel plate shims are most appropriate for levelling the end of a beam (they should be welded together and to the beam)

Wood beams can sit on wood shims, although they should provide continuous bearing on the top and bottom of the shim. The shims should be secured in place with adhesive or mechanical fasteners. The shims should be of a wood at least as hard and dense and the beams. Cedar is soft and doesn't make good shims.

Beams Rest On Solid Masonry

Beams on masonry walls should rest on a depth of at least 7½ inches of solid masonry. Many recommend that the beam ends rest on solid masonry or concrete all the way down to the footing. In any case, beams should not rest on a hollow concrete block.

*Space Around
Beams In
Foundation
Pockets*

Where beams sit in foundation walls, the end, top and sides should have a ½ inch air space to allow the wood to dry out. If a wood beam is buried in a concrete or masonry foundation wall, it is more likely to rot. In some cases, the end of the beam in the foundation is coated with pressure treating chemicals to make the beam more rot resistant.

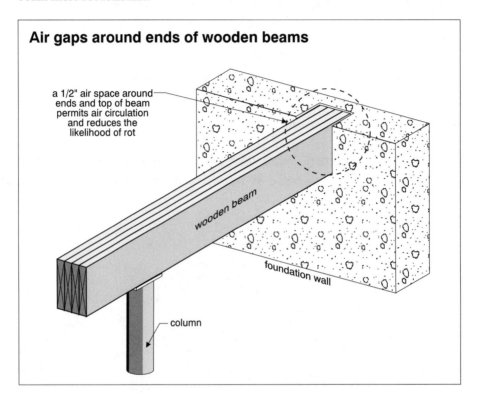

Air gaps around ends of wooden beams

a 1/2" air space around ends and top of beam permits air circulation and reduces the likelihood of rot

wooden beam

foundation wall

column

5.1.5 ROTATED OR TWISTED BEAMS

Causes

Beams may rotate or twist because of natural warping on drying, or they may twist as a result of the live loads imposed on them. Tall slender wood structural members in a horizontal orientation (beams and joists) will want to twist to the flat position when loaded from the top. This tendency to twist can cause point loads and crushing.

Strategy

Watch for beam rotation creating point bearing situations and crushing at joists, columns and foundations.

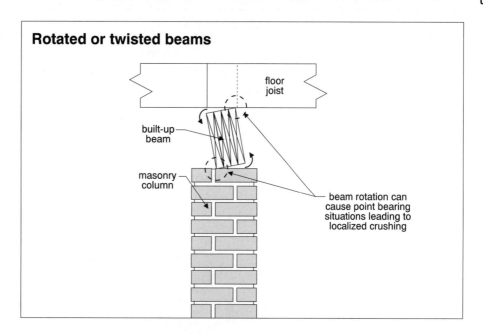

Rotated or twisted beams

floor joist

built-up beam

masonry column

beam rotation can cause point bearing situations leading to localized crushing

5.1.6 SPLIT OR DAMAGED WOOD BEAMS

Causes

Checks

Wood may split as it dries, forming **checks**. Checks generally have a starting and ending point within the beam itself (assuming the beam is solid wood). **Checking** is not considered serious unless the checks go all the way through the beam. Checking in the sides of beams is somewhat more serious than in the tops or bottoms. In most cases, it's not a problem.

Splits

Splits in beams are more serious than checks and are usually the result of notching of the beams or weak end bearing connections. Splitting of beams is a shear failure. Shear failures in beams are unusual without a considerable amount of bending, unless the beam has been weakened by notching or drilling.

Strategy

Where you see gaps in a beam, try to identify whether they are the result of checking caused by drying of the wood, or splitting. Splits usually begin at an edge or end of the beam or a notch. Checks are more likely to start and stop within the length of the beam.

Watch for any places where the beam may be split. Depending on the size and location of the split, the problem may be serious or trivial. You should be able to evaluate the performance of the beam given the damage that it has incurred. Is the beam sagging, twisting or showing evidence of any distress as a result? Has the bearing of the beam been lost or weakened as a result of the split? The older the split is, the more time there has been for problems to manifest themselves.

5.1.7 NOTCHES OR HOLES

Beams should not be notched and holes should not be drilled. Where this has been done, check for sag, splitting or rotation of the beam, especially if the notches are in the middle third of the span.

Repairs can be made relatively inexpensively to wood beams, and may make sense as a preventative measure even if you see no signs of distress.

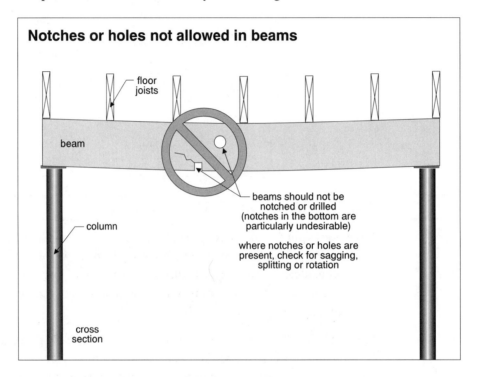

Notches or holes not allowed in beams

floor joists

beam

beams should not be notched or drilled (notches in the bottom are particularly undesirable)

where notches or holes are present, check for sagging, splitting or rotation

column

cross section

5.1.8 WEAK CONNECTIONS OF BUILT-UP COMPONENTS

Rather than a single solid beam, a beam may be **built-up** out of two inch dimensional lumber.

Built-up wood beams are typically made up of three, four or five 2 x 8s or 2 x 10s. These must be nailed or bolted together so that all the individual members act as a single component. Generally speaking, two sets (one for each side) of 2 nails are visible every 18 inches along the length of the beam.

Nailing of built-up wooden beams

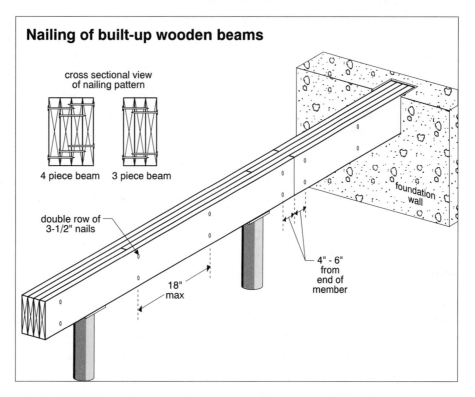

cross sectional view
of nailing pattern

4 piece beam   3 piece beam

double row of
3-1/2" nails

foundation
wall

18"
max

4" - 6"
from
end of
member

Bolting of built-up wooden beams

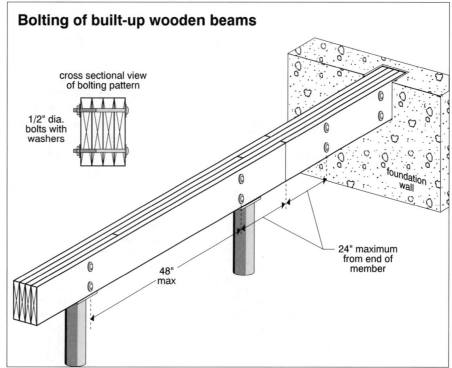

cross sectional view
of bolting pattern

1/2" dia.
bolts with
washers

foundation
wall

48"
max

24" maximum
from end of
member

Joints in **individual** beam members are best made over bearing points. Continuous span beams (not simple span beams) may have joints within 6 inches of the end quarter point of the beam span. In this area, the bending forces and the shear forces are relatively low. The joint is permitted near interior supports only, not near the foundation wall. There shouldn't be more than one joint at each quarter point. If there are four, two by eights in the beam, three must be continuous through the quarter point. Joints should be at least four feet apart.

Strategy Look for evidence of built-up beam members pulling apart. Where butt joints occur in beam components, ensure that there is no individual sag of these components, nor separation of the joint ends. Sight along the underside of the beam for sagging.

5.1.9 WEAK CONNECTIONS TO COLUMNS

Causes This is an installation issue, typically, although it can be a result of column or beam movement.

Strategy We've talked about the importance of adequate bearing surface for beams on columns. The column bearing plates should be as wide as the beam, and at least $3\frac{1}{2}$ inches in length for each beam end supported. Plate modifications are often required on steel columns to achieve this bearing. Where it is not provided, recommend changes.

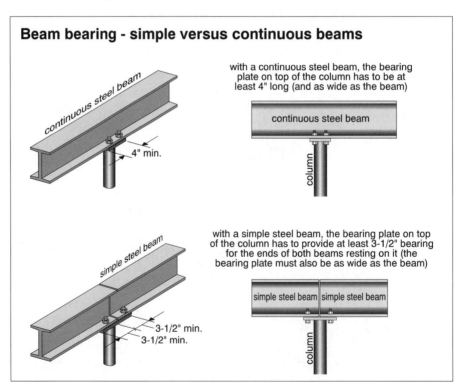

Beam bearing - simple versus continuous beams

continuous steel beam

with a continuous steel beam, the bearing plate on top of the column has to be at least 4" long (and as wide as the beam)

continuous steel beam

column

4" min.

simple steel beam

with a simple steel beam, the bearing plate on top of the column has to provide at least 3-1/2" bearing for the ends of both beams resting on it (the bearing plate must also be as wide as the beam)

simple steel beam | simple steel beam

column

3-1/2" min.
3-1/2" min.

We've also talked about steel columns to steel beam connections. Watch for bolts, welds or tabs that are not secure.

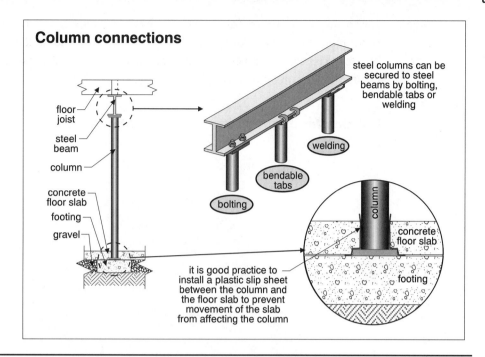

Column connections

floor joist

steel beam

column

concrete floor slab

footing

gravel

steel columns can be secured to steel beams by bolting, bendable tabs or welding

welding

bendable tabs

bolting

column

concrete floor slab

footing

it is good practice to install a plastic slip sheet between the column and the floor slab to prevent movement of the slab from affecting the column

5.1.10 WEAK CONNECTIONS TO JOISTS

Joists must be properly secured to beams to successfully transfer their load. There are several joist/beam connection methods, some of which are better than others.

Strategy   Watch for evidence of movement of the joists relative to the beams. The joists and beams should act as a unit. Pay particular attention to notched joists resting on beams or ledger boards, and to mortise and tenon joints.

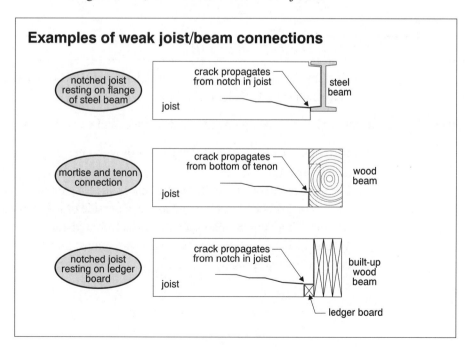

Examples of weak joist/beam connections

notched joist resting on flange of steel beam

crack propagates from notch in joist

steel beam

joist

mortise and tenon connection

crack propagates from bottom of tenon

wood beam

joist

notched joist resting on ledger board

crack propagates from notch in joist

built-up wood beam

joist

ledger board

Joist Hangers   Joist hangers must be the right size for the joists, and must have an adequate number of the proper nails (not roofing nails!) Typically, all nail holes in the hangers should be used. You can't comment on nail type, other than to make sure the head is big enough that it won't pull through. You can check whether there's a nail in each hole.

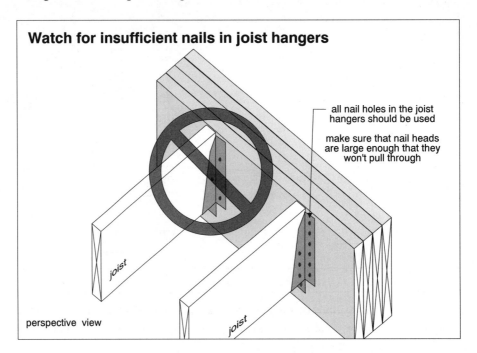

Watch for insufficient nails in joist hangers

all nail holes in the joist hangers should be used

make sure that nail heads are large enough that they won't pull through

joist

joist

perspective view

Watch for joists that are sagging or twisted. Either of these may weaken the joist/beam connection. Joists must extend at least 1½ inches onto or into the beam support.

5.1.11 LATERAL SUPPORT

A vulnerable arrangement with respect to lateral support is wood joists resting on top of a steel beam. Let's look at a few situations.

Strategy   Look for lateral bracing on either side of steel and wood beams.

1. Floor joists nailed to the tops and sides of wood beams provide adequate lateral bracing.
2. Ribbon boards (one by two, for example) run along either side of the top flanges of steel beams are nailed to the underside of joists to provide lateral bracing. These boards also keep the joists from twisting.
3. Where joists rest inside steel beam flanges against the web, the joists provide adequate lateral support.

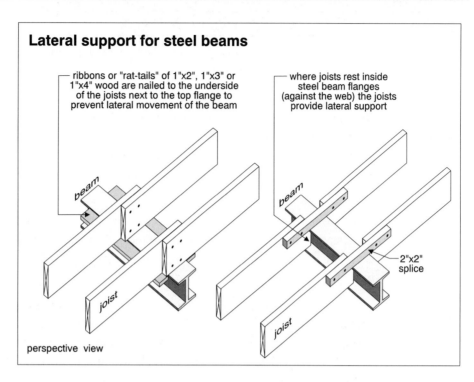

Lateral support for steel beams

— ribbons or "rat-tails" of 1"x2", 1"x3" or 1"x4" wood are nailed to the underside of the joists next to the top flange to prevent lateral movement of the beam

— where joists rest inside steel beam flanges (against the web) the joists provide lateral support

— 2"x2" splice

beam

joist

joist

perspective view

4. Where joists are hung off the sides of beams with joist hangers or ledger boards, adequate lateral support is provided.

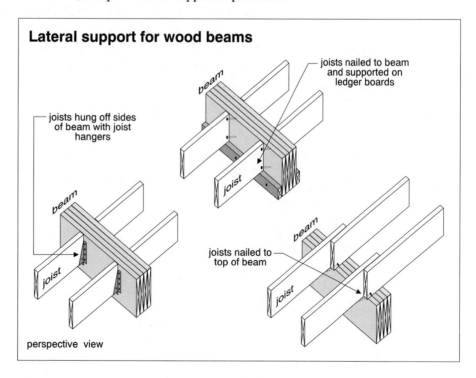

Lateral support for wood beams

— joists nailed to beam and supported on ledger boards

— joists hung off sides of beam with joist hangers

joists nailed to top of beam

beam

joist

perspective view

Most other joist/beam connections inherently provide lateral support.

55

5.1.12 CONCENTRATED LOADS

Where a beam is loaded near its midpoint by a column from above, for example, the beam may be overstressed.

Two Columns Instead Of Several Joists

Most beams are **uniformly loaded**. This means that several floor joists and wall studs rest on top of the beam along its length. Where a wall is removed or rooms are rearranged above a beam, loads from the next story may be collected and transferred down through one or two columns instead of a continuous bearing wall. This changes the loading on the beam below from a widely distributed load to a concentrated load.

As a general rule, concentrated loads should be carried straight down through the building to a footing. Where a column bears on the mid-span of a beam, the beam is likely to deflect excessively. The solution is to provide a column under the beam, immediately below the column above.

Columns On Subfloors

There is another problem that sometimes occurs when a column rests on a subfloor. It's common for the subfloor to be supported by joists, and the joists rest on top of a beam. A column may be resting on the subfloor between two joists. The subfloor will deflect once the live loads are applied, by people, furniture, wind and snow.

Think Vertically

The load from the column must be carried continuously. Blocking is required under the subfloor immediately below the column. The blocking can carry the load from the column through the subfloor, down to the beam. The beam, in turn, should have a column immediately below the blocking. At the bottom of the column should be a footing. Any discontinuity in this vertical transferring of loads can lead to structural distress.

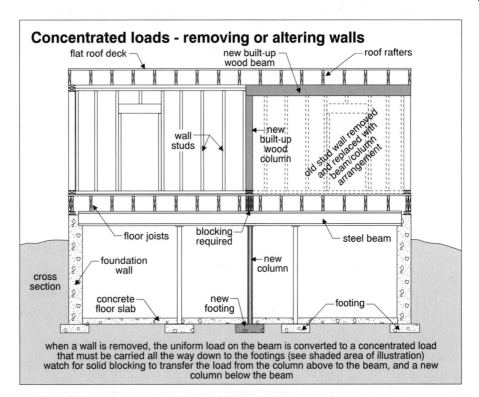

Concentrated loads - removing or altering walls

flat roof deck — new built-up wood beam — roof rafters

wall studs

new built-up wood column

old stud wall removed and replaced with beam/column arrangement

floor joists

blocking required

steel beam

cross section

foundation wall

new column

concrete floor slab

new footing

footing

when a wall is removed, the uniform load on the beam is converted to a concentrated load that must be carried all the way down to the footings (see shaded area of illustration) watch for solid blocking to transfer the load from the column above to the beam, and a new column below the beam

As a general rule, when thinking about how structures react, think vertically, try to follow loads down through the building and watch for the weak connections or off-sets. We'll talk more about offset vertical loads when we talk about bearing walls.

5.1.13 MISSING BEAM SECTIONS

Beams Removed

It's rare for beams to be missing entirely. However, it's not unusual for individual sections of beams to have been removed. These areas are usually easy to identify because of the discontinuity in the beams and the lack of support for joists.

Joists Hanging In Mid Air

It is strange how joists, in some cases, can remain seemingly supported in mid air. In reality, the subfloor is holding the joists up and the loads are being transferred to supported joists on either side. If joists are unsupported for long enough, the live loads will usually deflect this area.

Delayed Reactions

The movement may not appear as soon as a section of beam is removed, but may occur with changes in lifestyle and house loading, which always occur when a house changes hands. Just because a beam has been cut out for some time and hasn't sagged or the joists haven't moved, does not mean that we can ignore the situation. When the new family brings their aquarium, bookcase or record collection into the house and puts it where the beam has been cut, the result will be significant.

5.1.14 PRIOR REPAIRS

Was Repair Successful?

As always, where a beam or any structural member has been repaired, you should ask yourself why the repair was necessary and whether it is likely to be successful. Some situations are difficult to analyze because a resupported beam has sagged. Has the sagging continued and worsened despite the reinforcing? Has the sagging been stopped by the repair?

Subsequent Movement

Some detective work is required here to evaluate the reinforcement and try to determine whether subsequent movement has occurred since the reinforcing was added. The reinforcing can be in the form of sistering of beams or adding columns below. Sometimes the columns added below are very informal. They are often too slender, do not provide enough bearing at the top, are not well connected at the top, do not rest on a footing, but simply on a thin concrete floor, and are often not connected directly to the floor and/or footing.

Where you see evidence of continued movement, further investigation and repair should be recommended. Where there is no evidence of on-going movement, you may want to recommend monitoring.

Monitor Movement

One way to monitor beam performance is to measure the distance from the mi point of the beam (where sag will be greatest) down to the floor, and write the results on the beam at the point you measured, with the date. You can measure periodically thereafter to find out if it's getting worse. This works great unless the floor moves!

Structure
MODULE

QUICK QUIZ 3

☑ INSTRUCTIONS

- You should finish reading Study Session 3 before doing this Quiz.

- Write your answers in the spaces provided.

- Check your answers against ours at the end of this Section.

- If you have trouble with this Quiz, re-read the Session and try the Quiz again.

- If you do well, move on to Field Exercise 1.

1. Beams carry loads from: (four answers)

   a. floors   d) footings
   b. walls   e) columns
   c. roofs

2. The two most common beam materials are:

   _____

3. List four types of engineered wood products used for beams.

   _____ _____ _____ _____

4. A beam notched at the top is more likely to cause failure than one notched at the bottom.
   True ☐   False ☐

5. Beams rest on: (two answers)

    a. foundations   d. joists
    b. columns   e. buttresses
    c. studs

6. The ends of beams should have at least _____ inches of bearing.

7. List 14 common beam problems.

    _____ _____

    _____ _____

    _____ _____

    _____ _____

    _____ _____

    _____ _____

    _____ _____

8. Where is rust most likely to be found on a steel beam?
    a. the top
    b. the end
    c. the middle
    d. in the web only

9. Beams sag because they are over – _____

    Another way of saying the same thing is that the beam is under – _____

10. Steel beams should be shimmed with wood.
    True ☐   False ☐

11. Wood beams should not be supported directly on hollow concrete block.
    True ☐   False ☐

12. Wood beams in pockets in masonry or concrete walls should have ½ inch of air space around the sides, top and end. Why?

    _____

    _____

13. Joists may sit on top of beams or be attached to the sides of beams.
    True ☐   False ☐

14. Checking of wood beams: (two answers)

    a. indicates failure

    b. requires repair, but not replacement

    c. results from drying

    d. is usually not serious

    e. indicates fire damage

15. Mortise and tenon joints between joists and beams are weaker than joists supported on top of the beam.

True ☐   False ☐

16. Columns that rest on the mid-point of beam spans may – (two answers)

    a. indicate very good design

    b. overstress the beam

    c. create a concentrated load

    d. prevent beam sag

    e. create a strong connection

If you had no trouble with the Quiz, you are ready for Field Exercise 1.

Keywords:

- *Beams*
- *Sag*
- *Girders*
- *Poor bearing*
- *Built-up*
- *Rotated or twisted*
- *Glulams*
- *Split or damaged*
- *LVL*
- *Notches and holes*
- *Parallel strand*
- *Poor connections to joists*
- *Engineered wood*
- *Concentrated loads*
- *Lateral support*
- *Missing sections*
- *End bearing*
- *Prior repairs*
- *Continuous span*
- *Shims*
- *Simple span*
- *Ribbon boards*
- *Rust*
- *Rot or insect damage*
- *Checking*
- *Joist hangers*
- *Poor connections of built-up beam components*
- *Ledger boards*

Structure
M O D U L E

FIELD EXERCISE 1

☑ INSTRUCTIONS

You should complete everything up to Quick Quiz 3 before doing this exercise.

For this Exercise, you are going to have to get into some houses. The houses should have sills, columns and beams visible. In some areas, these may be hard to find. In other areas, this means getting into sub-grade areas or crawlspaces. Be prepared to get dirty! Your sample size should be large as possible and certainly no less than 5 homes.

Allow yourself 15–30 minutes in each house that you look at. We are going to concentrate just on the sills, beams and columns for this exercise.

The purpose of this exercise is to give you some first hand field experience in looking at these components. This is an opportunity for you to apply the knowledge you have gained and to use the inspection strategies that we have been discussing.

For each house, answer as many of these questions as possible:

1. Sill material:

_____

2. Sill size:

_____

3. Were the sills located on the inner or outer part of the foundations?

_____

4. How were the sills anchored? (e.g., bolts or embedding in concrete)

_____

5. If bolts were used, what was the spacing?

_____

6. Are sills in direct contact with concrete or masonry? (Were sill gaskets used?)

_____

7. Are sills above or below the outside grade level? By how much?

_____

8. Did you find any of these problems? (review the text for inspection strategies)

    a.   rot or insect damage
    b.   gaps below sills
    c.   crushed sills
    d.   poor anchoring
    e.   sills missing

9. Column materials:

_____

10. Column dimensions:

_____

11. How are columns secured at the bottom?

_____

12. How are columns secured at the top?

_____

13. Did you see any of these problems? (review the text for inspection strategies)

    a. missing

    b. settled

    c. crushed

    d. leaning

    e. buckling

    f. rust

    g. poorly secured at the top or bottom

    h. mortar deterioration

    i. spalling concrete or brick

    j. mechanical damage

    k. rot or insect damage

    l. heaved

    m. prior repairs

14. Beam material:

_____

15. Beam dimensions:

_____

16. Are beams simple spans or continuous spans?

_____

17. What supports the beams? (e.g., columns, foundations)

_____

18. Did you find any of the following problems? (review the text for inspection strategies)

    a. rust

    b. rot or insect damage

    c. sag

    d. poor bearing

    e. rotated or twisted beams

    f. split or damaged beams

    g. notches or holes

    h. poor connections of built-up components

    i. weak connections to columns

    j. weak connections to joists

    k. inadequate lateral support

    l. concentrated loads

    m. missing beam sections

    n. prior repairs

19. Note the most common materials you saw for sills, beams and columns.

_____

20. Note the most common problems you came across in your sampling for each of sills, beams and columns.

_____

When you have completed this Exercise, you are ready for Study Session 4.

Structure

MODULE

STUDY SESSION 4

1. You should have completed Study Sessions 1, 2 and 3, and Field Exercise 1 before starting Sessions 4. This Session covers joists.

2. By the end of this Session you should be able to –

   - List two joist materials and seven types of floor joists and trusses
   - Explain in one sentence how joists can support masonry walls
   - Explain in one sentence fire-cut joists
   - Explain in one sentence why joists should be laid crown up
   - Explain in one sentence rim joists
   - List twelve common joist problems
   - List twelve problems common to engineered wood floor systems

3. This Session may take roughly one hour to complete.

4. Quiz 4 is included at the end of this Session.

Keywords:

- *Joists*
- *Trusses*
- *Wood I joists*
- *PSL*
- *LVL*
- *LSL*
- *OSB*
- *Lateral support*
- *Fire cut*
- *Rim joists*
- *Crown up*
- *Rot*
- *Insect damage*
- *End bearing*
- *Twisted*
- *Blocking, bridging, strapping*
- *Notches and holes*
- *Split*
- *Cantilevers*
- *Weak openings*
- *Repairs*
- *Concentrated loads*
- *Spans*
- *Sistering*
- *Excess overlap*
- *Joist hangers*

► 6.0 JOISTS

Function Joists can be thought of as several small beams. Their function is primarily the same as beams. Joists transfer the dead load of the subfloor and floor finishes as well as the live load of people and furnishings to beams, walls, headers, sills or foundation walls.

Joists are traditionally solid wood, although there are a large number of engineered wood products, including –

1. trusses
2. plywood
3. wood I beams with flanges (top and bottom pieces) of conventional lumber or laminated veneer lumber and webs (vertical middle piece) of plywood or oriented strand board, (OSB)
4. laminated veneer lumber (LVL)
5. parallel strand lumber (PSL)
6. laminated strand lumber (LSL)

Joists can also be made of steel. These may be sheet metal, open web steel joists (trusses) or trusses made of wood and metal.

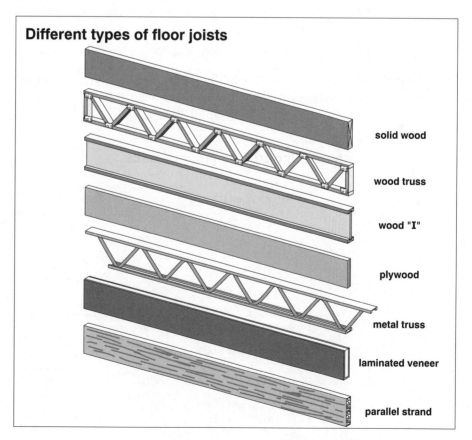

Different types of floor joists

solid wood

wood truss

wood "I"

plywood

metal truss

laminated veneer

parallel strand

For the rest of this section, we'll focus on conventional joists.

Materials Solid wood joists may be made of several species of lumber and may be one of several grades. Softwoods such as spruce, pine and fir are common. Cedar is not commonly used because it is not very strong and is expensive in many areas. Joist sizes range from two by sixes to two by twelves and can be spaced at 12, 16, 20 or 24 inches on center. Spacing of 16 inches is most common.

Factors Joist spans are a function of the species, grade, size, spacing, and the live load it's
Affecting Spans likely to see. For residential construction, it's common to design for 40 pound per square foot (psf) live loads. Some authorities allow a 30 pound per square foot (psf) load in bedroom areas, for example.

The Forces Joists see vertical loads from above and lateral soil loads from foundation wall
That Exist thrust and lateral wind loading from above grade walls, for example. Joists provide lateral support for walls.

Supporting Masonry Walls

Joists that rest on masonry walls or in pockets in masonry walls are often secured to the walls with steel straps that are typically 1½ inches wide by ³/₁₆ inches thick. The straps are embedded in the mortar at one end and nailed to the joists at the other.

Joists Where joists are at right angles to the wall, the straps are nailed to the bottoms
Perpendicular or sides of the joists. The straps extend 12 to 18 inches typically, along the
To Walls joists. Every 4th joist is usually strapped.

Joists Parallel Where the joists are parallel to the wall, the straps run perpendicular to the
To Walls joists and are secured to 3 or 4 joists moving in from the wall. The strapping can be nailed to either the top or bottom of the joists.

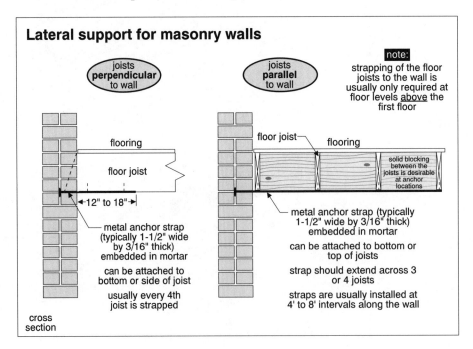

Bowing Walls

Many people do not think of this function of floor joists, and those who build without thinking about it often end up with bowing masonry walls, particularly at a second floor level. Masonry walls are typically tied into the foundation at the bottom, and to the roof structure at the top. In a two story house, the masonry wall may bow outward near its midpoint, especially if the joists are parallel to the masonry wall and the support strapping is not effective or has been omitted.

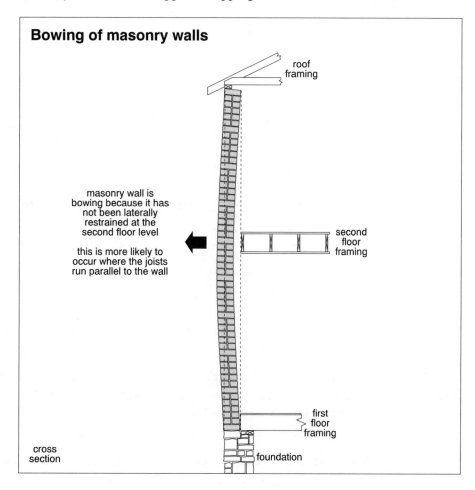

Bowing of masonry walls

roof framing

masonry wall is bowing because it has not been laterally restrained at the second floor level

this is more likely to occur where the joists run parallel to the wall

second floor framing

first floor framing

cross section

foundation

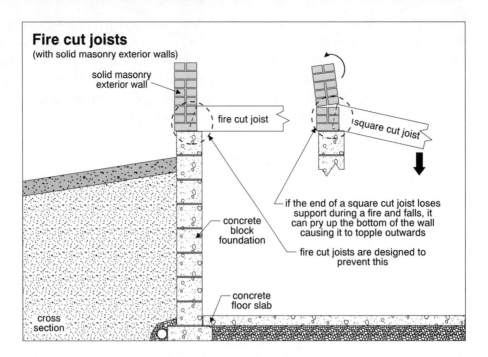

Fire cut joists
(with solid masonry exterior walls)

solid masonry
exterior wall

fire cut joist

square cut joist

if the end of a square cut joist loses
support during a fire and falls, it
can pry up the bottom of the wall
causing it to topple outwards

fire cut joists are designed to
prevent this

concrete
block
foundation

concrete
floor slab

cross
section

Fire Cut Joists

Joists that are embedded in solid masonry (not brick veneer) walls should be cut
back on a taper so the bottom of the joist is longer than the top of the joist by about
two inches. This results from problems that firefighters experienced with burning
buildings. Buildings with masonry walls and wood floor framing systems often
had the masonry walls topple outward, sometimes injuring or killing firefighters.

Joists Act
As Levers

As the floor joists collapsed or lost their support due to beam or column failure in
a fire, the joists embedded in the masonry walls would act as levers to pry the bottom of the masonry wall up as the other end of the joist dropped. This lever action
tipped the masonry walls outward, resulting in sudden collapse.

When joists are fire cut, they can fall out of a masonry wall without acting as a
lever. The masonry walls are less likely to be tipped over.

Joists Laid Crown Up

Many houses have uneven floors that at first glance appear to indicate settlement.
However, the careful home inspector will notice that it is only a result of the
uneven joist surfaces. Most joists have a natural bend along their length. Framing
carpenters should install joists with the crown on the high side. When the joist is
loaded, it will deflect, tending to straighten out. Sometimes the joists are installed
crown down. This creates a low spot in the floor which is exaggerated when the
floor is loaded and deflects.

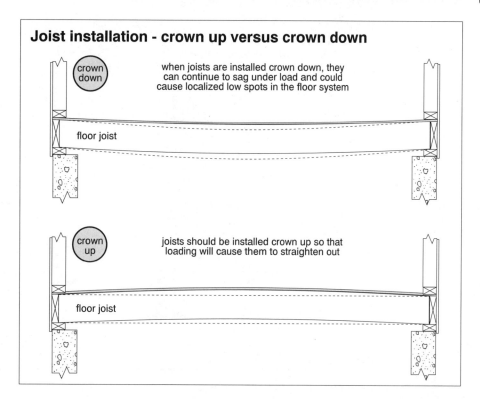

Joist installation - crown up versus crown down

crown down — when joists are installed crown down, they can continue to sag under load and could cause localized low spots in the floor system

floor joist

crown up — joists should be installed crown up so that loading will cause them to straighten out

floor joist

Look From Below

If you're in an unfinished basement or crawlspace, you can look along the underside of the joists and identify any that were installed crown down. You should look above to determine whether there is a concentrated load such as a partition wall immediately above that joist that may be causing it to deflect. If no particular load can be seen, chances are it was a joist that was simply installed crown down.

Rim Joists

The rim joist, header joist or band joist as it is sometimes called, runs around the perimeter of the house. This joist, which is usually the same dimension as the floor joists, is toe-nailed down into the sill and end-nailed into the joists.

Functions

The rim joist –

1. secures the joist ends
2. lends support to the walls and floor systems above
3. provides a nailing surface for exterior sheathing and siding

Rim joists do not have to be two by tens, for example. They can be one by tens.

Doubling Rim Joists

Where basement windows or crawlspace vents leave the rim joist and sill plate unsupported (because there's no foundation wall under them) the rim joist should be doubled.

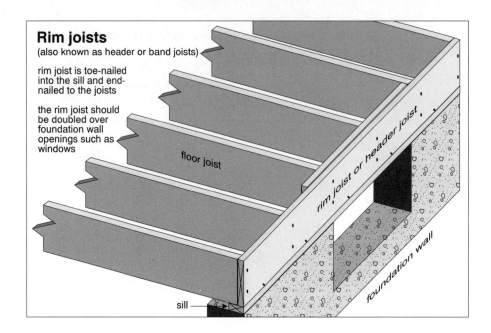

Rim joists

(also known as header or band joists)

rim joist is toe-nailed into the sill and end-nailed to the joists

the rim joist should be doubled over foundation wall openings such as windows

floor joist

rim joist or header joist

foundation wall

sill

6.1 CONDITIONS

Common joist problems include –

1. rot and insect damage
2. sagging joists (often part of a springy floor)
3. poor end bearing
4. rotated or twisted joists
5. no blocking, bridging or strapping
6. inappropriate notching or holes
7. split or damaged
8. weak cantilevers
9. weaknesses created by openings around stairs, chimneys and windows, etc.
10. prior repairs
11. concentrated loads
12. missing joists

6.1.1 ROT AND INSECT DAMAGE

We've talked about these on other parts of the floor systems. The causes and strategies are the same. Joists should be 12 to 18 inches above the soil in earth-floor crawlspaces.

6.1.2 SAGGING JOISTS

Causes

Sagging joists may be the result of –
1. Overspanning
2. Joists weakened by rot, insect attack, notches, holes, fire damage
3. Joists installed crown down
4. Concentrated loads.

Strategy

Overspanned joists are identified by measurement. There are span tables in code books and wood design books. Most home inspectors carry some rough rules around in their head. Here are some very broad rules assuming number 1 or 2 grade spruce joists 16 inches on center,

Rough Span Rules

• two by sixes can span about nine feet
• two by eights can span about twelve feet
• two by tens can span about fourteen feet
• two by twelves can span about sixteen feet

Spacing joists 12 inches on center results in longer allowable spans:

• two by sixes can span about ten feet
• two by eights can span about twelve and three quarters feet
• two by tens can span about fifteen feet
• two by twelves can span about eighteen feet

Use these rough guidelines with caution.

Watch For Additions And Converted Attics

Sagging and overspanned joists are very common on additions and on attics that have been converted to living space. Reinforcing joists during construction work is not expensive or difficult, but stiffening floors once interior finishes are applied is expensive and disruptive.

Sistering Joists Or Adding A Beam

Overspanned, sagging joists are often **sistered** with additional lumber of the same size. Joists may also be supported by a midpoint beam that cuts the joist span in half.

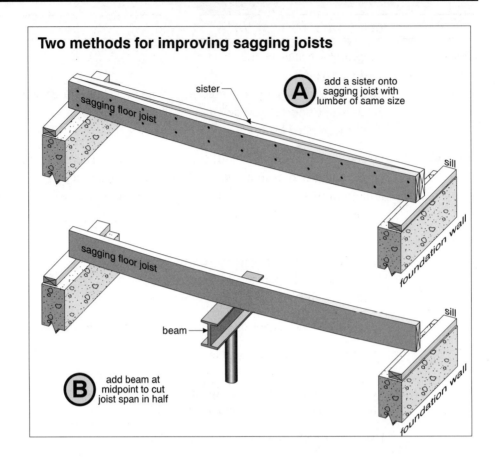

Two methods for improving sagging joists

sister

(A) add a sister onto sagging joist with lumber of same size

sagging floor joist

sill

foundation wall

sagging floor joist

beam

(B) add beam at midpoint to cut joist span in half

sill

foundation wall

Stiff
Subfloors
Help Share
Loads

Joists are more likely to sag if there is very little load sharing between joists. The stiffer the subfloor, the more load sharing there is from one joist to the joists on either side. Gluing and screwing the subfloor to the joists, creates a T-shaped beam or truss out of the joists and subfloor that is effective at transferring loads among joists. The goal is to make the floor act as a single strong unit, rather than several individual pieces.

Bridging
Or Blocking

While it is a somewhat controversial issue, many feel that bridging or blocking helps to transfer loads from one joist to the joists on either side. Bridging or blocking also prevents joists from twisting, and damp vibrations.

Strapping

Strapping the bottom of the joists together prevents twisting but does little to transfer loads among joists.

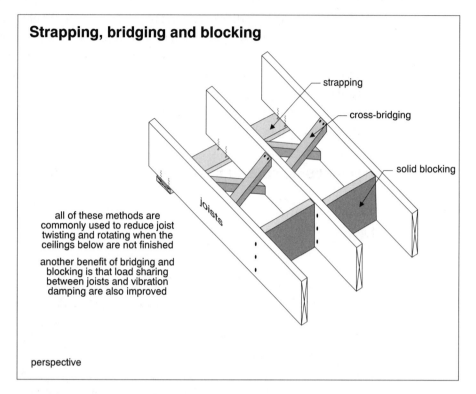

Strapping, bridging and blocking

strapping

cross-bridging

solid blocking

joists

all of these methods are commonly used to reduce joist twisting and rotating when the ceilings below are not finished

another benefit of bridging and blocking is that load sharing between joists and vibration damping are also improved

perspective

Lots Of Strength

Most floor joist systems are strong enough, since they are designed for maximum deflection. Deflection limits are usually far more restrictive than strength limitations. The exceptions are when joists are weakened by rot, insect damage, fire or mechanical damage. Also, look for concentrated loads from walls, columns or heavy furniture above.

Sagging Is Not Sloping

Sagging joists have their low spot in midspan. **Sloping** joists are lower at one end. Sloping joists indicate footing, foundation, beam or column movement, rather than joist failure. Sloping floors are often more serious than sagging floors.

Vibration Or Springiness

Test for the vibration potential or springiness of the floor. By bouncing on the floor, and watching the movement of pieces of furniture (especially china cabinets) you can get a sense for the susceptibility of the floor to vibration. Listen to the noise generated as things shake. Bridging, blocking and strapping help to dampen this problem, especially if they are installed in a continuous line across the floor. Some authorities call for sets of bridging, blocking or strapping every 7 feet, other recommend that they be closer together, roughly every 4½ feet.

Where the joists are exposed in a crawlspace or basement you can suggest bridging or blocking as an inexpensive solution for a springy or bouncy floor.

Other Causes of Springy Floors

Other causes of bouncy, vibrating floors include long joist spans, smaller depth joists, wide joist spacing, wood species that flex easily, thin subflooring and cantilevered floor joists.

*Joists
Overlapping
Beams
Too Far*

Watch for joists that overlap and extend beyond the beam. Where the joist from one side of a beam extends several inches past the beam on the other side, a hump may appear in the floor at the end of the joist because the joist deflects slightly as it's loaded. As the joist deflects, the end that extends beyond the beam will kick up, causing a hump in the floor just past the beam. The floor joist is acting like a teeter-totter, with the beam as the fulcrum. This isn't a serious problem, but a red herring that can look serious.

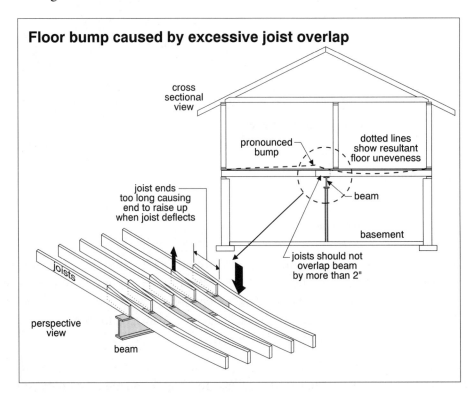

Floor bump caused by excessive joist overlap

cross
sectional
view

pronounced
bump

dotted lines
show resultant
floor unevenness

joist ends
too long causing
end to raise up
when joist deflects

beam

basement

joists
joists should not
overlap beam
by more than 2"

perspective
view

beam

Joists should not extend beyond the face of the beam by more than two inches. Where joists are overlapped, some say the minimum overlap should be 4 inches and the maximum overlap 12 inches.

6.1.3 END BEARING

*Joists Need
Less Bearing
Than Beams*

Joists require 1½ inches of end bearing, considerably less than the 3½ inches required for beams. That's because the live load carried by individual joists is much smaller than the beam's load.

Note: Some jurisdictions call for 3 inch end bearing on masonry. Check standard practices in your area.

*Joists on
Beams*

Where joists rest on beams, best practice is to have the joist rest on the full width of the beam, rather than just 1½ inches. Good practice also includes splicing joists that overlap from opposite side of the beam.

End Support For Joists

Joists can be supported in many ways:

1. They can rest on sill plates on top of foundation walls
2. They can be embedded in masonry or concrete foundation walls
3. They can be supported on the sides of beams with **joist hangers**
4. They can be supported on the sides of beams with **ledger boards**
5. They can be supported in a **mortise and tenon joint** where the end of the joist is trimmed to form a tenon and the beams have a mortise cut-out to receive the tenon
6. Joists can be notched at the end so that only the top part of the joist sits on a beam
7. Joists can be supported on the bottom flange or top flange of steel beams

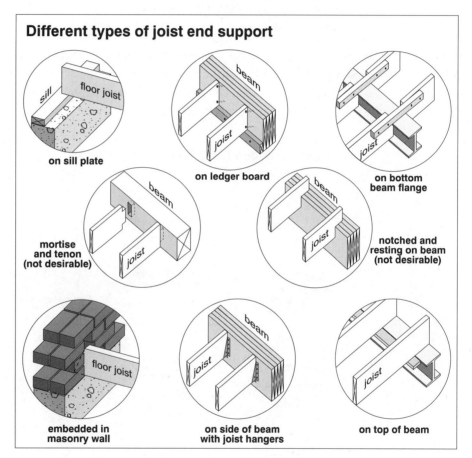

Different types of joist end support

on sill plate

on ledger board

on bottom beam flange

mortise and tenon (not desirable)

notched and resting on beam (not desirable)

embedded in masonry wall

on side of beam with joist hangers

on top of beam

Causes

Joists may not have enough end bearing because of –

1. original construction mistakes
2. sagging joists
3. differential settlement or heaving of the footing/foundation system
4. bowing or leaning walls
5. notched bearing arrangements
6. rotted joist ends, sills, beams or foundations

Strategy

Where joists are supported on the bottom flange of a steel beam, it's good practice to have the joists slightly taller than the beam, and a wooden splice across the top of the steel beam.

Joists On The Side Of Steel Beams

The bottom of the splice should be at least half an inch above the top flange of the beam to allow for vertical shrinkage of the wood members. It's not unusual to get 4% shrinkage across the grain in wood frame members

Notched Bearing Is Bad

One of the weakest configurations is when the joist is notched and only the top inch or so of the joist rests on a beam or foundation wall. This reduces the strength of the joist, and concentrates loads in the top part. Expect to see cracks radiating out horizontally from the top of the notch. This can result in serious structural movement, especially if more than one joist shows this crack. The solution involves supporting the bottom of the joist, often with joist hangers.

Notching At Bottom Is a Little Better

A better, but still less than desirable arrangement, is to notch the bottom one inch or so of the joist and rest the majority of the joist on a ledger board or steel beam flange, for example. The joists are weakened slightly by such an arrangement. Again, watch for horizontal cracks running out from the notch.

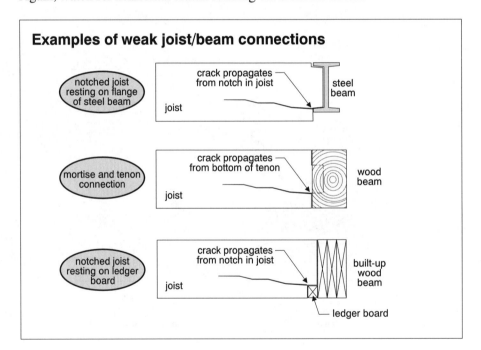

Examples of weak joist/beam connections

Joist Hangers

Steel joist hangers can provide excellent support for joists on the sides of beams. This maximizes the head room in basements and crawlspaces because the beams don't have to project below the joists. However, joist hangers have to be installed correctly to work properly.

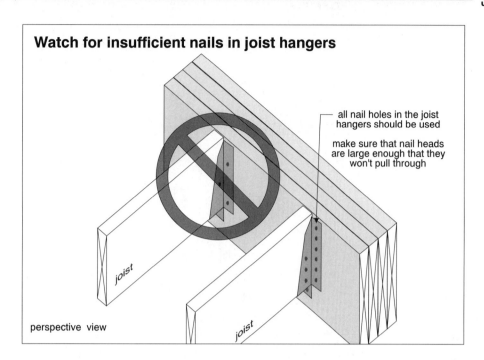

Watch for insufficient nails in joist hangers

all nail holes in the joist hangers should be used

make sure that nail heads are large enough that they won't pull through

joist

joist

perspective view

Let's look at joist hanger issues:

1. There are different sized joist hangers for different sized joists. A joist hanger designed for two by fours should not be used on two by tens.

2. Joist hangers have lots of holes in them for nails. Generally speaking, every hole should be filled with a nail. It is very common to find that people have skimped on the number of nails.

3. The right type of nails should be used. Some joist hangers have special nails made for them. Nails used with joist hangers need considerable shear strength and large enough heads that the head won't pull through the joist hanger. Many people mistakenly use roofing nails because of the large heads. Roofing nails do not have good shear strength and may not be able to adequately transfer the loads from the joists to the beam.

4. Joists should rest squarely in the bottom of the joist hangers. When joists don't sit on the bottom, they will settle to the bottom when loaded. This may cause cracking or sagging above, and may pull out some nails in the hangers.

5. Joists should extend fully into the hanger to achieve adequate support.

6. Perpendicular joist hangers should not be used when joists meet beams at a 45° angle for example.

7. Special joist hangers should be used to support doubled joists.

Ledger Boards

Ledger boards need to be well secured to beams in order to transfer the loads from the joists to the beam. Watch for inadequate nailing here. Generally speaking, you're looking for two nails securing the ledger board to the beam below each joist. The joist should also be toe-nailed into the beam.

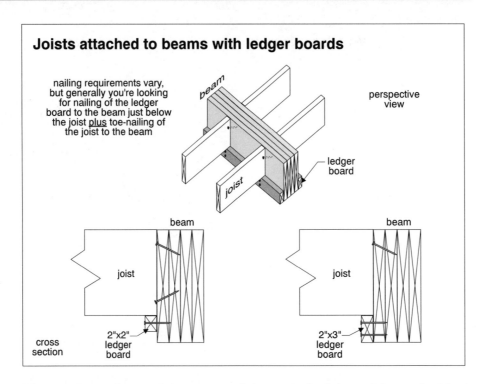

Joists attached to beams with ledger boards

nailing requirements vary, but generally you're looking for nailing of the ledger board to the beam just below the joist <u>plus</u> toe-nailing of the joist to the beam

beam

joist

perspective view

ledger board

beam

joist

beam

joist

cross section

2"x2" ledger board

2"x3" ledger board

Mortise And Tenon Joints Weak

The mortise and tenon joints are weak because the joist end is notched both at the top and bottom. Cracking along the bottom of the tenon is common. Extra support below the joist is often required to stop movement.

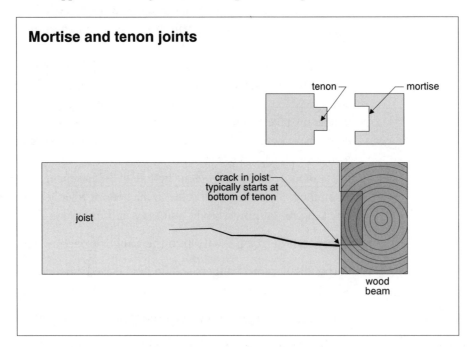

Mortise and tenon joints

tenon

mortise

joist

crack in joist typically starts at bottom of tenon

wood beam

6.1.4 ROTATED OR TWISTED JOISTS

Causes

Twisted joists may be the result of –

1. Live loads
2. Warping when drying

Strategy

These are common only where there is no ceiling provided on the underside of the joists. Drywall or plaster ceilings provide good restraint. Where the ceiling is unfinished, strapping with one by four boards stops joists twisting. Twisting is a

Ceilings Or Strapping

natural tendency for tall thin loadbearing members like joists. The strapping should be nailed to the underside of each joist, and should be provided every six or seven feet (some say every 4½ feet) along the length of the joists.

Blocking Or Bridging

Solid blocking or bridging also effectively resists rotating or twisting.

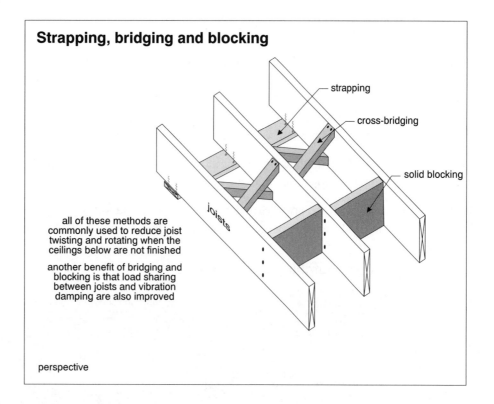

Strapping, bridging and blocking

strapping

cross-bridging

solid blocking

joists

all of these methods are commonly used to reduce joist twisting and rotating when the ceilings below are not finished

another benefit of bridging and blocking is that load sharing between joists and vibration damping are also improved

perspective

6.1.5 NO BRIDGING, BLOCKING OR STRAPPING

We've talked about the role that these members play. Their functions include

1. transferring loads from one joist to adjacent joists,
2. damping vibration, and
3. preventing twisting or rotating of joists under load.

Causes   These may be missing due to –

1. poor installation, or
2. removal during home "improvements."

Strategy   We recommend that you be careful in criticizing floor assemblies based on an absence of bridging, blocking or strapping. Many floors perform adequately without these. If these have been left out, either in whole or in part, look for evidence of the problems (sagging, vibration or twisting). If you don't see any problems and the system has been in place for some years, improvements are probably not required.

Bridging Not Nailed   Watch for diagonal bridging that is not nailed to the joists at the bottom. This is a common problem due to construction work sequences. Bridging that isn't nailed at the bottom is useless.

6.1.6 NOTCHING AND HOLES

Where Forces Concentrate   **The Home Reference Book,** most code books and carpentry books set out rules for notching and holes. It's surprising how varied the code requirements are. Some consider the fact that shear stresses are great near ends of joists and bending stresses are great near the midpoint. Bending stresses are more extreme at the top and bottom of joists, and are negligible near the midpoint.

Wood is slightly better in compression than in tension and that's why it's better to notch the top rather than the bottom of joists.

No Holes Near Top Or Bottom   Holes can be anywhere along the length of the joists (although not too close to the ends) and are better near the middle than the top or the bottom.

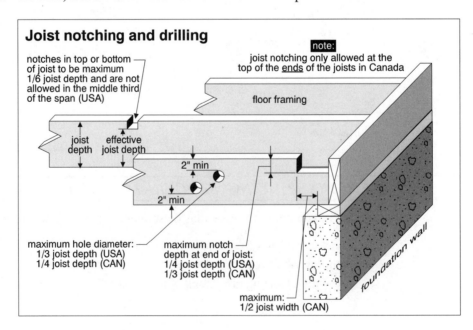

Joist notching and drilling

notches in top or bottom of joist to be maximum 1/6 joist depth and are not allowed in the middle third of the span (USA)

note:
joist notching only allowed at the top of the ends of the joists in Canada

floor framing

joist depth

effective joist depth

2" min

2" min

maximum hole diameter:
1/3 joist depth (USA)
1/4 joist depth (CAN)

maximum notch depth at end of joist:
1/4 joist depth (USA)
1/3 joist depth (CAN)

maximum:
1/2 joist width (CAN)

foundation wall

Causes   Notches and holes are caused by tradespeople making room for house components, and sometimes by homeowners who don't understand the importance of joists.

Strategy   Don't memorize a bunch of rules. You can look at the performance of joists which have been notched or drilled. If the joists have cracked or sagged, you can be reasonably sure that the notching or holes were excessive.

Judge The Performance   Watch for holes drilled near the bottom of joists. It's easier to drill low than get the drill up between the joist spaces and drill through the middle. Also watch for 3 or 4 inch diameter holes cut for waste plumbing from toilets. These weaken joists considerably. Headers and trimmers around 3 inch pipes are a better solution than drilling holes. Watch also for a whole series of holes drilled through joists. Even if they're in the middle, a row of holes 2 feet long will weaken joists considerably.

6.1.7 SPLIT OR DAMAGED JOISTS

Causes   Splits may be caused by –

1. poor end bearing configurations
2. notches and holes
3. flaws such as knots, localized rot, etc.
4. mechanical damage

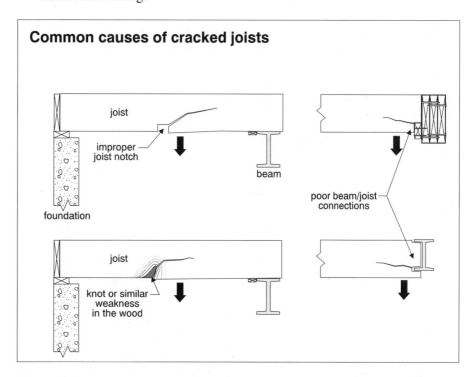

Common causes of cracked joists

Strategy   Split or damaged joists are common, particularly in unfinished basements where the joists are exposed to the home improvement enthusiast. Follow each joist, end to end. Look at both sides of each joist.

6.1.8 WEAK CANTILEVERS

Amount Of
Cantilever

Cantilevers are inherently weak structural details and exterior cantilevers are particularly weak. Most modern conventions restrict cantilevers to two feet or ⅙ of the length of the wood member, unless there has been special engineering consideration. In some areas, and with some older sets of rules, up to 1/3 of the length of the joist could be cantilevered.

Causes

Weak cantilevers are caused by –

1. poor original design or installation
2. deterioration (usually rot) of the cantilevered members

Strategy
Teeter-Totter
Effect

Hump In
Floor Inside

Cantilevering creates a joist that is unsupported at one end and, consequently, subject to deflection and springiness. The other reality of cantilevers is the teeter-totter effect. If joists are cantilevered over an outside wall, for example, bouncing on the cantilevered end puts an upward force on the other end of the joist inside the house. The outside wall is the fulcrum. You'll sometimes find humps in floors at the inner end of the cantilevered joists.

Leakage
And Rot
Outside

The design may minimize deflection and springiness and there may be no hump. That still leaves a significant problem. Cantilevered joists are vulnerable to leakage and rot where they pass through an exterior wall.

Cantilevers

There can be a lot of concealed water damage. Cantilevered joists may rot at the wall penetration point creating an unsafe condition which is difficult to identify.

Water
Damage

Look very closely at cantilevers for deflection and springiness, and pay special attention to water damage at the joist/wall joint on outdoor cantilevers.

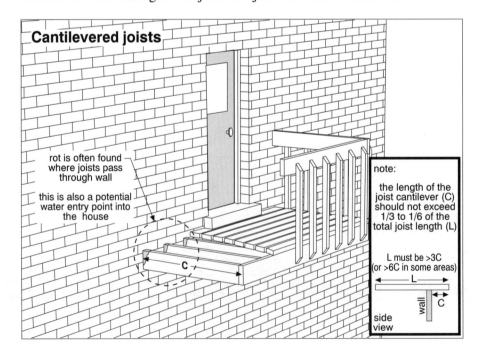

Cantilevered joists

rot is often found where joists pass through wall

this is also a potential water entry point into the house

note:

the length of the joist cantilever (C) should not exceed 1/3 to 1/6 of the total joist length (L)

L must be >3C (or >6C in some areas)

C

L

wall

C

side view

6.1.9 WEAK OPENINGS

Stairwell Openings

Where a floor joist system is interrupted, there will be more connections and concentrated loads. **The Home Reference Book** discusses load transfers around stairwells. We need to double headers and trimmers for modest openings and to engineer the header and trimmer sizes for larger openings.

Causes

Opening problems are caused by –
1. Undersized or missing headers and/or trimmers, or
2. poor connections.

Strategy

Where joists cannot rest on walls because of windows, for example, headers are necessary. Headers may be missing or weak, adjacent joists may be overloaded, tail joist-to-header connections may be weak, and header-to-trimmer joist connections may be weak. Watch for deflection around all floor openings.

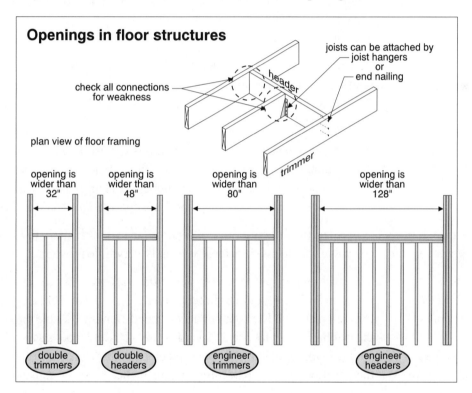

Openings in floor structures

check all connections for weakness

joists can be attached by joist hangers or end nailing

header

trimmer

plan view of floor framing

opening is wider than 32"	opening is wider than 48"	opening is wider than 80"	opening is wider than 128"
double trimmers	double headers	engineer trimmers	engineer headers

Fireplaces

Fireplaces and chimneys may also interrupt the floor framing system. Framing members should not touch fireplaces or chimneys. Watch for overheating (charring) of wood framing around fireplaces and chimneys. The weight of a concrete hearth and/or masonry mantle can affect the joists.

Rim Joists

Where rim joists are not supported by foundation walls, because of a basement window, for example, watch for sagging. The rim joists should be doubled over these openings.

6.1.10 PRIOR REPAIRS

Strategy   We've talked about what prior repairs mean and what to watch for. Try to figure out why the joists were repaired and whether or not the repairs are effective. Look for evidence of subsequent movement.

6.1.11 CONCENTRATED LOADS

We've talked about some examples of concentrated loads already. Watch for these, including jack posts below lintels, columns, water beds, spiral staircases, pianos, fish tanks, book cases, record collections and bath tubs (especially the big ones designed for two or more people).

Partition Walls   Another big enemy of floor joists is the non-loadbearing or partition wall. These walls are often not given much structural attention, because they are not carrying the weight of a floor or ceiling joist system above. But partition walls have their own nasty habits.

Considerable Loads   Partition walls have considerable dead weight in the lumber and plaster on both sides. A typical wall weighs 15 pounds per square foot. Every foot along an 8 floor high partition wall weighs 120 pounds. A 10 foot long partition wall weighs 1,200 pounds!

But more than that, people put heavy things against partition walls. Whether it's a dining room with a buffet, sideboard or china cabinet, a kitchen with a refrigerator, stove, dishwasher, base cabinets and upper wall hung cabinets, or a bedroom with a triple dresser and/or water bed, there are considerable loads on joists.

Walls Perpendicular   Where partition walls run perpendicular to joists, their load is spread over several joists. In this case, there is usually very little problem.

Walls Parallel To Joists

Double The Joist Below   The problem crops up where partition walls run parallel to floor joists. A partition wall may end up directly over a floor joist. This can deflect a single joist dramatically. The common recommendation is to double the floor joist under the partition. This makes it awkward to run wires and pipes up through the partition wall (a favorite trick of plumbers and electricians). Joists are often doubled under the partition but set apart three or four inches so services can run up through.

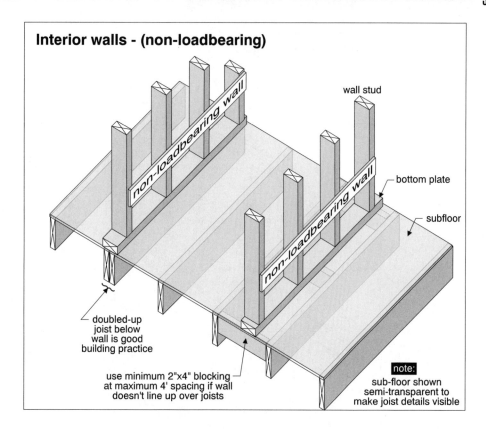

Interior walls - (non-loadbearing)

non-loadbearing wall

non-loadbearing wall

wall stud

bottom plate

subfloor

doubled-up joist below wall is good building practice

use minimum 2"x4" blocking at maximum 4' spacing if wall doesn't line up over joists

note:
sub-floor shown semi-transparent to make joist details visible

Use Blocking To Span The Bridge Between Joists

Where the partition wall sits mid-span on the subfloor between two joists, the subfloor is likely to deflect considerably. Two by four blocking below the wall spaced every four feet, bridging between the joists, helps transfer the wall load to the two joists.

Doubling Not Enough

There is a common condition found in houses that creates sagging floors despite joist doubling. A stairwell opening typically has double trimmers at either end because these joists are helping to carry the tail joist loads through the header.

A partition wall may be above and parallel to one of the trimmer joists. Doubling or tripling of this trimmer joist may not be enough. It's puzzling because when you go down stairs thinking about the partition wall, you say, *"Great! They've doubled the joist under the partition wall."* If you look downstairs thinking about the stairwell opening, it also looks okay. The problem is that the joist had to be doubled for the partition wall and doubled or tripled for the trimmer joist. You need to be thinking about both the partition and the staircase opening.

We need a beam, a loadbearing wall or columns under the trimmer joists to carry the concentrated loads. Watch out for this one.

This helps explain why the floor systems sag around stairwell openings in most old houses. The same thing applies around other openings, of course.

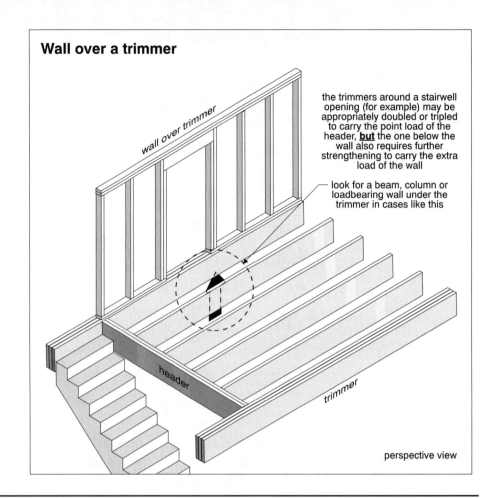

Wall over a trimmer

wall over trimmer

the trimmers around a stairwell opening (for example) may be appropriately doubled or tripled to carry the point load of the header, **but** the one below the wall also requires further strengthening to carry the extra load of the wall

look for a beam, column or loadbearing wall under the trimmer in cases like this

header

trimmer

perspective view

6.1.12 MISSING

Causes   Joists are often cut or removed by inexperienced home improvement enthusiasts.

Strategy   Strangely, the house will often not move immediately and/or dramatically as a result of one missing joist. Over the long term, however, the effects may show up, particularly if loads are concentrated in this area. Any missing or compromised joist should be written up for immediate repair.

6.2 ENGINEERED WOOD

This topic is beyond the scope of this program. We will touch briefly on some of the issues.

Long Spans   These systems are becoming popular because they can have much longer spans than conventional lumber, and are less prone to shrinkage and warping problems than conventional lumber.

Materials   Wood I joists may have conventional lumber top and bottom plates, or the top and bottom plates (flanges) may be LVLs (Laminated Veneer Lumber), PSLs (Parallel Strand Lumber), or LSL's (Laminated Strand Lumber). Webs may be plywood, oriented strandboard (OSB) or metal. Wood based webs are glued to wood based flanges or chords. Trusses may be all wood, all metal or a combination. Open web steel joists can be used and you may find plate steel joists.

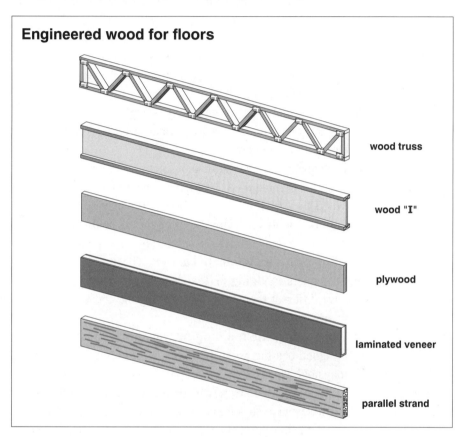

Engineered wood for floors

wood truss

wood "I"

plywood

laminated veneer

parallel strand

LVLs, PSLs, and LSLs can also be used as joists, beams, sills, lintels, columns, studs, rafters, etc. Glulams (glue laminated lumber) made up of conventional lumber pieces glued together can also be used for many wood structural members.

The Rules Change   With engineered wood, the rules change, and some of the rules are specific to the individual manufacturers. When looking at wood I or truss system, you are wise to have the manufacturer's installation guides handy. Some of the areas in which these systems differ from conventional wood joists are outlined below. This list is not all-inclusive, and these issues do not necessarily apply to all engineered wood systems.

6.2.1 CONDITIONS

1. **Holes** may be too big or in the wrong place (many systems have knockouts that indicate where the holes must be).
2. **Joist hangers** may be too short, too wide, the wrong type, and may not have enough nails or the wrong kind of nails.
3. Proper **rim joist material** may not be used. Wood I joists should have $^3/_4$ inch plywood or special rim joist materials. Rims should not be conventional lumber. Inadequate load transfer through rim joists is a common problem.
4. **Blocking** (squash blocks) may be missing or incomplete where joists rest on beams or where loads from bearing walls above are transmitted down through I joists to beams or sills.
5. Split, notched or **cut flanges** may be a problem. The top and bottom flanges of wood I joists and trusses are critical. Any weakening will seriously affect the strength of the system.
6. Inadequate **end bearing** is a problem. A larger end bearing than conventional joists is often required. $1^3/_4$ inches is a common minimum.
7. Wood I joists should not be **bevelled or fire cut**. The ends of wood I joists must be cut off vertically. Tapering the cut so that the top flange is shorter than the bottom flange seriously reduces the strength.
8. When I joists are **laminated** to form a beam, **blocking** must be used between.
9. Inadequate **bridging or load sharing** can be a problem. Different systems have different requirements for bridging. Individual manufacturers' requirements should be referenced.
10. **Trusses may be too long or too short.** Most trusses must rest on their designed bearing point. If trusses are too long or too short, the load transfer may not be in the right place.
11. **Concentrated loads** may be on the top of weak points in **trusses**. Top chords in trusses have strong and weak points along their length. Watch for deflection in the top chord of a truss where concentrated loads end up on weak points.
12. **Trusses** may be installed **upside down**. Trusses are designed to rest on either their top chord or bottom chord. It's often difficult to know by looking whether trusses have been installed upside down. Watch for sagging, deflection, rotation, twisting, etc.

Structure
M O D U L E

QUICK QUIZ 4

☑ INSTRUCTIONS

• You should finish reading Study Session 4 before doing this Quiz.

• Write your answers in the spaces provided.

• Check your answers against ours at the end of this Section.

• If you have trouble with this Quiz, re-read the Session and try the Quiz again.

• If you do well, move on to Session 5.

1. The function of joists is to: (three answers)

    a. transfer live loads to beams
    b. transfer dead loads to foundations
    c. transfer live and dead loads directly to columns
    d. transfer live loads to walls
    ev transfer dead loads to subfloors

2. Name five engineered wood products that may replace conventional joists.

_____

_____

_____

_____

_____

3. Joists see vertical loads only.
    True ☐   False ☐

4. Joists are often used to provide lateral support for solid masonry walls.
    True ☐   False ☐

5. Fire-cutting joists is a serious structural error.
    True ☐   False ☐

6. List 12 common joist problems you will see on inspections.

    _____   _____   _____

    _____   _____   _____

    _____   _____   _____

7. Joist sag may be the result of – (4 answers)

    _____   _____

    _____   _____

8. Roughly how far can these common joists span if spaced 16 inches apart?
    2 x 8 _____   2 x 10 _____   2 x 12 _____

9. Possible functions of bridging and blocking are – (3 answers)

    a. reduce joist spacing
    b. support weak subflooring
    c. prevent joist twisting
    d. help transfer loads to more than one joist
    e. vibration damping

10. The joist resting on a beam should not extend past the beam more than
    2 inches. Why?

    _____

11. Joists typically need _____ inches of end bearing.

12. Joists notched at their end are stronger than normal joists?
    True ☐   False ☐

13. Joists resting on foundation walls at or near grade level are prone to rot.
    True ☐   False ☐

14. List six possible joist hanger problems.

_____   _____   _____

_____   _____   _____

15. How does a ledger board support joists?

_____

_____

16. List four things that can prevent joist twisting.

_____   _____

_____   _____

17. Holes in joists should be near the bottom rather than the middle of the joists.
True ☐   False ☐

18. What is a cantilever?

_____

_____

19. Outdoor cantilevers are particularly vulnerable to moisture damage. Where is the problem most likely to occur and why?

_____

_____

20. Sketch the framing for a typical stairwell opening in a floor joist system. Label headers and trimmers

21. Partition walls exert no load on floor joists because they are not load bearing walls.
True ☐   False ☐

22. List eight common engineered wood flooring problems.

_____

_____

_____

_____

_____

_____

_____

_____

If you had no trouble with the Quiz, you are ready for Study Session 5.

Keywords:

- **Joists**
- **Trusses**
- **Wood I joists**
- **PSL**
- **LVL**
- **LSL**
- **OSB**
- **Lateral support**
- **Fire cut**
- **Rim joists**
- **Crown up**
- **Rot**
- **Insect damage**

- **Twisted**
- **Blocking, bridging, strapping**
- **Notches and holes**
- **Split**
- **Cantilevers**
- **Weak openings**
- **Repairs**
- **Concentrated loads**
- **Spans**
- **Sistering**
- **Excess overlap**
- **Joist hangers**
- **End bearing**

Structure
MODULE

STUDY SESSION 5

1. You should have completed Study Sessions 1, 2, 3 and 4, and completed Field Exercise #1 before starting this Session.

2. After completing this Session you should be able to –

- Describe subflooring materials and their function in one sentence each
- List nine subflooring problems
- Describe in one sentence each, pre-stressed and post tensioned concrete floors
- List seven concrete floor problems

3. This Session may take about one hour to complete.

4. Quick Quiz 5 is lurking at the end of this Session.

Keywords:

- *Planking*
- *Plywood*
- *Waferboard*
- *Span*
- *Tongue-and-groove*
- *Rot*
- *Insect damage*
- *Condensation*
- *Overspanned*
- *Damaged or cut*
- *Cantilevers*
- *Concentrated loads*
- *Squeaks*
- *Swollen waferboard*
- *Cracked ceramic tiles*
- *Prestressed concrete*
- *Post-tensioned concrete*
- *Supported slab*
- *Suspended slab*
- *Cracked*
- *Settled*
- *Heaved*
- *Hollow below*
- *Shaling*
- *Spalling*
- *Rusted rebar*

► 7.0 SUBFLOORING

Materials   Subflooring is typically wood planking, plywood or waferboard.

Function   Think of the subfloor as a series of many small joists or beams. The function is similar to joists and beams. Subfloors carry live loads to the joists, which carry the loads to the beams, which carry the loads to the columns and foundation walls, which carry the loads to the footings, which carry the loads to the soil below. We hope the soil stays put.

Span   Subflooring usually spans 12 to 24 inches, with 16 inches being most common. Subflooring is a nominal 1 inch thick plank (about ¾ of an inch of actual thickness), or about ⅝ inch plywood or waferboard, assuming 16 inch centers on the joists.

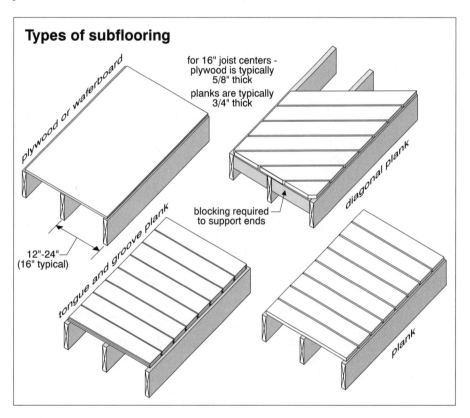

Types of subflooring

plywood or waferboard

for 16" joist centers -
plywood is typically
5/8" thick

planks are typically
3/4" thick

12"-24"
(16" typical)

tongue and groove plank

blocking required
to support ends

diagonal plank

plank

Plank   If the subflooring is plank, it can be tongue-and-groove although it's usually butt jointed. Tongue-and-groove is typically used where resilient flooring is going to be applied above. Butt joints are used where hardwood flooring will overlay the subflooring.

Perpendicular *Or Diagonal*   The plank subflooring is usually perpendicular to the joists although it can also be installed on the diagonal. Diagonal subflooring is considered to have better rigidity with respect to racking of the building, although it can create some problems. All subflooring must be supported at its edges. Diagonal subflooring requires additional blocking at the perimeters to support ends of pieces. Spongy floors are often due to unsupported ends of diagonal planking.

Plywood

Plywood subflooring should be installed with its long dimension and face grain perpendicular to the joists. Installing plywood with the subfloor parallel to the joists makes the flooring weaker.

Making Little Trusses

Using glue and screws to fasten the subfloor to the joists makes the whole floor act as a rigid truss.

Stagger The Joints

Joints in plywood or waferboard subflooring should be staggered to increase the rigidity of the floor. Unsupported butt joints and panels should be supported with two by two blocking, or the panels should be tongue-and-groove.

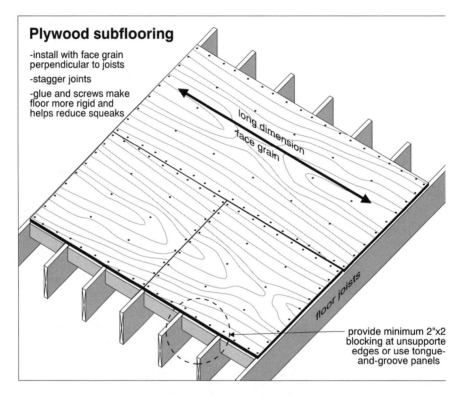

Plywood subflooring

-install with face grain perpendicular to joists

-stagger joints

-glue and screws make floor more rigid and helps reduce squeaks

long dimension face grain

floor joists

provide minimum 2"x2 blocking at unsupporte edges or use tongue-and-groove panels

Support The Joints

Small gaps between adjacent panels allow for swelling due to moisture changes without buckling. Gaps of $\frac{3}{32}$ of an inch are typical.

7.1 CONDITIONS

Subfloor problems include –

1. rot and insect damage
2. sagging or springy subflooring (as a result of being overspanned or undersized)
3. damaged or cut
4. cantilevered/unsupported ends
5. prior repairs
6. concentrated loads
7. squeaks
8. swollen waferboard
9. cracking ceramic tiles

7.1.1 ROT AND INSECT DAMAGE

Causes

Damage is caused by –

1. moisture
2. insects (especially wet or rotted wood).

Strategy

Rot Around Plumbing

We've talked about this with respect to other wood members. Rotted subfloors are common around toilets, bathtubs, shower stalls, etc. Rotted subflooring is also common below radiators on heating systems. Anywhere water might leak, rotted subflooring could be an issue.

At Perimeters

Rotted subflooring may also be found around building perimeters where there is exterior wall or window leakage or condensation which gets hung up on subflooring.

At Sliding Glass Doors

Subfloor damage is common at exterior doorways, particularly at sliding glass doors. Sliding glass doors often suffer condensation. Subflooring may be rotted along the entire length of the door. Watch for this from below, or if you can lift up an edge of the finish flooring, you will sometimes see the damage.

7.1.2 OVERSPANNED OR UNDERSIZED SUBFLOORING

Cause

This is an installation issue.

Strategy

Subflooring should not deflect more than 1/360th of its span. Weakened or under-sized subflooring can make flooring spongy. This is often localized. A weakened joist will cause subflooring to be springy in that area. Diagonal subflooring with unsupported ends at walls is common.

7.1.3 DAMAGED OR CUT SUBFLOORING

Cause   Mechanical damage may be done by tradespeople or homeowners.

Strategy   Many people cut through subflooring recklessly to accommodate ductwork, piping, etc. Resupporting may be necessary. In carpeted rooms, it's common to find that an opening was cut for a heating register in the wrong place. The heating register was not provided, but the hole in the subfloor gets carpeted over. Whenever someone steps on that area, the floor is very weak. Repairs are easy if the subfloor is accessible from below.

Abandoned Heat Register Holes

7.1.4 CANTILEVERED SUBFLOORING (POOR END BEARING)

Causes   Problems are installation issues in most cases.

Strategy   Edges of subflooring should be supported. Where subflooring is cut or terminated and is not over a joist, blocking should be provided. Diagonal plank subflooring that is missing blocking at perimeter walls is very spongy.

Where subflooring edges on plywood or OSB are butted and not tongue-and-groove, you should see blocking. Unsupported edges should have blocking added.

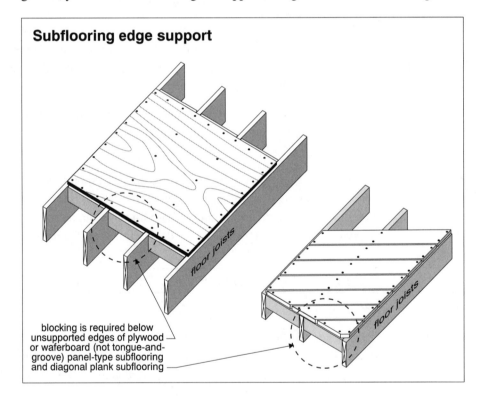

Subflooring edge support

blocking is required below unsupported edges of plywood or waferboard (not tongue-and-groove) panel-type subflooring and diagonal plank subflooring

floor joists

7.1.5 PRIOR REPAIRS

As we've discussed, you should try to identify why the repair was necessary and whether it is performing satisfactorily.

7.1.6 CONCENTRATED LOADS

Causes

Pianos, columns, or heavy pieces of furniture with only four legs can create such large point loads that will deflect or crack the subfloor.

Strategy

Watch for evidence of this and recommend resupporting from below the subfloor.

7.1.7 SQUEAKS

Causes

Squeaks are often the result of poor fastening of the subfloor to the joists. This is especially true where the subflooring is nailed (not screwed and/or glued) to the joists. The squeaking noise is usually the nails sliding in and out of their holes. In some cases, the squeaky noise is wood-on-wood.

Squeaks may be caused by unsupported edges of plywood or waferboard panels rubbing against each other as people walk across the floor.

Strategy

In the Section 1.2 of the **Interior** chapter of **The Home Reference Book**, there is a discussion about squeak control for floors. There is no structural impact.

Supporting panel edges, leaving gaps between panels, or using tongue-and-groove panels help reduce squeaks.

7.1.8 SWOLLEN WAFERBOARD

Causes

Waferboard is vulnerable to moisture damage. Wet waferboard swells and gets much thicker than it was originally. This weakens the subflooring.

Strategy

Where swollen waferboard is noted, watch for sagging or breaking. Replacement may be necessary. Fasteners often pull through the swollen subfloor.

7.1.9 CRACKED CERAMIC TILES

Causes

Subfloor that is not rigid enough will allow ceramic tiles to crack.

Strategy

A common problem in relatively new homes is cracking ceramic tile floors. This is not a structural problem but a failure to recognize that tiles cannot tolerate much deflection without cracking. The subflooring should be more rigid to prevent cracking. There are several strategies for this. They include –

  a. setting the tiles in at least 1¼ inches of concrete,
  b. using thicker or double subflooring (total thickness of roughly 1¼ inches)
  c. using blocking to support the subflooring between the joists.

Cracking tile is most often a cosmetic issue, although it can be a big one.

In some areas ⁵⁄₈ inch subflooring with tiles set in lightly reinforced thinset mortar are acceptable. This may or may not be a successful approach, depending on several variables.

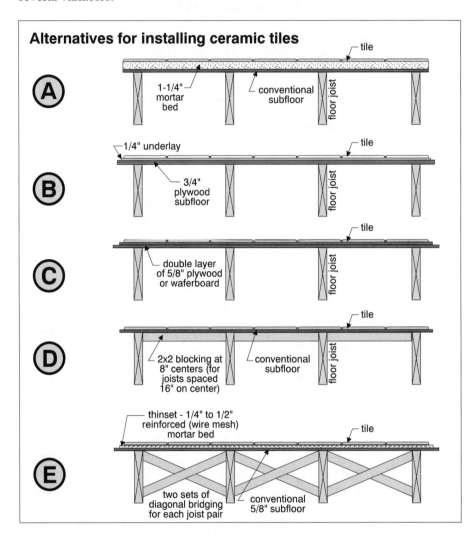

Alternatives for installing ceramic tiles

A — tile; 1-1/4" mortar bed; conventional subfloor; floor joist

B — 1/4" underlay; tile; 3/4" plywood subfloor; floor joist

C — tile; double layer of 5/8" plywood or waferboard; floor joist

D — tile; 2x2 blocking at 8" centers (for joists spaced 16" on center); conventional subfloor; floor joist

E — thinset - 1/4" to 1/2" reinforced (wire mesh) mortar bed; tile; two sets of diagonal bridging for each joist pair; conventional 5/8" subfloor

Determining Subfloor Make-up   The subfloor composition can sometimes be determined by lifting floor heating or cooling registers. Other floor openings may also allow checking the subfloor.

Support Edges Of Panel-Type Subflooring   Ceramic tile is less likely to crack if the edges of subflooring are supported by solid blocking, even if the panels are tongue-and-groove type.

Plywood Subflooring May Be Best   Some manufacturers and flooring associations recommend plywood rather than OSB (Oriented Strand Board), waferboard or particleboard subflooring.

▶ 8.0 CONCRETE FLOOR SLABS

Concrete Defined

Concrete is a mixture of cement, water and aggregates. There is usually fine aggregate (sand) and coarse aggregate (gravel). The cement is the glue that bonds things together. It is typically a fine gray powder made by burning a mixture of limestone and clay.

Structural?

Concrete floor slabs may or may not be an integral part of the structure. You will not usually know whether the floor slab is structural.

Reinforced?

Similarly, you won't be able to identify, in most cases, whether the flooring was reinforced, or whether it is a special flooring such as pre-stressed or post tensioned concrete. These are rare systems in single family homes, but we'll briefly describe them. They are common in some areas.

Prestressed Concrete

Prestressed concrete floor slabs use steel cables or tendons that are put under tension (stretched) before the concrete is poured. The tensioned cables are pulled tight like a piano wire and the concrete is poured around them. As the concrete cures, the cables are let go. This strengthens the floor.

Post-tensioned Concrete

Post-tensioned concrete is similar in that there are steel cables or tendons laid in the forms before the concrete is poured. The difference is that these cables are usually put in a sheathing, and as the concrete cures, the cables are pulled tight from one end (usually with hydraulic jacks), while the other end is anchored. This applies the tension after the concrete is in place. The floor is strengthened by putting the concrete in compression.

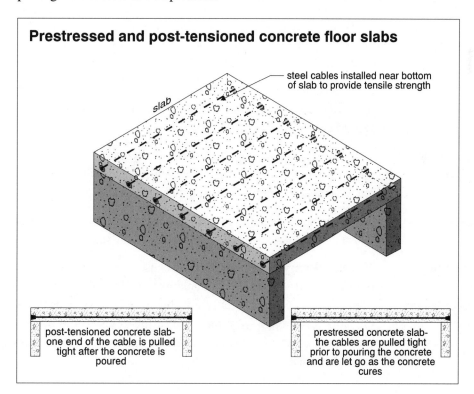

Prestressed and post-tensioned concrete floor slabs

steel cables installed near bottom of slab to provide tensile strength

slab

post-tensioned concrete slab- one end of the cable is pulled tight after the concrete is poured

prestressed concrete slab- the cables are pulled tight prior to pouring the concrete and are let go as the concrete cures

Supported Or   Most concrete floor slabs are supported on granular fill or native soil below.
Suspended   Some slabs are suspended with living space, garages, etc., below. Suspended slabs
                 are clearly structural. Suspended slabs may be pre-cast or cast-in-place. They are
                 common commercially, but rare residentially except in high rise construction.
                 Inspection of these can be challenging, and where you suspect any non perfor-
                 mance, a specialist should be consulted.

Slab Thickness We have seen concrete floor slabs that are ½ inch thick, and those that are ten inches
                  thick. The most common thickness of supported slabs is three to four inches.

8.1 CONDITIONS

Common problems in floor slabs include –

1. cracked
2. settled
3. heaved
4. hollow below slab
5. scaling and dusting
6. spalling
7. rusting reinforcing bar

8.1.1 CRACKED

Causes   Cracked slabs may be due to –

1. shrinkage,
2. settling, or
3. heaving.

Concrete cures for several years after pouring but most of the curing occurs
within the first month. Concrete shrinks as it cures, as much as ⅛ inch over 20
feet. Many slabs crack as they cure.

Shrinkage   Shrinkage cracks are usually a result of drying too fast or the slab being held in
Cracks   place too tightly while the concrete is curing. Control joints help determine where
                  cracks appear, but don't prevent cracks.

Rebar   Some people think putting reinforcement into concrete stops shrinkage cracks. It
                  doesn't stop the cracks, but it does control their size.

Strategy   You can identify shrinkage cracks because they are random and usually show up
                  over the entire floor area. Cracks that follow straight lines or form circles
Identifying   around columns are probably not shrinkage cracks. Shrinkage cracks have no
Shrinkage   elevation difference from one side of the crack to the other and are rarely ⅛
Cracks   inch wide, often much smaller. These cracks may or may not go all the way
                  through the slabs

Settling Or Heaving Cracks

These cracks indicate movement of parts of the slab relative to other parts.

Causes include –

Causes

1. footing or foundation settlement
2. soil compaction or erosion below the slabs
3. excess concentrated loads on the slabs
4. footing or foundation heaving due to
   a. frost
   b. expansive soils
   c. tree roots
5. soil heaving below the slabs due to
   a. frost
   b. expansive soils
6. Uneven slab settlement due to service trenches (disturbed soils) or large rocks against slab preventing uniform settlement

Implications

Cracks in slabs may be

1. unnoticed,
2. cosmetic,
3. sources of leakage or insect entry (including termites),
4. safety and comfort issues because floors are uneven, or
5. structural issues if the building is unsound.

Strategy

Use the yardsticks we discussed in the Footing and Foundation section to quantify the problem. Recommend further investigation where you are unsure.

Identifying Settling And Heaving Cracks

There are often elevation differences on either side of the crack. The slab surfaces may be tilted on either side of the crack. Walls may not be plumb or floors may not be level.

Cold Joints Aren't Cracks

Watch for cold joints that occur along the edges of slabs. If the concrete foundation and the floor slab are poured at different times, you will get a cold joint around the perimeter of the house between the top of the foundation and the bottom of the floor slab. This is often visible from outside and looks at first glance like a crack. Do not mistake this for a structural crack.

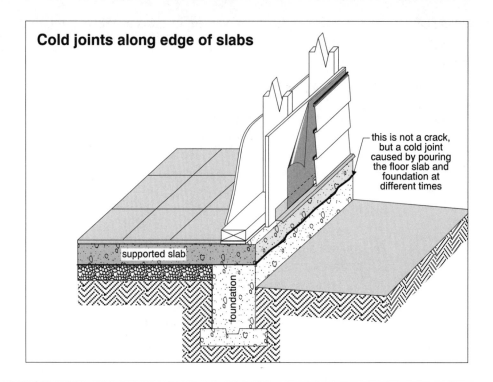

Cold joints along edge of slabs

this is not a crack, but a cold joint caused by pouring the floor slab and foundation at different times

supported slab

foundation

8.1.2 SETTLED

Slabs may settle with or without cracking.

Causes   Slabs may settle because of

1. inadequate support from foundations and footings,
2. compacting or eroding soil below, or
3. overloading from above.

Settling is usually accompanied by cracking.

Implications   The implications may be trivial or significant.

Strategy   **Sounding** (tapping on the floors) for hollowness below will tell you whether there is erosion or missing fill below the slab. This can occur where there are underground streams or expansive soils which have dried out and shrunk. It can also occur where the slab is on organic material which is decomposing, or the subgrade material was disturbed and is recompacting.

Other Movement In Building   Look for other movement in the building. If walls have moved as a result, the slab may be structural and corrective action may be necessary. This can include excavation and repair or replacement of footings, **mud jacking** (injecting a concrete slurry under the slab to fill voids), or monitoring the situation.

8.1.3 HEAVED

Slabs may heave with or without cracking.

Causes This is usually the result of frost, tree roots or expansive soils getting wet. Heaving floors will often be accompanied by cracks.

Implications These can form a trip hazard and may weaken the structure. Walls may be out of plumb as a result of the heaved slabs.

Strategy Heaved slabs generally require monitoring and investigation by a specialist. It is very dangerous to offer any conclusions about heaved floors based on a one-time visit.

8.1.4 HOLLOW BELOW

Causes This may be due to settled fill, or erosion due to air conditioning condensate drains, leaking plumbing or heating pipes. On sloped lots, erosion can also be the result of surface water run off.

Implications Loss of support for the slab below can cause settlement.

Strategy We talked earlier about sounding the floor for hollow areas. Again, mud jacking is a possible solution, although this is expensive and not used commonly residentially. Depending on the extent of the hollow area, this may not be an appropriate solution and other approaches may have to be investigated. Again, you won't be making any final decisions during a home inspection. Your task is simply to identify the problem.

8.1.5 SCALING OR DUSTING

This surface deterioration of the concrete is not related to the structure. Scaling and dusting are pitting or erosion of the concrete surface. There are several causes and a determination is not usually necessary. In rare cases, there may be enough deterioration to warrant further investigation.

8.1.6 SPALLING

Spalling is a breaking away of the concrete surface in chunks or flakes. It may be the result of too much water in the concrete or freeze/thaw action. It is rare in floor slabs, except around the perimeter. Damage is usually localized but should be identified.

8.1.7 RUSTING REBAR

Causes One of the most troublesome areas is suspended garage floor slabs. In areas where salts are used on roads, vehicles carry salts and slush into garages during the winter months. This moisture leaks down into slabs and the salt water rusts the steel reinforcing bar quickly.

Rusting may occur on any slab where moisture is present, of course.

Implications
Steel expands to 6 or 10 times its original volume as it corrodes. This will crack or spall the concrete dramatically. This deterioration is sometimes called **delamination**. The strength of suspended concrete slabs is dramatically reduced when the rebar rusts. Repairs can be expensive and replacement may be necessary. There are several strategies to address this problem, although they are not common on single family homes.

Strategy
Watch for evidence of rusting at slab surfaces, particularly on suspended slabs (tops and bottoms) where you can get a look.

Where you see suspended slabs and evidence of rusting, either on the top of bottom, recommend further investigation by a specialist.

Summary

Concrete floor slabs may experience problems for three general reasons:

• deterioration of the concrete or rebar itself
• excessive loads
• loss of support for the slab.

Cracking, scaling, dusting and rusting rebar are failures of the concrete slabs itself. Settling and heaving are usually the result of excessive loads or loss of support.

Structure

MODULE

QUICK QUIZ 5

☑ INSTRUCTIONS

• You should finish reading Study Session 5 before doing this Quiz.

• Write your answers in the spaces provided.

• Check your answers against ours at the end of this Section.

• If you have trouble with this Quiz, re–read the Session and try the Quiz again.

• If you do well, move on to Field Exercise 2.

1. Name 3 common subfloor materials.

_____   _____   _____

2. Subfloors act like – (two answers)

    a. joists
    b. foundations
    c. columns
    d. footings
    e. beams

3. What is one possible disadvantage of diagonal plank subflooring?

_____

4. Plywood should be installed with its long dimension parallel to joists.
True ☐   False ☐

5. Common subflooring problems include – (give nine)

_____   _____   _____

_____   _____   _____

_____   _____   _____

6. Subflooring below ceramic tiles should be stiffened to prevent tile cracking. Name three ways this can be done.

_____   _____   _____

7. Briefly describe pre-stressed concrete flooring.

_____

_____

8. Briefly describe post-tensioned concrete flooring.

_____

_____

9. All concrete floors in houses are suspended slabs.
   True ☐   False ☐

10. List seven common concrete floor problems.

_____

_____

_____

_____

_____

_____

_____

11. Shrinkage crack patterns in concrete floors are usually –

   a. in circles
   b. in straight lines
   c. random
   d. at 45^0 to walls
   e. at 90^0 to walls

12. Concrete slabs may settle or heave because of – (give five reasons)

_____

_____

_____

_____

_____

13. How can you tell if slabs have had their support undermined?

_____

14. In what part of the building is rusting steel reinforcing bar in concrete slabs likely to be a problem?

_____

If you had no trouble with the Quiz then you are ready for Field Exercise 2.

Keywords:

- **Planking**
- **Plywood**
- **Waferboard**
- **Span**
- **Tongue-and-groove**
- **Rot**
- **Insect damage**
- **Condensation**
- **Overspanned**
- **Damaged or cut**
- **Cantilevers**
- **Concentrated loads**
- **Squeaks**

- **Swollen waferboard**
- **Cracked ceramic tiles**
- **Prestressed concrete**
- **Post-tensioned concrete**
- **Supported slab**
- **Suspended slab**
- **Cracked**
- **Settled**
- **Heaved**
- **Hollow below**
- **Shaling**
- **Spalling**
- **Rusted rebar**

Structure
MODULE

FIELD EXERCISE 2

☑ INSTRUCTIONS

This exercise is based on Study Sessions 4 and 5.

Again, you are going to have to get into a number of houses. We are going to look at both wood and concrete floor systems. The concrete floor systems can be in the house, basement, garage or crawlspace. The wood flooring can be on the first, second or third floor, although you may see most of the details looking at the unfinished underside of a first floor level. Rarely is much of the framing visible on the underside of a second or third floor.

You should inspect at least 10 floor systems.

Allow yourself roughly 15 minutes to look at each floor system.

For each of the houses you look at, try to answer the following questions:

1. Joist material (e.g., solid wood, engineered wood, metal) –

    _____

2. Species of wood (you may be able to get this from the stamp on the wood):

    _____

3. a. joist size _____
    b. joist spacing _____
    c. joist span _____

4. What supported the joist?(e.g., beams, foundations, sills)

    _____

5. What was the end bearing?(e.g., 2 inches)

_____

6. Did you see any fire cut joists?

_____

7. Did you see bridging, blocking or strapping?

_____

8. Did you see any headers? Where?

_____

9. Did you see any trimmers? Where?

_____

10. Did you see any doubled joists? Could you tell why they were doubled?

_____

11. Did you see any cantilevers? Were they entirely indoors, or were they partly indoors and partly outdoors? Where did you look for problems?

_____

_____

12. Could you see the rim joists?

_____

13. Did you find any of these problems?

    a.   rot and insect damage
    b.   sagging joists
    c.   poor end bearing
    d.   rotated or twisted joists
    e.   incomplete blocking, bridging or strapping
    f.   inappropriate notching or holes
    g.   split or damaged joists
    h.   weak cantilevers
    i.   weaknesses created by openings around stairs, chimneys and windows, etc.
    j.   prior repairs
    k.   concentrated loads
    l.   missing joists

14. Which was the most common?

_____

15. What kinds of subflooring did you see?

_____

16. Did you see any of these problems?

    a.   rot and insect damage
    b.   sagging or springy subfloorings
    c.   damaged or cut subflooring
    d.   cantilevered or unsupported ends
    e.   prior repairs
    f.   concentrated loads
    g.   squeaks
    h.   swollen waferboard
    i.   cracking ceramic tiles

17. Which of these was the most common?

_____

18. Did you find:

    a.   supported concrete slabs
    b.   suspended concrete slabs
    c.   pre-stressed concrete slabs (can't usually tell by looking)
    d.   post–tensioned concrete slabs (can't usually tell by looking)

19. Did you find any of the following conditions?

    a.   cracked
    b.   settled
    c.   heaved
    d.   hollow below slab
    e.   scaling or dusting
    f.   spalling
    g.   rusting reinforcing bar

20. Try to contact local builders or framing carpenters who have worked in your area for several years. Ask them what the most common floor framing materials are. Ask them what the most common problems have been.

_____

_____

_____

_____

21. Speak to local builders who work with concrete floors. Are the majority of floors supported? Are there any prestressed or post-tensioned concrete floor slabs in 1 to 4 family dwellings in your area? If so, why are these used? What are the most common problems these people have found in concrete floors?

_____

_____

_____

_____

Finished with the exercise? Great! Then it is time to look at the Inspection Tools and Inspection Checklist on the next two pages.

► 9.0 INSPECTION TOOLS

1. **Flashlight**

   To examine dark area, such as crawlspaces.

2. **Screwdriver/Awl**

   To probe suspect surfaces.

3. **Moisture Meter**

   To identify high moisture content in building materials.

4. **Tape Measure**

   To evaluate foundation height and thickness against grade height, for example.

5. **Plumb Bob**

   Is used to quantify leaning or bowing wall conditions.

6. **Mason's Level**

   To help quantify out–of–plumb situations.

► 10.0 INSPECTION CHECKLIST

Location Legend   N = North S = South E = East W= West
B = Basement 1 = 1st story 2 = 2nd story 3 = 3rd story

LOCATION		LOCATION	
	SILLS		**JOISTS**
	• Missing		• Missing
	• Rot or insect damage/fire damage		• Rot or insect damage/fire damage
	• At or below grade level		• Sag or springy
	• Gaps under sills		• Poor end bearing/joist hanger connections
	• Crushed		• Weak mortise and tenon joints
	• Anchor bolts missing		• No blocking, bracing or bridging
	• Anchor nuts missing		• Ineffective blocking, bracing or bridging
	• Anchor washers missing		• Inappropriate notching or holes
	• Anchor bolts not secure in foundation		• Split or damaged
	• Anchor bolts too short		• Weak cantilevers
	• Anchors not centered in sill		• Weak openings (stairs, chimneys, etc.)
	• Sill split at anchor bolts		• Concentrated loads
	• Anchor nuts not tightened		• Prior repairs
	COLUMNS		**SUBFLOORING**
	• Missing		• Rot or insect damage/fire damage
	• Settled		• Sag or springy
	• Crushed		• Damaged or cut
	• Leaning		• Poor end support/cantilevered
	• Buckling		• Prior repairs
	• Poorly secured at top or bottom		• Concentrated loads
	• Mortar deterioration		• Squeaks
	• Spalling concrete or brick		• Swollen waferboard
	• Mechanical damage		• Cracking ceramic tiles
	• Rot or insect damage/fire damage		• Plywood in wrong orientation
	• Heaved		• Poor fastening (nailing, screwing, gluing)
	• Prior repairs		
	• Undersized, too slender		
	• Missing footing?		**CONCRETE SLABS**
			• Cracked
	BEAMS		• Settled
	• Rust		• Heaved
	• Rot or insect damage/fire damage		• Hollow below slab
	• Sag		• Scaling or rusting
	• Poor bearing, crushed or loose shims		• Spalling
	• Rotated or twisted beams		• Rusted rebar
	• Notches or holes		
	• Poor connections of built-up components		
	• Weak connections to columns		
	• Weak connections to joists		
	• Inadequate lateral support		
	• Concentrated loads		
	• Missing beams or sections of beams		
	• Prior repairs		

Now you're ready for the Final Test!

► ANSWERS TO QUICK QUIZZES

Answers to Quick Quiz 1

1. Foundations, floor structures, wall structures, ceiling structures, roof structures

2. Sills, columns, beams, joists, subfloors

3. c

4. True

5. True

6. Avoid moisture and possible rot

7. To connect the top of the foundation to the wood floor system

8. 1. Rotted sills may be crushed and lead to differential settlement
   2. Rotted sills often mean rotted joists and studs
   3. Rotted sills means the house frame is not well anchored to the foundation

9. Sills are typically bolted to the foundation

10. 1. Sills below grade
    2. Rot or insect damage
    3. Gaps between the sill and foundation
    4. Crushed sills
    5. Not properly anchored
    6. Missing

Answers to Quick Quiz 2

1. b

2. 1. Concrete
   2. Concrete block
   3. Brick
   4. Steel
   5. Wood

3. 1. Missing
   2. Settled
   3. Crushed

4. Leaning

5. Buckled

6. Rust

7. Poorly secured at the top or bottom

8. Mortar deterioration

9. Spalling concrete or brick

10. Mechanical damage

11. Rot or insect damage

12. Heaved

13. Prior repairs

4. 1. No footing
    2. Undersized footing
    3. Poor soil conditions under the footing
    4. Larger load than intended

5. 1. Concrete
    2. Wood

6. The same width

7. 1. Bolts
    2. Welding
    3. Bendable tabs

8. A level or plumb bob

9. 1. Expansive soils
    2. Tree roots
    3. Frost

10. c

Answers to Quick Quiz 3

1. a, b, c & e

2. 1. Wood
    2. Steel

3. 1. Glulams
    2. LVL – Laminated Veneer Lumber
    3. LSL – Laminated Strand Lumber
    4. PSL – Parallel Strand Lumber

4. False

5. 1. a
    2. b

6. $3\frac{1}{8}$ inches

7. 1. Rust
2. Rot or insect damage
3. Sag
4. Poor bearing
5. Rotated or twisted beams
6. Split or damaged
7. Notches or holes
8. Poor connections of built-up components
9. Weak connections to columns
10. Weak connections to joists
11. Inadequate lateral support
12. Concentrated loads
13. Missing sections
14. Prior repairs

8. b

9. Overspanned or undersized

10. False

11. True

12. To avoid rot

13. True

14. d

15. True

16. both b and c

Answers to Quick Quiz 4

1. a, b, & d

2. 1. Trusses
2. Plywood
3. Wood I-joists
4. Laminated Veneer Lumber (LVL)
5. Parallel Strand Lumber (PSL)
6. Laminated Strand Lumber (LSL)

3. False

4. True

5. False

6. 1. Rot and insect damage
2. Sagging joists
3. Poor end bearing
4. Rotated or twisted joists
5. No blocking, bridging or strapping
6. Inappropriate notching or holes
7. Split or damaged
8. Weak cantilevers
9. Weaknesses created by openings around stairs, chimneys and windows, etc.
10. Prior repairs
11. Concentrated loads
12. Missing joists

7. 1. Overspanning
2. Weakened by rot, insects, notches, holes or fire
3. Joists installed crown down
4. Concentrated loads

8. 1. Two-by-eights - twelve feet
2. Two-by-tens - fourteen feet
3. Two-by-twelves - sixteen feet

9. a, c & e

10. The end of the joist may kick up, creating a high spot in the floor.

11. 1½ inches

12. False

13. True

14. 1. Undersized
2. Inadequate nails
3. Wrong type of nails
4. Joist not bottomed in hanger
5. Joist doesn't penetrate fully into hanger
6. Joists connected to beam at other than 90° with conventional hanger.
7. Doubled joists connected to beam with single joist hanger

15. The ledger board is fastened to the beam near the bottom and the joist rests on the top of the ledger board.

16. 1. Bridging
2. Blocking
3. Ceilings
4. Strapping

17. False

18. The member is supported at one end and partway along the length. One end is unsupported.

19. The problem is most likely to occur where the joists pass through the walls because this is the area that is likely to stay wet.

20. Refer to the illustration in Section 6.1.9.

21. False

22. 1. Holes too big or in the wrong place
    2. Incorrect joist hangers
    3. Improper rim joist material
    4. Missing or incomplete blocking
    5. Split, notched or cut flanges
    6. Inadequate end-bearing
    7. Joists beveled or fire-cut
    8. Inadequate blocking on laminated I-joists
    9. Inadequate bridging or load-sharing
    10. Trusses that are either too long or too short
    11. Concentrated loads on the top of trusses
    12. Trusses installed upside down

Answers to Quick Quiz 5

1. Planking, plywood, waferboard

2. both a & e

3. Unsupported edges may be springy

4. False

5. 1. Rot and insect damage
   2. Sagging or springy subflooring
   3. Damaged or cut
   4. Cantilevered or unsupported ends
   5. Prior repairs
   6. Concentrated loads
   7. Squeaks
   8. Swollen waferboard
   9. Cracking ceramic tiles

6. 1. 1¼ inches of concrete
   2. Using thicker or double subflooring
   3. Using blocking to support the subflooring between the joists

7. Prestressed concrete floors use steel cables under tension put in place before the concrete is poured. The concrete is poured around the cables and then the cables are let go.

8. Post-tensioned concrete has steel cables in a sheathing, typically. The concrete is poured around the cables when they are relaxed, and as the concrete cures, the cables are pulled tight, from one end while the other end is anchored. The tension in the cables puts the concrete under compression.

9. False

10. 1. Cracked
    2. Settled
    3. Heaved
    4. Hollow below slab
    5. Scaling or dusting
    6. Spalling
    7. Rusting reinforcing bar

11. c

12. 1. Footing or foundation settlement
    2. Soil compaction or erosion below slab
    3. Excess concentrated loads on the slab
    4. Footing or foundation heaving due to frost, expansive soils or tree roots
    5. Soil heaving due to frost or expansive soils

13. Tap on the slab and listen for a hollow sound

14. Suspended garage floor slabs

3

WALL
SYSTEMS

Structure

MODULE

► TABLE OF CONTENTS

► 1.0 OBJECTIVES

During this section we will –
- learn the three types of wall systems
- learn the key components that make up a wall
- learn the common conditions that may be found in each type of wall system
- learn how to identify these conditions
- learn how to evaluate the seriousness of the conditions and the implications of non-repair

Not The
Last Word

This program is not an in-depth Structure course and you should not assume that you have all the knowledge of a professional engineer, architect, designer, carpenter, mason, etc. after studying this material. This program does not qualify you to design or build homes. There are many places to go to learn more and we encourage you to continue expanding your knowledge.

Structure
MODULE

STUDY SESSION 1

1. This Session assumes that you have read Section 6.1 in the Structures chapter of **The Home Reference Book**. If you have not read this, please do that now.

2. At the end of this Session you should be able to –

- List seven functions of walls.
- List four types of masonry walls.
- List seven common masonry wall problems.
- List eight items in a general approach to looking at cracks.
- List nine steps in crack analysis.

3. This Session may take you about 1 hour to complete.

4. Try Quick Quiz 1 when you are finished the Session.

Key Words:

- *Live and dead loads*
- *Solid masonry*
- *Cavity walls*
- *Reinforced masonry walls*
- *Veneer walls*
- *Headers*
- *Stretchers*
- *Metal tiles*
- *Diagonal brick bond*
- *Lateral support*
- *Arches*
- *Lintels*
- *Leaning, bowing, bulging*
- *Corbelling*
- *Truss uplift*

► 2.0 SCOPE AND INTRODUCTION

2.1 SCOPE

The following is the Structure Section of the ASHI® Standards of Practice, effective January 2000. The Purpose and Scope, General Limitations and Exclusions, and Glossary are included in the Footings and Foundations section.

3.0 STRUCTURAL SYSTEM

3.1 The *inspector* shall:

    A. *inspect:*
  1. the *structural components* including foundation and framing.
  2. by probing a *representative number* of structural components where deterioration is suspected or where clear indications of possible deterioration exist. Probing is NOT required when probing would damage any finished surface or where no deterioration is visible.

    B. *describe:*
  1. the foundation and *report* the methods used to *inspect* the *under-floor crawl space*
  2. the floor structure.
  3. the wall structure.
  4. the ceiling structure.
  5. the roof structure and *report* the methods used to *inspect* the attic.

3.2 The *inspector* is NOT required to:

    A. provide any *engineering service* or *architectural service*.
    B. offer an opinion as to the adequacy of any *structural system* or *component*.

2.2 INTRODUCTION

Masonry And Wood Frame Walls

In this section we're going to deal with masonry and wood frame walls only. We will not be dealing with log, post and beam, stacked plank, steel, or concrete walls, either precast panels or poured-in-place.

Exterior And Interior Finishes

These are addressed in the Exterior Module and, as such, we won't be dealing with them extensively here. Similarly, interior finishes will be dealt with in the Interior Module. Here we will focus on the structure.

Functions

Walls have several functions including –

1. Carrying the live and dead loads to the flooring or foundation system. These loads include –

Live And Dead Loads

  a. the dead load from floors, walls and roofs above
  b. snow loads
  c. wind loads
  d. earthquake loads
  e. loads from people, furnishings and contents of houses

Resist Racking

2. Walls help houses resist racking forces. Houses are generally built as rectangles, and walls help keep them rectangles rather than parallelograms.

Support Finishes

3. Walls support interior and exterior finishes. Exterior siding and interior drywall, for example, are attached to wall systems. In some cases, the wall structure is also the exterior and/or interior finish. For example, in solid masonry construction, the load carrying brick is also the exterior finish.

Hide Mechanicals

4. Walls provide chases for wires, pipes and ductwork for the house electrical and mechanical systems.

Thermal Insulation

5. Exterior walls accommodate thermal insulation to minimize heat loss and heat gain.

Sound Insulation

6. Wall assemblies provide sound isolation.

Privacy

7. Walls provide spatial separation within dwellings, affording privacy.

► 3.0 SOLID MASONRY WALLS

Materials

Masonry walls may be made of brick, stone, concrete block, cinder block, clay tile or glass block. Walls may be single, double or triple **wythe (thickness)**. Six inch single wythe masonry walls are common on one-story buildings with walls less than 9 feet high.

There are four general types of masonry walls.

1. **Solid masonry walls** may be single, double or triple wythe, with no space between.

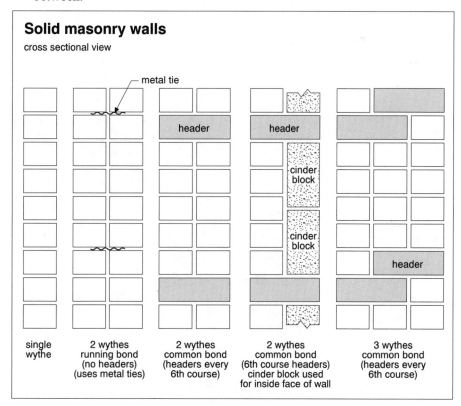

Solid masonry walls
cross sectional view

| single wythe | 2 wythes running bond (no headers) (uses metal ties) | 2 wythes common bond (headers every 6th course) | 2 wythes common bond (6th course headers) cinder block used for inside face of wall | 3 wythes common bond (headers every 6th course) |

2. **Cavity walls** are at least two wythes with an air space between. The air space provides some insulation and a moisture barrier, in effect. The inner and outer wythes are typically joined with metal ties.

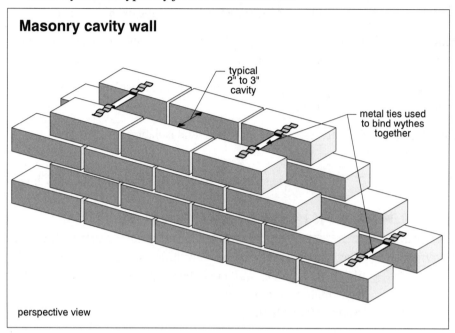

Masonry cavity wall

typical 2" to 3" cavity

metal ties used to bind wythes together

perspective view

3. **Reinforced masonry walls** are double wythe with steel reinforcement embedded in grout in the space between the wythes. This type of construction is common in earthquake areas.

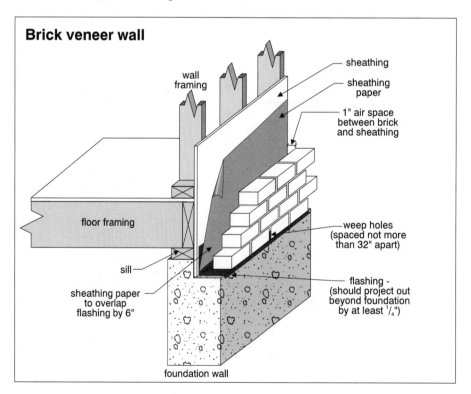

Brick veneer wall

wall framing

sheathing

sheathing paper

1" air space between brick and sheathing

floor framing

weep holes (spaced not more than 32" apart)

sill

sheathing paper to overlap flashing by 6"

flashing - (should project out beyond foundation by at least $\frac{1}{4}$")

foundation wall

4. Veneer walls are wood frame walls with a single wythe of brick or stone applied on the outside. In this case, the masonry is acting as a siding rather than a structural component. The heavy masonry has to sit on the foundation and footing system. A masonry veneer cannot rest on a wood frame wall.

What We'll Look At

We'll focus on solid walls in this section and veneer walls in section 3.0. In many cases, you won't be able to differentiate solid, cavity and reinforced walls unless the interior of the wall system is accessible. The inspection techniques for solid walls are similar to cavity and reinforced walls, in any case.

Holding The Wythes Together

There are three ways of holding the masonry wythes together, two of which are common.
• Header bricks
• Metal ties
• Diagonal brick bond (rare)

1. Header bricks

Headers are masonry units that are turned into the wall and straddle both wythes. When the wall is finished, you see only the end of the headers. They look like short bricks.

Bricks installed with their long dimension parallel to the wall face are called **stretchers**, if they are horizontal. Sometimes, bricks are installed over windows their long face parallel to the wall, but the brick is standing on its end. These are commonly called **soldiers**.

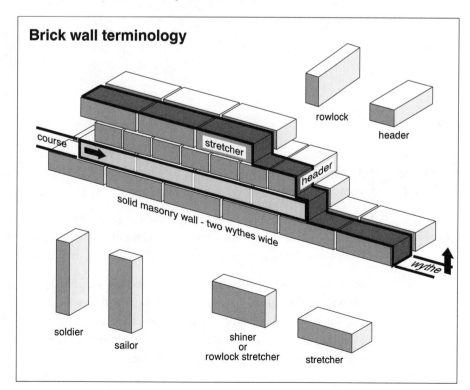

Brick wall terminology

9

2. Metal ties

There are several types of metal ties (brick ties) that can be used to hold the two wythes of a masonry wall together.

3. Diagonal brick bond (rare)

Within the wall, bricks are laid flat, but on the diagonal so they straddle the two wythes of brick. With a diagonal brick bond, the diagonal bricks are not exposed on the face of either the inside of the outside of the wall. You can think of a diagonal brick bond as headers that aren't turned fully 90°.

This would be more common in a three wythe masonry wall than a two wythe wall.

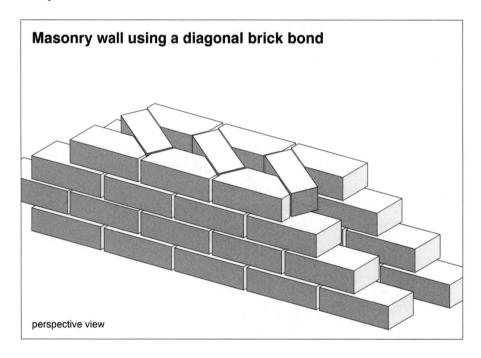

Masonry wall using a diagonal brick bond

perspective view

Foundations And Footings Are Needed

All masonry walls, including veneer walls, require foundations and footings designed to carry the considerable weight of these wall systems. (Yes, there are a few exceptions!)

Lateral Support

Masonry walls are generally not freestanding. Lateral support can be provided either by vertical or horizontal members. Horizontal support is provided by floor or roof systems. Vertical support is provided by interior or end walls.

The distance between either horizontal or vertical supports should be no more than 20 times the thickness of solid masonry loadbearing wall. If the walls are hollow units, such as concrete block, supports are typically provided every 18 times the wall thickness. This means that masonry walls should not be taller than 12 feet without support. This is usually not an issue.

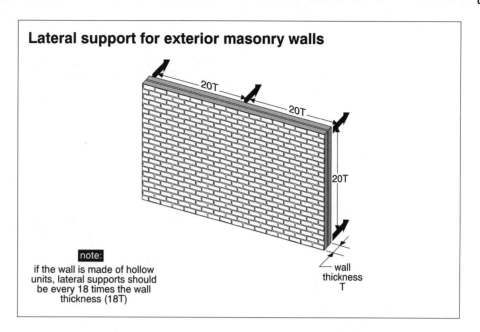

Lateral support for exterior masonry walls

20T

20T

20T

wall thickness T

note:
if the wall is made of hollow units, lateral supports should be every 18 times the wall thickness (18T)

Walls Bow If Laterally Unsupported

Most lateral support failures occur near the midpoint, either top to bottom or between the ends. Most walls are supported at the top and bottom, but on a two-story house, for example, there may not be good support at the second story floor level.

When Walls Extend Above The Ceiling Joists

Masonry walls that extend above the ceiling joists and support roof rafters are susceptible to leaning outward. The lateral thrust of the rafter bottoms pushes out on the masonry walls when the roof is loaded (wind or snow, for example.) Ceiling joists at the same height as the rafter bottoms are tied to the rafters, preventing spreading. When the rafter bottoms are above the ceiling joists, the rafters may spread outward.

Sometimes the rafters slide out off the top of the walls. Sometimes they push the top of the masonry walls out. This can be a very dangerous condition, because the top of the wall may fall.

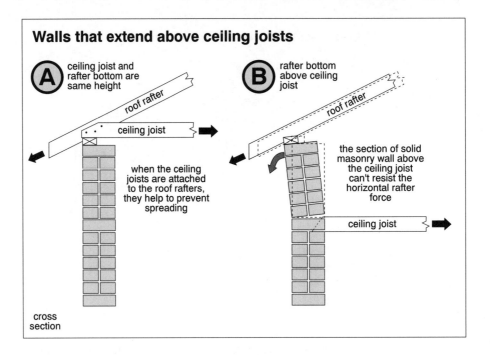

Walls that extend above ceiling joists

(A) ceiling joist and rafter bottom are same height

roof rafter

ceiling joist

when the ceiling joists are attached to the roof rafters, they help to prevent spreading

(B) rafter bottom above ceiling joist

roof rafter

the section of solid masonry wall above the ceiling joist can't resist the horizontal rafter force

ceiling joist

cross section

Mortar *Joints* *Re-pointing*	The strength of a masonry wall depends on the quality of the mortar and the strength of the bond between the mortar and the brick. The mortar discussion in the Exterior Module applies here, too. Missing mortar needs to be replaced. This process is called re-pointing.
Strong In *Compression* *Not Strong* *In Tension* *Creep*	Most masonry walls are several times stronger than they need to be in compression. The strength of mortar is not a big issue when it comes to walls carrying their vertical loads. Wind and earthquakes exert bending forces on walls. Bending includes tension. If the wall starts to lean or bow, bending forces are also introduced. Masonry walls are a good deal weaker in tension than they are in compression. Tension failures in bowing walls usually occur at mortar joints. Sometimes cracks will appear, but there may be no visible cracks, especially if the movement is very slow. The wall will **creep** as it bows and can move without cracking.
	If the masonry wall is loadbearing, the wall must rest on concrete, masonry or metal (usually steel, occasionally aluminum). While this is good practice for any masonry, brick veneer walls which are not loadbearing are, in some cases, allowed to rest on wood. Because of the different expansion and contraction properties of these materials, we consider this configuration vulnerable, although some authorities allow it.
Openings In *Masonry* *Walls*	Openings for doors and windows use masonry **arches**, or steel, concrete or masonry **lintels** to span the opening. While wood was occasionally used in old construction, wood exposed to the elements may be subject to rot and insect attack. Where you find wood supporting masonry, look closely.

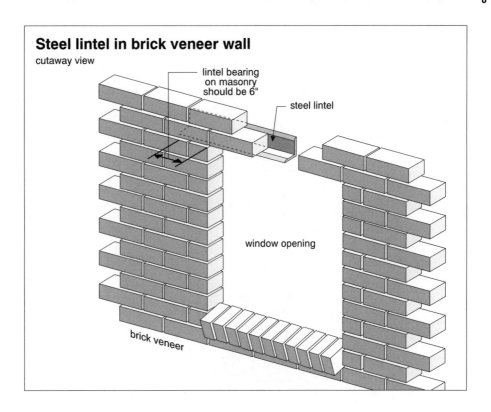

Steel lintel in brick veneer wall

cutaway view

lintel bearing on masonry should be 6"

steel lintel

window opening

brick veneer

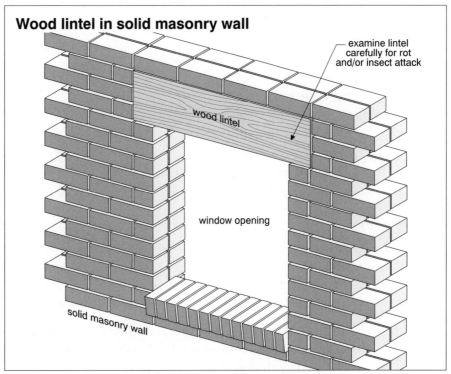

Wood lintel in solid masonry wall

examine lintel carefully for rot and/or insect attack

wood lintel

window opening

solid masonry wall

Arch Outside And Lintel Inside

In some cases, there will be a masonry **arch** for the outer wythe, but a wood **lintel** for the inner wythe of a solid masonry wall. This is not normally visible, but can help explain a cracking pattern related to differential movement between the inner and outer wythes of masonry walls.

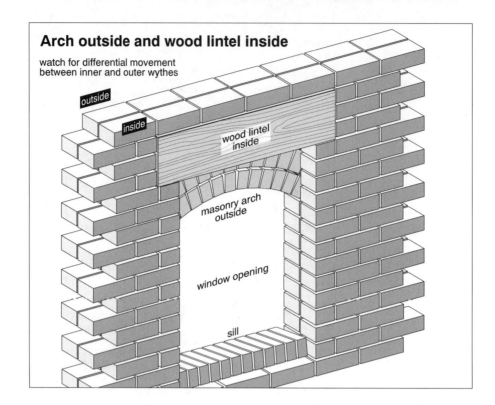

Arch outside and wood lintel inside

watch for differential movement
between inner and outer wythes

outside

inside

wood lintel inside

masonry arch outside

window opening

sill

3.1 CONDITIONS

Let's look at some of the common problems you'll find on masonry walls.

1. cracks
2. leaning, bowing or bulging
3. mortar deteriorating or missing
4. wavy brick walls
5. excess corbelling
6. bricks installed on sides
7. prior repairs.

3.1.1 CRACKS

Complex

Cracks in masonry walls could be a topic for an entire course. We will discuss the issue in relatively simple terms. These comments will apply to solid masonry, cavity, reinforced and brick veneer walls, for the most part.

When looking at cracks in walls, make sure you don't jump to conclusions. There is a strong temptation to do so. We'll outline a general approach to evaluating cracks and then discuss a step-by-step process.

GENERAL APPROACH TO CRACKS

1.What kind of wall is it? Is it solid masonry, wood frame brick veneer or something else?

2. What has moved? Has the whole house moved or only part of it? If part, which part is moving and which part is staying still? Perhaps both are moving.

3. Which way has it moved? Walls or parts of walls may move up, down, sideways or they may rotate.

4. How far have things moved?

5. Is it still moving?

Causes

6. Why has it moved? Common causes include –

1. footing or foundation settlement
2. heave due to frost or tree roots
3. expansive soil heave and/or settlement,
4. connection failure due to
   • poor original construction,
   • amateurish renovations,
   • mechanical damage,
   • rot or insect attack,
   • increased loading from heavy furnishings such as bookcases, fish tanks, etc.,
5. component failures
6. thermal expansion and contraction of materials
7. moisture related expansion and contraction of materials.

7. What are the implications? These can range from practically nothing to imminent collapse.

8. What should we do about it? Again, the answers can range from, "Ignore it" to, "Bulldoze the house."

A STEP-BY-STEP APPROACH

Number

1. How many cracks are there? Document all the cracks in the house inside and out from top to bottom. Many inspectors make sketches. Do not draw conclusions until you have looked everywhere and found all the cracks.

Continuity

2. Are they continuous through various components?

• Do the cracks go from the top of the house to the bottom? How long are they?

• Do they go through above grade walls and foundations down to the footing?

• Look to see if they are continuous through the wall. On an exterior wall, if there is a crack on the outside, does it show up on the inside as well? If it doesn't show on the inside, it may be patched. Can you see evidence of patching?

Steps **1** and **2** will help you learn what has moved and what hasn't.

Type

3. What types of cracks are they? Are they

- horizontal
- vertical
- diagonal (usually at 45°)
- random, alligatored or map cracks?

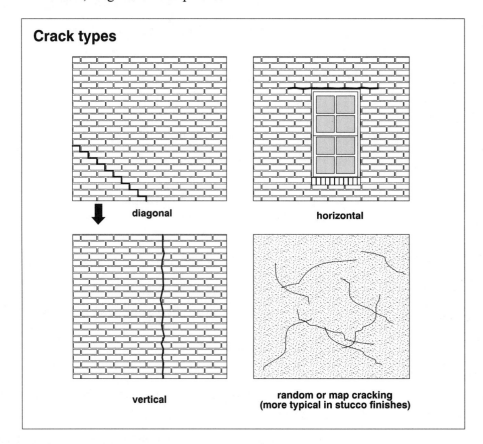

Crack types

diagonal

horizontal

vertical

random or map cracking
(more typical in stucco finishes)

Amount And Direction of Movement

4. What kind of movement do the cracks show? Try to quantify the cracks with respect to the following:

- Hairline separation (less than $1/16$ inch).
- Wide separation (make a note of the crack width).
- One surface sliding against another (very often up and down). In this case, the crack won't be wide, but there may be considerable movement.

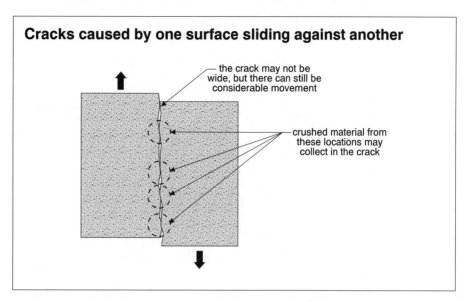

Cracks caused by one surface sliding against another

the crack may not be wide, but there can still be considerable movement

crushed material from these locations may collect in the crack

• Is one surface moving in or out relative to another? Sometimes part of the wall is leaning out while the rest stays stable.

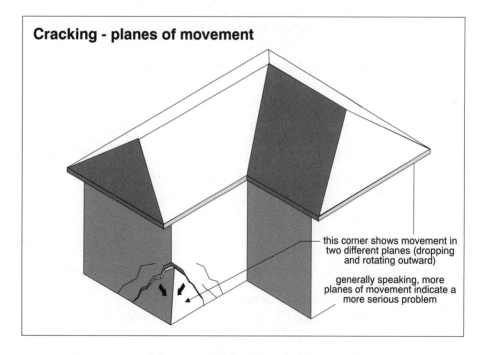

Cracking - planes of movement

this corner shows movement in two different planes (dropping and rotating outward)

generally speaking, more planes of movement indicate a more serious problem

• Are the cracks wider at one end than another? This often indicates rotation.

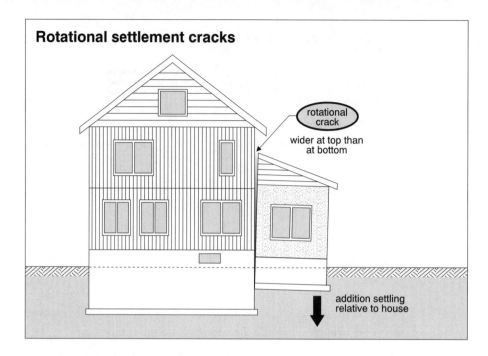

Rotational settlement cracks

rotational crack

wider at top than at bottom

addition settling relative to house

Related Problems

5. Are there other problems that go with the cracks? For example –

- Are the walls leaning, bowing or bulging?
- Are floors sloping or sagging?
- Are doors and windows
  - out of square,
  - difficult to operate,
  - full of gaps,
  - obviously trimmed to open and close?
- Are stairs sloped or leaning?
- Is the roofline displaced?

Steps **3**, **4** and **5** help tell you which way things have moved, and how far.

Active

6. Is it still moving? There are several possibilities including –

- the movement has stopped,
- the movement is ongoing at a constant rate,
- the movement is decelerating,
- the movement is accelerating,
- the movement is cyclical
- the movement is ongoing but on an unpredictable basis.

Age of Cracks

The age of the cracks may provide clues. Paint or debris in the cracks, and worn edges suggest old cracks. Patches that have re-opened, sharp edges and clean inner surfaces suggest recent movement. As we discussed in the Footing and Foundation Section, it's difficult to know based on a one-time visit. Don't go out on a limb here.

Cause **7. Why has the movement taken place?** Look for factors that lead you to the causes listed under the GENERAL APPROACH. Rule out those conditions that clearly don't fit. You may be left with more than one possibility.

Implication **8. What will happen to the house?** It is great if you can say that the movement has stopped and the house is stable. While it's not great news, it's also valuable to be able to say for sure the house is about to fall down. Unfortunately, most cases are in between and you can't be definitive. Unless your experience and knowledge allows you to be conclusive, be careful here.

Recommended **9. Give your client some direction.** Again, the choices are similar to what we
Action discussed in the Footing and Foundation Module. You might tell your client to –

a) ignore it,
b) monitor it,
c) call in a specialist for further evaluation
d) make repairs or replacements.

Again, if you haven't been able to answer all questions **1.** to **8.** with confidence, don't guess at **9**. Tell your client what you know and what you can't determine. That will help your client understand why you can't make a call. The default recommendation is for further evaluation and advice.

Strategy Many inspectors will sketch the cracks. This may help you to understand the pattern and the mechanism. Remember, you're not just identifying cracks, you're looking at their direction, length, size, direction of movement (the more directions, the worse usually), and the age.

Deductive Once you have documented as much as you can, your deductive powers have to
Reasoning take over. What type of movement is consistent with this crack pattern? If the building moves up, would you get these cracks? If the building moves down, would you get these cracks? If part of the house is sliding down the ravine, would you get these cracks?

Cracks Can you isolate the part that is moving? Walls will crack at their weakest points.
At Weak These are typically changes in direction or where there are openings, such as doors
Points and windows. These do not always line up exactly with the footing/foundation movement. Grouping cracks that are in the same direction and same plane can help simplify your mental picture of what's happening.

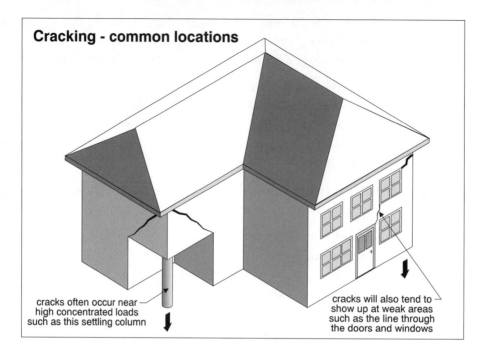

Cracking - common locations

cracks often occur near high concentrated loads such as this settling column

cracks will also tend to show up at weak areas such as the line through the doors and windows

Figuring Out If It's Still Moving

We talked in the Footing and Foundation section about some of the clues to determine whether or not things are still moving. You may want to review these. Even with these clues, this is perhaps the most difficult piece of information to determine. Unless you can be sure the crack is very, very old or very, very young, don't draw conclusions.

Brittle Vs. Flexible Materials

Brittle materials such as brick, concrete, plaster, gypsum, stucco, ceramic tile and glass will crack without much movement. In most cases, the cracks go all the way through these materials. However, other materials such as wood can move considerably without visible cracking. Exterior siding made up of several small components may not show any cracking. This includes vinyl and aluminium siding as well as wood clapboard, shingles and shakes. Masonry walls often look worse with less actual movement.

Look In Neglected Areas

One of the ways to discover cracks and get a sense of their age is to look in areas that are not frequently decorated. This includes closets, furnace rooms, etc.

Look For Wall/Floor Or Wall/Ceiling Separation

Sometimes there will be a crack on the outside, but on the inside you'll simply see a gap between the floor and the wall. This may indicate wall movement, but more often indicates floor movement. In the case of wall/ceiling gaps, sometimes the ceiling is actually going up due to truss uplift, although it looks as though the wall is falling.

Truss Uplift Some gaps between the wall and the floor are also caused by truss uplift. If the truss is well secured to an interior partition wall, when the truss lifts (usually near the center of the house) the wall will be picked up and a gap will appear at the wall/floor junction. At first glance, it will appear as though the floor has dropped. We're all prisoners of gravity, and always think when we see a gap like this that something has dropped. You can get fooled.

We'll talk about truss uplift in the Roof Framing section.

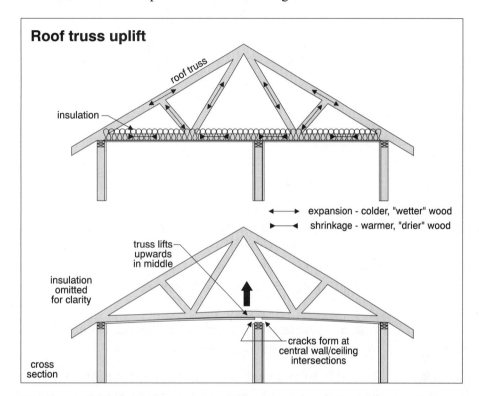

Roof truss uplift

Additions And Projections Watch additions and projections. It's very common for projections and additions to settle differentially from the rest of the house. The house may settle more than the projection because it's much heavier, or the projection settles relative to the house because it doesn't have proper footings.

Garages Settle Attached garages often settle relative to houses even in new construction. This often causes cracking near the intersection of the garage and house. Sometimes these cracks are rotational.

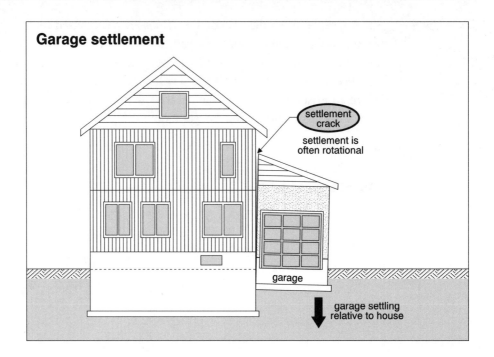

Garage settlement

settlement crack

settlement is often rotational

garage

garage settling relative to house

Cracks Over Openings   Cracks may indicate localized problems. An undersized or overspanned lintel may sag, causing cracks above either corner of a window or door opening. The cracks usually radiate up from the opening corners in toward the center of the opening. This is a lintel problem and doesn't suggest major distress in the structure.

Arch Failure   A similar problem occurs with arches that have failed. We'll talk about those more later. Again, it's a localized problem.

Horizontal Cracking At Lintels   This kind of cracking radiating out horizontally from the tops of door or window openings is often the result of rusting steel lintels expanding.

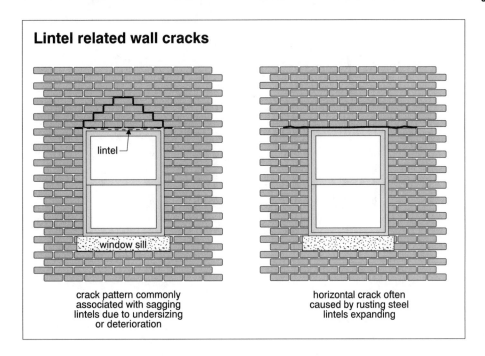

Lintel related wall cracks

lintel

window sill

crack pattern commonly
associated with sagging
lintels due to undersizing
or deterioration

horizontal crack often
caused by rusting steel
lintels expanding

*Heat
Cracking
Of Chimneys*

Chimneys that have experienced high temperatures or have metal dampers or lintels tied in too tightly, may crack as a result of thermal expansion. Vertical cracks above fireplace openings close to the midpoint may indicate an overly hot fire or an expanding lintel that was installed without provision for expansion.

*Chimney
Fires*

In severe cases, where there have been chimney fires, the chimney may be cracked part way or even all the way up. This is often visible only from the outside. This type of crack is a fire hazard and structural concern. If a crack is visible on the outside of the chimney, there are often cracks on the inside. Subsequent fires may allow products of combustion into the house through these cracks.

Structure
M O D U L E

QUICK QUIZ 1

☑ INSTRUCTIONS

• You should finish reading Session 1 before doing this Quiz.

• Write your answers in the spaces provided.

• Check your answers against ours at the end of this Section.

• If you have trouble with the Quiz, re-read the Session and try the Quiz again.

• If you do well, move on to Session 2.

1. Exterior and interior finish condition is part of the Structure inspection.
True ☐   False ☐

2. List seven functions of walls.

_____

_____

_____

3. List five loads that walls may see.

_____

_____

4. List six materials that may be used for masonry walls.

_____

_____

5. Which two masonry walls are most common on homes in North America?

    a. solid
    b. reinforced
    c. cavity
    d. veneer
    e. dry laid

6. In a solid masonry wall, how are the two thickness (wythes) held together? (Name the two most common ways.)

_____

_____

7. Lateral support for masonry walls can be provided by –

    a. floor systems
    b. roof systems
    c. interior walls
    d. end walls
    e. all of the above

8. Masonry walls that extend above the top floor ceiling joists are susceptible to:

_____

9. Masonry walls are strongest in:

    a. compression
    b. tension
    c. bending

10. List ten common problems with masonry walls.

_____

_____

_____

_____

_____

_____

_____

_____

_____

_____

11. When looking at cracks, what eight questions should you ask yourself as a general approach?

_____

_____

_____

_____

12. Briefly outline the nine steps involved in a step-by-step approach to crack analysis.

_____ _____ _____

_____ _____ _____

_____ _____ _____

13. To help evaluate the cracks, many inspectors make a _____.

14. Crack analysis should be done only from the outside of the building.
True ☐   False ☐

15. Cracks over openings do not always indicate severe problems.
True ☐   False ☐

If you had no trouble with the Quiz, move on to Study Session 2!

Key Words:

- *Live and dead loads*
- *Solid masonry*
- *Cavity walls*
- *Reinforced masonry walls*
- *Veneer walls*
- *Headers*
- *Stretchers*
- *Metal tiles*
- *Diagonal brick bond*
- *Lateral support*
- *Arches*
- *Lintels*
- *Leaning, bowing, bulging*
- *Corbelling*
- *Truss uplift*

Structure
M O D U L E

STUDY SESSION 2

1. You should have completed Study Session 1 and Quick Quiz 1 before starting this Session.

2. By the end of this Session, you should be able to –

- List six common problems with masonry walls in addition to cracks.
- List six causes of leaning, bowing or bulging brick walls.
- List seven causes of mortar deterioration.
- Describe **corbelling** in one sentence.

3. This Session may take you about 45 minutes to complete.

4. Quick Quiz 2 is at the end of the Session.

Key Words:
- *Leaning*
- *Bowing*
- *Bulging*
- *Rafter spread*
- *Failure of ties*
- *Expansion of brick*
- *Corbelling*

3.1.2 LEANING, BOWING OR BULGING BRICK

Causes Walls may lean, bow or bulge because

1. **There is no lateral support.** We talked about this earlier in this section. Lateral support may be missing as a result of –
   • an original construction mistake,
   • rotted or rusted supporting components,
   • renovations that remove supports, or
   • footing and foundation settlement.

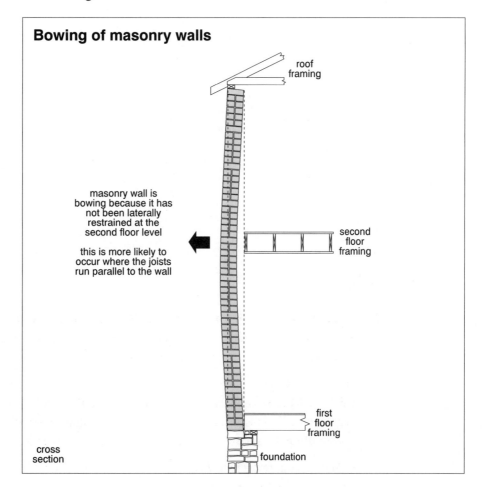

Bowing of masonry walls

roof framing

masonry wall is bowing because it has not been laterally restrained at the second floor level

second floor framing

this is more likely to occur where the joists run parallel to the wall

first floor framing

cross section

foundation

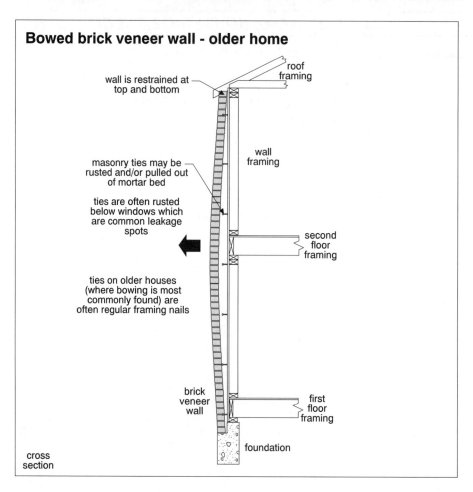

Bowed brick veneer wall - older home

wall is restrained at top and bottom

roof framing

wall framing

masonry ties may be rusted and/or pulled out of mortar bed

ties are often rusted below windows which are common leakage spots

second floor framing

ties on older houses (where bowing is most commonly found) are often regular framing nails

brick veneer wall

first floor framing

foundation

cross section

2. **Foundation movement.** If the foundation wall rotates outward, the wall may bow, since the base of the wall sits on top of the foundation. It will tend to follow any movement of the foundation.

3. **Sagging or sloping floor systems.** In this case, the ends of the floor joists which are let into the masonry wall may act as long levers which pry the wall up and out as the joists sag or slope along their length. If the joists are fire cut, this should not happen. You won't often know whether joists are fire cut.

4. **Rafter spread.** If the bottom of the roof rafters push out hard enough, without sliding over the top of the wall, they can cause the top part of the wall to lean out. This usually doesn't happen near the corners, since the sidewalls prevent movement. The leaning will be most noticeable near the midpoint of the wall.

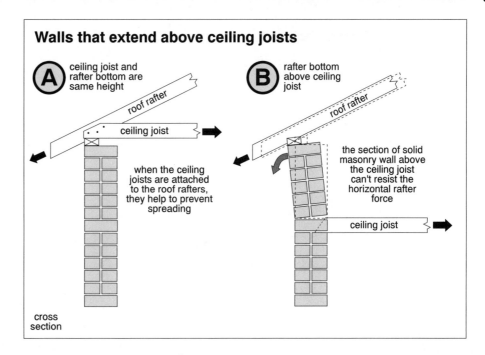

Walls that extend above ceiling joists

A ceiling joist and rafter bottom are same height

roof rafter

ceiling joist

when the ceiling joists are attached to the roof rafters, they help to prevent spreading

B rafter bottom above ceiling joist

roof rafter

the section of solid masonry wall above the ceiling joist can't resist the horizontal rafter force

ceiling joist

cross section

5. **Failure of ties.** We've talked about how the wall may not have adequate lateral support, often near the midpoint of a two-story masonry wall. There is another situation where walls may bow. Solid masonry walls are commonly two wythes thick. When the wythes are secured to each other with metal ties, the ties may fail. This could be because –

• there weren't enough ties
• the ties were not the right type,
• the ties were not well secured in the mortar joints,
• the mortar has deteriorated,
• the ties have rusted,
• the nails holding the ties have rusted (veneer wall)
• the wood supporting the nails has rotted (veneer wall)

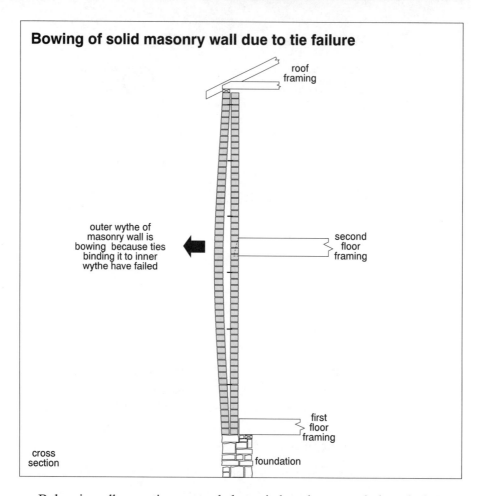

Bowing of solid masonry wall due to tie failure

roof framing

outer wythe of masonry wall is bowing because ties binding it to inner wythe have failed

second floor framing

first floor framing

cross section

foundation

Bulges Below Windows

Bulges in walls sometimes occur below windows because windows leak. Water that gets in around windows runs down between the wythes rusting the metal ties.

Expansion Cracks In Clay Brick Walls

6. Expansion of brick. Clay brick expands slightly over time for many years after it is manufactured. Tall or long masonry walls, built without room to allow the movement, can expand causing bowing and cracking problems. This is more common in commercial than residential buildings, but may be an issue.

Brick expansion on long walls may cause vertical cracks at corners of buildings. In this case, the wall gets longer after it is built and pushes on the corners. The forces may be enough to shear the wall at the corner, creating a full height vertical crack as the long wall pushes past the end wall.

Cracks Around Windows

Similar cracks can be set up in long walls with windows. The windows break up the brick and take up the expansion in the plane of the windows. However, the brick above and below the windows may experience considerable expansive forces along their length. Horizontal cracks may appear near the tops and bottoms of windows. Diagonal cracks in the field of the brick between windows are also common.

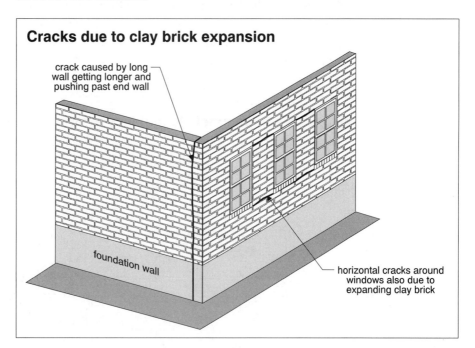

Cracks due to clay brick expansion

crack caused by long wall getting longer and pushing past end wall

foundation wall

horizontal cracks around windows also due to expanding clay brick

Again, these are more typical of commercial buildings, but can occur on large residential buildings as well, townhomes or row houses, for example.

No Expansion In Concrete Masonry Walls

While we've said that brick walls get slightly longer and taller over time, wood frame, concrete brick or block walls shrink over time. You won't see expansion problems with wood or concrete masonry.

Implications

The implications of leaning, bowing or bulging walls include collapse. The walls may collapse, or the floors may lose their endbearing as the walls lean, bow or bulge. Masonry walls that have moved need careful analysis.

Strategy

You need to look from a distance as well as up close. If you get too close to a wall, you may not see the lean or bow.

Sight along the length and up the height of the wall. Where movement is seen, a plumb line can help to quantify it. Where the movement is horizontal, pulling a tape measure or string tight along the wall can help to measure the amount.

Where movement is noted follow through the whole house, top to bottom, inside and out to get the entire picture. Is the problem localized or wide spread? Consider all of the connection points. Will floors, walls and roof systems still be well supported, given this movement?

Corrective
Actions

Has anything been done to stop the movement? Look for large metal plates on opposite exterior walls. These plates are usually attached to rods or cables that tie opposing walls together and keep them from pulling away from the building. These plates which may be square, rectangular, circular or star shaped, are often found at the second story floor level.

Metal
Plates

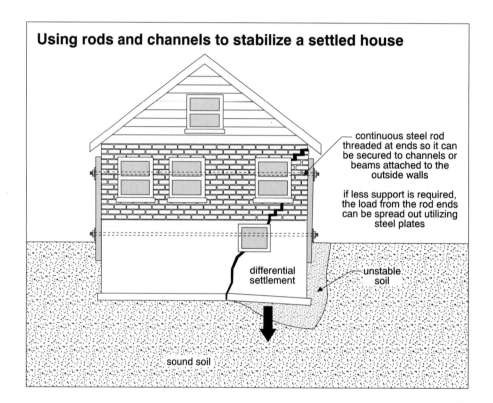

Using rods and channels to stabilize a settled house

continuous steel rod threaded at ends so it can be secured to channels or beams attached to the outside walls

if less support is required, the load from the rod ends can be spread out utilizing steel plates

differential settlement

unstable soil

sound soil

Pilasters

Look for external pilasters, sometimes in the form of steel channels bolted to the inside or outside of the building. In some cases, these, too, are interconnected with steel cable.

What To Tell
Your Client

When you identify masonry walls that are leaning, bowing or bulging you should recommend further investigation, unless you are sure there are no structural implications. Some destructive investigation is often necessary to closely examine important connections.

Not Okay
Just Because
It's Old

Do not assume because the bowing, bulging or leaning is old that it is not a problem. This kind of movement can take place slowly over a long period of time. At some point, it becomes serious. You may be close to that point during your inspection.

3.1.3 MORTAR MISSING OR DETERIORATED

Mortar is an important structural component in the wall assembly. In most cases, missing or deteriorated mortar is a maintenance issue. However, if walls are severely cracked, or show bowing, bulging or leaning, deteriorated mortar may become important structurally. If the wall is allowed to move as several small units rather than a large single slab, the chances of failure are much greater.

Causes   Mortar may deteriorate for a number of reasons including –

1. weathering
2. poor quality mortar
3. a poor job of laying the mortar (too thin or thick, uneven, incomplete, etc.)
4. the weather was too hot to lay brick
5. the weather was too cold to lay brick
6. the mortar set too long before being used
7. additives to the mortar affected its strength

Implications   These are the same as we've discussed for other masonry wall problems.

Strategy   If the mortar is in place uniform and looks intact, no further testing is necessary. Mortar joints are typically ½ inch wide. No individual joint should be more than ¾ inches wide. If you are suspicious about the mortar quality, dragging a key or screwdriver along it will tell you quickly what kind of shape it's in. If you deeply score the mortar or it falls out as you drag the screwdriver along with moderate force, there may be a serious mortar problem.

As we mentioned, unless the deteriorated mortar is accompanied by severe cracking or wall movement, repair is a maintenance issue rather than a major structural concern.

3.1.4 DETERIORATION OF THE MASONRY ITSELF

Brick, stone or concrete walls may suffer deterioration of the masonry units themselves. This often appears as **spalling**, which is deterioration of the surface with chunks or flakes of material coming off the masonry units.

Causes   Deterioration may be the result of –

• Sandblasting
• Freeze-thaw damage due to such things as overflowing or leaking gutters, ice dams and chimney condensation

• Masonry too close to grade

• Moisture deterioration due to excessive wetting. This may be the result of water getting into the top of parapet or garden walls, or water splashing brick from sidewalks. Water may also be dumped on to bricks from defective gutter and downspout systems or poor roof drainage arrangements, for example. While freeze-thaw damage may be associated with moisture damage, it is not necessary to cause damage.

Implications   If deterioration is local, this situation may be simply cosmetic. Weather-tightness may be an issue if wind-driven rain, for example, can get into the wall assembly.

Widespread   If the damage is widespread, there may be structural implications. If more than an inch of a typical masonry unit (about 3½ inches thick) is gone, there may be some question about structural integrity.

Strategy   Look at masonry units for missing sections, rough surfaces or masonry debris at the base of the walls. Where damaged masonry is accesible, dragging a screw-driver or key, for example, across the surface may reveal how extensively the units are deteriorated.

Where there is doubt about structural integrity, recommend further investigation.

3.1.5 EFFLORESCENCE

Efflorescence is a white salt, typically, that shows up on the surface of masonry walls. The salts are dissolved from the masonry or the mortar as moisture moves through the wall. The dissolved salts are left behind as crystals when the moisture that has moved through the wall evaporates from the surface. The water leaves but the salts are left behind on the surface.

Causes   Moisture is the main cause of efflorescence. In some cases, the mortar and/or the masonry units are susceptible to efflorescence.

Implications   Efflorescence is usually a cosmetic problem. In most cases it can be washed away and will not reappear.

Strategy   While efflorescence is not likely to be a structural problem, it should be identified and noted. Explain to the client the cause of efflorescence. Walls subject to excessive wetting may be vulnerable to efflorescence. Walls exposed to the weather on both sides (garden walls, railings and fences, for example) are also prone to efflorescence. Masonry close to grade level may wick moisture up and suffer efflorescence. Efflorescence may mask spalling or other deterioration of the masonry. Dragging a screwdriver or key across the surface should remove the efflorescence easily. Check to see whether the masonry units behind have been damaged.

Chemically Cleaning   Masonry walls that have been chemically cleaned may be susceptible to efflorescence for a period of time. Repeated wetting by rain or washing the wall will usually remove the efflorescence in a few weeks. Where efflorescence persists, it can be a cosmetic concern and specialists should be consulted.

3.1.6 TOO CLOSE TO GRADE

While some types of brick can be installed at and below grade, most bricks should be kepts six inches above grade. Brick that is exposed to damp soil may deteriorate unless it is suitable for this application.

Causes   Brick too close to grade me be an original construction issue or may be caused by re-grading.

Implications   Masonry and mortar may deteriorate as a result of the constant exposure to moisture. Efflorescence may also develop.

Strategy   Where masonry is at or near grade, check carefully for deterioration of masonry or mortar. Where you see very old masonry in contact with the ground and there is no deterioration, you need to make a note. On newer buildings, you may note the possibility of deterioration even if none is visible during your inspection. Explain to your client that some types of brick can stand up to this application and others cannot. You can't tell by looking which bricks will be durable.

3.1.7 WAVY BRICK WALLS

Some walls have an irregular surface, visible as you look up the wall. It can appear that the wall has several **crests** in it as you look up. This is discussed in Section 6.1 of the Structure chapter of **The Home Reference Book** and is usually a problem related to initial laying of the brick, rather than movement after construction. In most cases, it is not serious.

Excess Speed   "The crests appear every five to seven courses and may be the result of building
Or Skimping   too quickly or skimping on the mortar bed at the back of the bricks."
On Mortar

3.1.8 CORBELLING

Corbelling is the practice of staggering bricks so that the higher bricks project beyond the lower bricks. There are several corbelling rules. Generally speaking, a
Rules   full brick can't be corbelled more than one inch from the brick below and the total corbelling in a wall can't be more than 1/3 of the wall thickness. With some types of masonry, the allowable projections are less. Find out what is acceptable in your area.

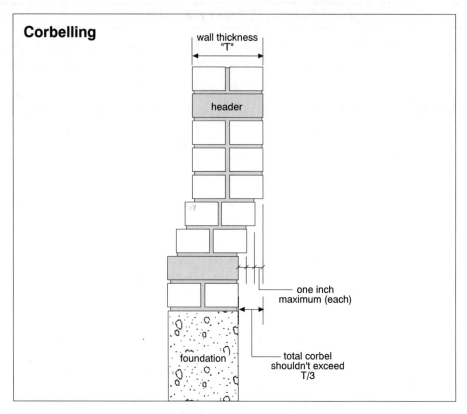

Corbelling

wall thickness "T"

header

one inch maximum (each)

foundation

total corbel shouldn't exceed T/3

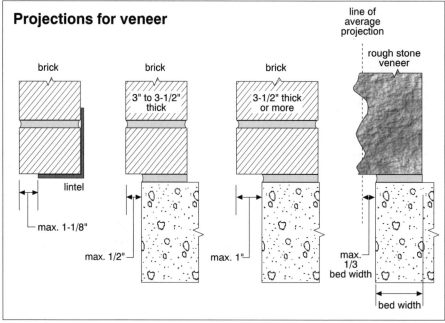

Projections for veneer

line of average projection

rough stone veneer

brick

lintel

max. 1-1/8"

brick

3" to 3-1/2" thick

max. 1/2"

brick

3-1/2" thick or more

max. 1"

max. 1/3 bed width

bed width

Causes   Excessive corbelling is caused by –

1. poor original installation
2. the foundation wall is pushed by expansive soils or frost, for example
3. the above grade wall is pushed out relative to the foundation. This can occur as a result of the expansive forces we talked about earlier.

Implications   The implications of excessive corbelling are leaning of the wall and ultimately collapse.

3.1.9 BRICKS OR BLOCKS ON THEIR SIDE

Hollow concrete blocks or cored bricks should be installed with the interior channels vertical. Their strength is greatly reduced if they are installed with the channels horizontal. There are a few clay tiles designed with horizontal channels, but these are rare exceptions.

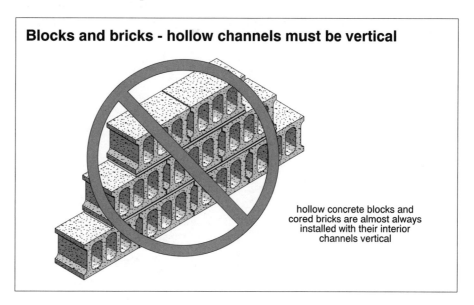

Blocks and bricks - hollow channels must be vertical

hollow concrete blocks and cored bricks are almost always installed with their interior channels vertical

Causes   This is an installation issue.

Implications   The masonry material itself may crush, resulting in the wall settling, leaning, bowing, bulging and ultimately collapsing.

Strategy   In many cases, you won't be able to see how the masonry has been laid, particularly if it's covered with stucco, for example. In some cases, gable end walls on masonry buildings are visible from the attic.

Use common sense to determine whether a problem has developed. Things may look wrong, but there may be no problem as a result of a very light load. For example, only the top two or three courses of a masonry wall may have been installed inappropriately. If it's not a loadbearing wall, there may be no implications.

Age Is Clue   If it's relatively new, alert your client to the possible problems. If it's old, describe it as being unconventional. If you do not see the performance failures that would result from this condition, recommend monitoring.

Window Sills   It is common in some areas to use bricks on their edge as window sill material. This puts the cores or channels through bricks in a horizontal orientation. Since window sills are not loadbearing members, this is not a structural issue. Leakage and premature deterioration of the bricks or mortar joints is a common problem with brick sills, but these are not structural problems.

3.1.10 PRIOR REPAIRS

Cause

Prior mortar deterioration or damage is obviously the cause. Most older brick walls have had some mortar repointed. Often, the repairs will be over openings that have been closed or moved. It's also common to find repairs to arches, lintels and sills around windows and doors.

Implications

Most often there are very few.

Strategy

When you see prior repairs, determine whether they are vulnerable points in the wall. If there are patched cracks, check to see if the patch has re-opened. If so, the movement was not a one-time issue and may or may not still be active.

Structure
M O D U L E

QUICK QUIZ 2

☑ INSTRUCTIONS

• You should finish reading Session 2 before doing this Quick Quiz.

• Write your answers in the spaces provided.

• Check your answers against ours at the end of this Section.

• If you have trouble with this Quiz, re-read the Session and try the Quiz again.

• If you do well, move on to Session 3.

1. List six common causes of leaning, bowing or bulging masonry walls.

    _____   _____

    _____   _____

    _____   _____

2. What is a common cause of bulging masonry walls below windows?

    _____

3. Which walls tend to expand over time, after original construction?

    a. concrete block
    b. poured concrete
    c. clay brick
    d. concrete brick
    e. wood frame

4. You see large metal plates or stars on the outside of the masonry walls at the top of the first floor level of an older two story building. Why are these here?

_____

_____

5. List seven causes of deteriorated mortar.

_____

_____

_____

_____

_____

_____

_____

6. What causes wavy brick walls?

_____

_____

7. Briefly describe **corbelling**. How much can a masonry wall be corbelled before it may become unstable?

_____

_____

_____

8. Hollow concrete blocks are weaker if laid on their side.
   True ☐   False ☐

9. Bricks laid on their sides forming window sills are a structural problem.
   True ☐   False ☐

10. Patched cracks on brick are a sure sign of serious structural movement.
    True ☐   False ☐

If you had no trouble with the Quiz, you are ready to move on to Study Session 3.

Key Words:

- *Leaning*
- *Bowing*
- *Bulging*
- *Rafter spread*
- *Failure of ties*
- *Expansion of brick*
- *Corbelling*

Structure

MODULE

STUDY SESSION 3

1. You should have completed Study Sessions 1 and 2 at this point.

2. After completing this Session on wood frame walls, you should be able to –

   • Describe platform and balloon frame construction in one sentence each.
   • Describe the difference between load bearing and partition walls in one sentence.
   • Describe two types of loads that walls see in one sentence each.
   • List three functions of sheathing.
   • List four ways to prevent racking of walls.

3. This Session assumes you have read the relevant sections of **The Home Reference Book** (Section 6.2 of Structure chapter). If you have not, please do that now.

4. This Session may take you about 1 hour to complete.

5. Quick Quiz 3 will help you check that you have learned the material in the Session.

Key Words:

- *Balloon framing*
- *Platform framing*
- *Loadbearing*
- *Partition*
- *Lintels*
- *Sole plate*
- *Top plate*
- *Jack studs*
- *Girts*
- *Sheathing*
- *Racking*
- *Oriented strandboard (OSB)*
- *Waferboard*
- *Holes*
- *Notches*

► **4.0 WOOD FRAME WALLS**

Balloon
And
Platform
Framing

Wood frame walls are very common in single family residential properties. **Balloon framing** and **platform framing** are discussed in **The Home Reference Book**. All new homes and many old homes have platform framing. Balloon framing has not been used for many years.

The main difference is that with balloon framing, the studs go down through the floor systems and rest on the sill plates or foundation walls.

Platform versus balloon framing

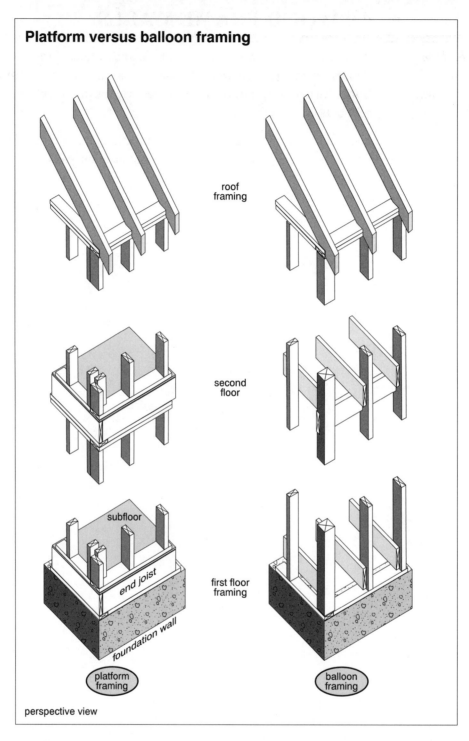

roof framing

second floor

subfloor

end joist

first floor framing

foundation wall

platform framing

balloon framing

perspective view

With platform framing, the wall studs rest on the subfloor at each floor level. Studs are shorter in platform framed houses than balloon framed houses. In houses with basements or crawlspaces, you can usually see how the house is framed by looking at the underside of the flooring around the perimeter and above beams.

Materials   Many different woods are used for studs. These include spruce, pine, fir and larch. There are several species of each of these woods. They come in several grades.

*Species
And Grade
Of Lumber*

Home inspectors don't get involved with grading lumber or, in most cases, identifying lumber species. Although lumber is supposed to be stamped as to species and grade, it's not always visible. Also, in old homes, the lumber will not be stamped and graded, or if it was, the stamps will no longer be visible. Again, this is not a big issue for home inspectors since our examination is performance based. This system is either working or it isn't. We are not analyzing the design of the structure.

*No Cedar Or
Hardwoods*

Cedar is not used as a framing lumber, typically. Cedar is weaker than the other woods we've mentioned. Hardwoods are usually not used because they are more difficult to work with, too expensive and heavy. Their additional strength is not necessary.

*Sole Plate,
Studs And
Top Plate*

Conventional wood frame walls are made up of a **sole plate**, (**bottom plate**, **base plate** or **sill plate**) – a two by four laid flat on the floor, **studs** (most often two by fours or two by sixes) and double **top plates** (two by fours or two by sixes.)

*Bearing And
Partition
Walls*

Loadbearing wood frame walls carry floor or roof loads from above. **Partition** (non-loadbearing) walls do not. However, they are built the same way. Both have bottom plates, studs and double top plates, typically.

*Partition
Walls Are
Heavy*

Loadbearing walls need to rest on something substantial such as a foundation wall or beam. Partition walls do not, although the walls are heavy. It is good practice to double joists under a partition wall or to put two by four blocking every four feet if a partition wall runs parallel to the joists and sits between two joists.

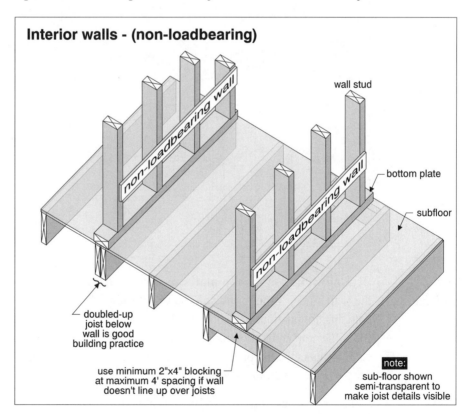

Interior walls - (non-loadbearing)

non-loadbearing wall

wall stud

non-loadbearing wall

bottom plate

subfloor

doubled-up
joist below
wall is good
building practice

use minimum 2"x4" blocking
at maximum 4' spacing if wall
doesn't line up over joists

note:
sub-floor shown
semi-transparent to
make joist details visible

Nailing　　Code and carpentry books set out appropriate nailing in terms of length, type and number of nails for each connection in a wood frame structure. You won't usually see how the studs were nailed together or nailed to the rest of the home. Those of you who build regularly or do new construction and/or code inspections, may well be familiar with nailing requirements, but most home inspectors focus on whether the connections are moving. Again, we're evaluating performance rather than design or code compliance.

Top Plates　　While we don't need **double** top plates on partition walls, these are common for a
In Partitions　　couple of reasons:

1. Partition walls can be secured to and brace loadbearing walls by overlapping the double top bearing plates, locking the walls together.

2. It is easier to cut all studs the same length to end up with an 8 foot high wall rather than to cut studs 1½ inches shorter for bearing walls than for partition walls. It's faster and cheaper to build everything the same way.

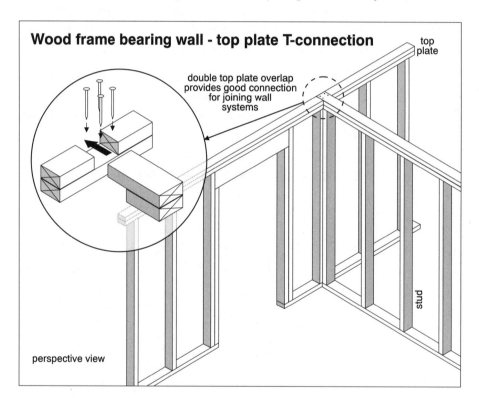

Wood frame bearing wall - top plate T-connection

top plate

double top plate overlap provides good connection for joining wall systems

stud

perspective view

Joints In　　Bearing walls use the top plates to transfer loads from joists above through
Top Plates　　the wall studs, through the sole plates, through the floor system to the beams, columns, foundations and footings. Joints in top plates have to be located over the studs. The top and bottom double plate should not both have joints over the same stud. Joints in the top plates should be offset by at least one stud. We can't usually see these details during a home inspection.

Cutting　　Holes or notches in top plates of bearing walls must have 2 inches of material
Top Plates　　intact, or the top plate should be reinforced with wood or metal.

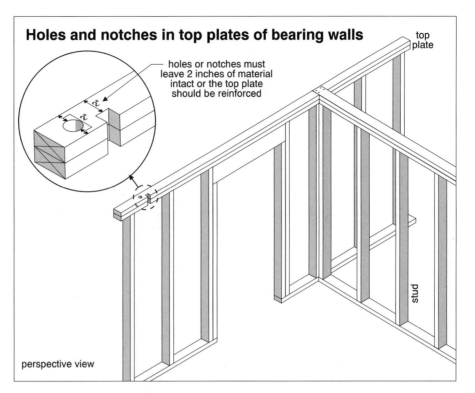

Holes and notches in top plates of bearing walls

top plate

holes or notches must leave 2 inches of material intact or the top plate should be reinforced

stud

perspective view

Double Top Plates Can Be Omitted

If the floor or roof joists resting on the stud wall have the joists line up directly over or within 2 inches of the studs, a double top plate is not required, since there will be no load on the plate other than at the tops of studs. As a practical matter, this is rarely done, since it requires considerable care and layout. There is often a reason to move a joist one way or another slightly, and the double top plate provides the flexibility to do that.

Metal Ties

If single top plates are used, you obviously can't use the double overlap method to lock wall corners and T intersections together. In this case, metal ties are used to secure the walls together. Metal ties are also used where lintels extend up flush with the top plate. This interrupts the continuity of the plate, and metal ties join each end of the lintel to the adjacent plate.

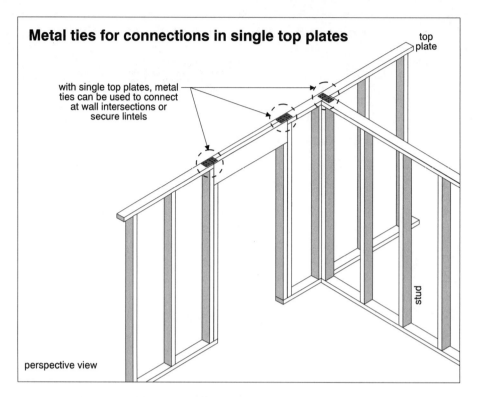

Metal ties for connections in single top plates

top plate

with single top plates, metal ties can be used to connect at wall intersections or secure lintels

stud

perspective view

Lintels   Openings in bearing walls require **lintels** (horizontal beams) to carry the loads around the openings. Openings in partition walls do not need lintels.

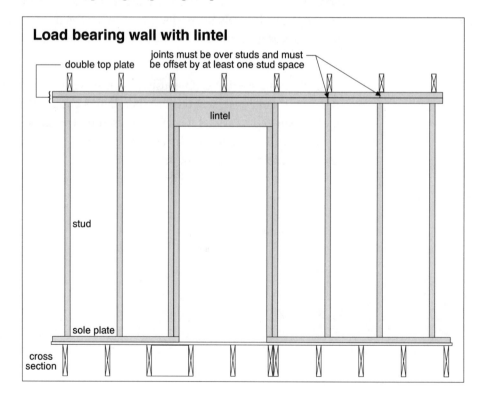

Load bearing wall with lintel

double top plate

joints must be over studs and must be offset by at least one stud space

lintel

stud

sole plate

cross section

What Loads Do Walls See?

As we've talked about earlier, walls see **compressive loads** as they transfer vertical live and dead loads down toward the foundation. Walls also see **bending loads** from the wind. In this sense, each stud acts like a small floor joist.

Compressive And Bending Loads

The wind pushing on a stud wall is much like furniture sitting on a floor. A floor joist is on its edge and sees a live load from above. A stud is on its edge, but in a vertical plane and sees the wind load from the side. Stud walls must be strong enough to carry the vertical (compressive) loads and the lateral (bending) loads.

Stud Spacing

Two by four and two by six studs are typically 16 inches on center. The maximum stud spacing permitted is 24 inches, but in most housing, 16 inch centers are standard.

Stud Sizes

Two by fours were the most common size for studs until the energy crisis of the mid 1970s. Two by six studs are now commonly used on exterior walls to accommodate the greater insulation levels common to new construction. While two by six studs are inherently stronger than two by four studs, the strength and stiffness is not needed. Houses were already strong enough with two by four studs.

Continuity Of Studs

Studs have to be continuous from the top to the bottom of the wall. The only exception is a factory made, finger jointed, glued assembly (not common). A splice in a loadbearing stud wall is usually a weakness. Spliced partition studs are more common.

Wall Strength

Two by four walls with studs 16 inches on center can typically carry the load from one floor level and the roof or two storys but no roof. This assumes that the walls are not taller than 10 feet. If a stud wall is asked to carry two storys plus a roof load, it's common to go to two by fours every 12 inches on center, or two by sixes, 16 inches on center. In some areas, two by fours cannot be used to support two storys plus a roof load.

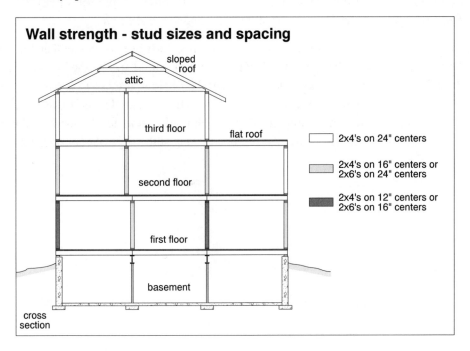

Wall strength - stud sizes and spacing

51

Walls Can Overhang The Floor

In some situations it's desirable to have the stud wall overhang the floor. If the stud wall projects out beyond the floor, only ⅓ of the wall width can overhang. Two thirds of the wall must rest on the floor surface.

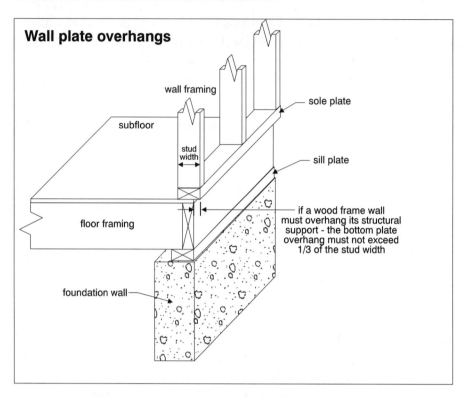

Wall plate overhangs

wall framing

sole plate

subfloor

stud width

sill plate

floor framing

if a wood frame wall must overhang its structural support - the bottom plate overhang must not exceed 1/3 of the stud width

foundation wall

Lintels For Openings In Loadbearing Walls

Partition walls don't need **lintels** for their openings. Loadbearing walls do require lintels. Lintels are usually two by fours, two by sixes, two by eights, or two by tens placed on edge, back-to-back above the opening. The lintel size depends on the opening width and the load above.

Concentrated Loads From Jack Studs

Lintels have to be supported by **jack studs** that are shorter than full studs. Jack studs are adjacent to full-height studs. Jack studs carrying the loads from the lintel create concentrated loads on the subfloor below. If these jack studs are over a joist, it's good practice to double the joist. If a jack stud rests between 2 floor joists, solid blocking below the stud can be used to transfer the loads to the joists on either side. This prevents subfloor sagging at the edge of door openings.

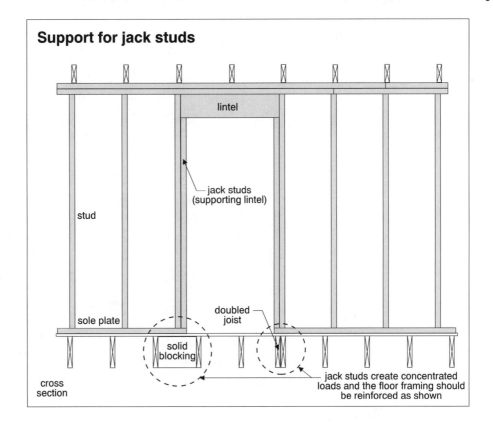

Support for jack studs

lintel

jack studs
(supporting lintel)

stud

sole plate

doubled
joist

solid
blocking

jack studs create concentrated
loads and the floor framing should
be reinforced as shown

cross
section

This is not as big an issue on exterior walls because the rim joists support the sub-floor between studs.

Walls Can Buckle

Studs in loadbearing walls should be supported so they do not buckle. Drywall or plaster is sufficient to provide this support. Most rigid exterior sheathings do, too. Where wood frame walls do not have any interior finish or exterior sheathing (for example, a loadbearing wall running through an unfinished basement) the wall needs solid blocking, called **girts** running horizontally through the wall near the midpoint. midpoint. You should not be able to walk between the studs in a loadbearing wall.

Drywall, Sheathing, or Girts

To summarize, loadbearing walls need one of –

• interior finish
• sheathing
• girts

to resist buckling.

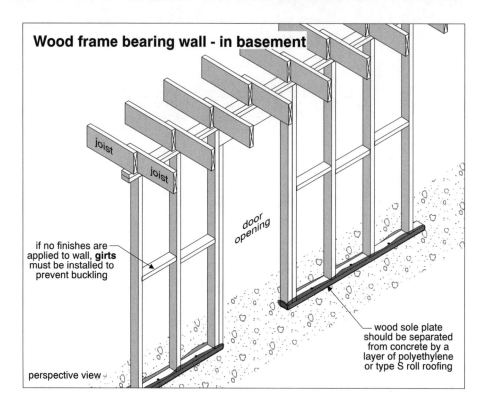

Wood frame bearing wall - in basement

joist

joist

door opening

if no finishes are applied to wall, **girts** must be installed to prevent buckling

wood sole plate should be separated from concrete by a layer of polyethylene or type S roll roofing

perspective view

Sheathing

Exterior sheathing has three functions:

1. support the siding,
2. stiffen the wood frame walls, and
3. help prevent wind and water entering the building.

Backing Or Nailing Surface For Siding

Sheathing may provide a solid backing for the siding or may be support fasteners for the siding between studs. For example, clapboard siding can be nailed at each stud, but wood shingles have to be nailed between studs because they aren't 16 inches wide.

Similarly, vertical wood siding 8 inches wide is supported either by the sheathing or by horizontal strapping over the sheathing and studs.

Racking

Racking is caused by a lateral force that can change a rectangular box into a parallelogram. Houses must be stiff enough to resist racking by the wind. Racking is a different problem than buckling of individual studs, but you'll see that the solutions are similar.

Resistance to racking may be provided several ways:

1. Drywall, plaster, plywood, waferboard, oriented strandboard (OSB) and hardboard work well.

2. Exterior sheathings such as diagonal lumber, plywood, oriented strandboard, waferboard, gypsum board and asphalt impregnated fiberboard also resist racking. **Insulating sheathings** such as rigid fiberglass, polystyrene, polyiso-cyanurate and phenolic boards **do not resist racking**.

3. Panel type sidings (e.g., four by eight sheets of plywood or oriented strandboard) protect against racking.

4. Diagonal bracing made of one by fours let into walls or metal strapping at a 45° angle on each story of each exterior wall resist racking.

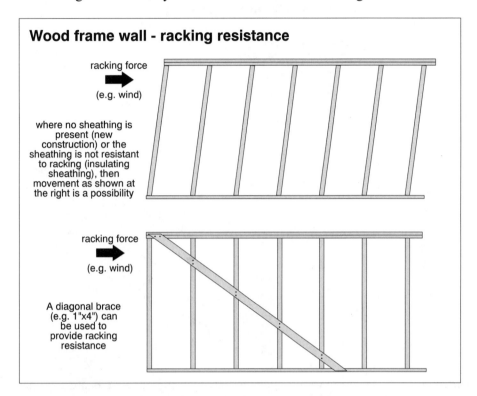

Wood frame wall - racking resistance

racking force (e.g. wind)

where no sheathing is present (new construction) or the sheathing is not resistant to racking (insulating sheathing), then movement as shown at the right is a possibility

racking force (e.g. wind)

A diagonal brace (e.g. 1"x4") can be used to provide racking resistance

Vulnerable During Construction

Houses under construction with no sheathing or interior finishes may be subject to racking problems during wind storms. Racking is not usually an issue once the house is built. Completed houses may suffer racking during hurricanes or earthquakes where the forces are great.

No Sheathing Required

Sheathing is not required if the siding is supported by wall studs the building is protected from racking (by drywall, for example) and from weather (wind-driven rain) by materials such as building paper. Remember, the functions of sheathing are to resist weather, support siding and resist racking. If these functions are all performed sheathing becomes unnecessary.

OSB Versus Waferboard

Both **oriented strandboard (OSB)** and **waferboard** are made from flakes or strands of wood mixed with glue and pressed together to form a board. In waferboard, the wafers or strands are oriented in a random fashion and the strength of waferboard is the same in either direction.

OSB Stronger Along Length

Oriented strandboard or OSB is a special kind of waferboard wherein the flakes or strands on each face are roughly parallel to the length of the panel. The interior layers may line up across the panel or may be randomly oriented. Oriented strandboard is stronger along the length of the panel than across the width.

OSB Perpendicular To Studs

The differences become important when fastening the material to studs or joists. With waferboard, it doesn't matter whether the long dimension of the panel is parallel to or across wall studs. OSB has to be installed perpendicular to the studs.

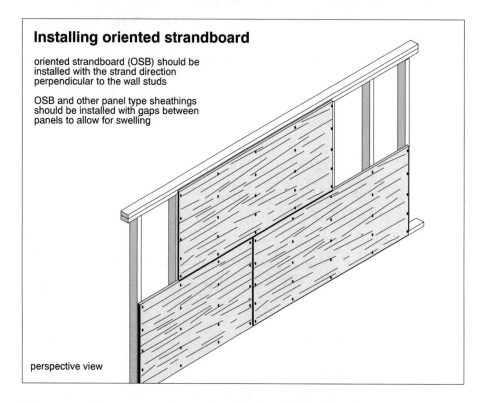

Installing oriented strandboard

oriented strandboard (OSB) should be
installed with the strand direction
perpendicular to the wall studs

OSB and other panel type sheathings
should be installed with gaps between
panels to allow for swelling

perspective view

Different Types

There are various types and strengths of both waferboard and oriented strandboard. They are typically used for floors, walls and roofs and may be designed for various spans. In some cases, these panels are designed to stand alone structurally. In other cases, they require additional support.

Gaps In Sheathing

Panel sheathing such as plywood, OSB and waferboard should have gaps at the edges to allow for expansion due to moisture. If the panels are tightly butted, they may buckle when they get wet and expand.

Sheathing Paper

Housewrap

Building paper or sheathing paper keeps moisture outside and prevents wind from driving through the wall system. Good sheathing papers do not act as vapor barriers; they allow moisture from inside the house to diffuse through the sheathing paper to the outside. The modern spun polyolefin fiber housewraps (such as TYVEK®) are good rain and wind barriers, but allow vapor diffusion.

Double Paper

Traditionally, sheathing papers have been installed over sheathing. In some cases, a double layer of sheathing paper is used without sheathing.

No Paper

In some cases, sheathing paper is not required. Weather-tight exterior siding such as synthetic stucco, plywood, hardboard or waferboard siding, needs no sheathing paper according to some manufacturers and authorities.

Holes And Notches In Studs

The size of holes and notches in studs is limited by whether

1. they are two by fours or two by sixes, and

2. whether they are loadbearing or not. The chart below provides rough rules, from two different authorities.

Holes And Notches In Studs

WALL SIZE AND TYPE	#1 MAXIMUM SIZE OF HOLES OR NOTCHES	#2 MAXIMUM SIZE OF HOLES OR NOTCHES
loadbearing	$^1/_3$ of width	Holes – 40% of width Notches – 25% of width
non-loadbearing	$1^5/_8$ inches of material must remain	Holes – 60% of width Notches – 40% of width
Note: "width" means the 4-inch dimension of a 2 by 4, for example.		

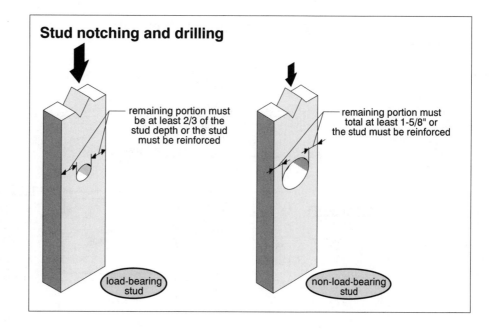

Stud notching and drilling

remaining portion must be at least 2/3 of the stud depth or the stud must be reinforced

load-bearing stud

remaining portion must total at least 1-5/8" or the stud must be reinforced

non-load-bearing stud

Identifying Bearing And Partition Walls

We have mentioned that loadbearing walls are built the same as partition walls. So how can you tell whether it's a loadbearing or partition wall? Those of you who answered, "Tapping on it," aren't really paying attention. Since the walls are built the same way, they're going to look and feel the same. The answer lies in what's above and below them.

1. Partition walls have no structural elements beneath them to transfer the loads to the foundations and footings.

2. Loadbearing walls must have foundations, beams and columns, or another wall system below them to transfer the loads to the soil.

3. Loadbearing walls have ends of floor or ceiling joists resting on them. Partition walls don't.

4. If there is another wall directly or almost directly above the wall, it's probably a bearing wall. When removing the wall would remove the support for structural members above, it's a loadbearing wall.

5. Door openings in partition walls do not normally require lintels. Openings in loadbearing walls do need lintels.

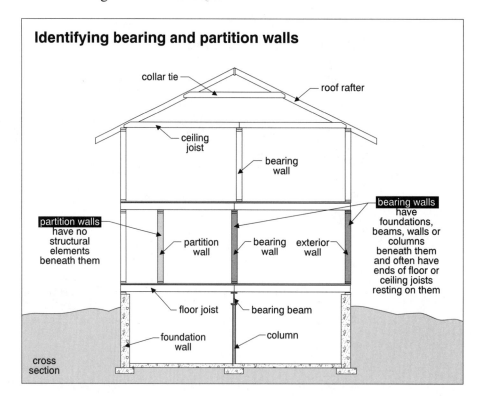

Identifying bearing and partition walls

collar tie

roof rafter

ceiling joist

bearing wall

bearing walls have foundations, beams, walls or columns beneath them and often have ends of floor or ceiling joists resting on them

partition walls have no structural elements beneath them

partition wall

bearing wall

exterior wall

floor joist

bearing beam

foundation wall

column

cross section

Structure

M O D U L E

QUICK QUIZ 3

☑ INSTRUCTIONS

• You should finish reading Session 3 before doing this Quiz.

• Write your answers in the spaces provided.

• Check your answers against ours at the end of this Section.

• If you have trouble with this Quiz, re-read the Session and try the Quiz again.

• If you do well, move on to Study Session 4.

1. In _____ framing, the wall studs extend through the subflooring.

2. All of these words mean the same thing except –

   a. sill plate
   b. top plate
   c. base plate
   d. bottom plate
   e. sole plate

3. Bearing walls and partition walls are built in substantially the same way.
   True ☐   False ☐

4. Walls see vertical loads only.
   True ☐   False ☐

5. Studs with splices are: (two answers)

    a. stronger
    b. weaker
    c. neither stronger nor weaker
    d. more common in partition walls
    e. more common in load bearing walls

6. Openings in partition walls need lintels.
   True ☐   False ☐

7. Jack studs:

    a. carry beam loads
    b. carry lintel loads
    c. carry window loads
    d. are only found in partition walls
    e. are only found in exterior walls

8. What are girts? (Include their function, location and material.)

    _____

    _____

    _____

9. Three functions of sheathing are:

    _____

    _____

    _____

10. List four ways to prevent racking of exterior wood frame walls.

    _____

    _____

    _____

    _____

11. No sheathing is needed if:

    _____

    _____

12. What is the difference between waferboard and OSB?

_____

_____

13. Adjacent pieces of plywood sheathing should be butted tightly to enhance weather-tightness.
True ☐   False ☐

14. Sheathing paper (building paper) should act as a vapor retarder.
True ☐   False ☐

15. Loadbearing wall studs should have holes no larger than:

a. $\frac{1}{4}$ to $\frac{1}{8}$ of width, depending on authority
b. $\frac{1}{4}$ to 50% of width, depending on authority
c. $\frac{1}{3}$ to 40% of width, depending on authority
d. $\frac{1}{3}$ to 60% of width, depending on authority
e. $\frac{1}{2}$ to 60% of width, depending on authority

16. List 5 differences between a bearing wall and a partition wall.

_____

_____

_____

_____

_____

If you had no trouble with this Quiz, you are ready for Study Session 4.

Key Words:

- **Balloon framing**
- **Platform framing**
- **Loadbearing**
- **Partition**
- **Lintels**
- **Sole plate**
- **Top plate**
- **Jack studs**
- **Girts**
- **Sheathing**
- **Racking**
- **Oriented strandboard (OSB)**
- **Waferboard**
- **Holes**
- **Notches**

Structure
MODULE

STUDY SESSION 4

1. You should have finished Study Sessions 1, 2 and 3 at this point.

2. At the end of this Session, you should be able to –

• List seven common wood frame wall problems
• Describe how condensation causes rot in three sentences

3. This Session may take you approximately 1 hour to complete.

4. Quick Quiz 4 is waiting to test you at the end of this Session.

Key Words:
• *Rot and insect damage*
• *Leaning*
• *Bowing or buckling*
• *Holes and notches*
• *Top plate*
• *Concentrated loads*
• *Lintels*
• *Condensation*
• *Racking*
• *Girts*
• *Loadbearing walls*
• *Partition walls*
• *Offset bearing walls*

Now let's look at some of the problems that we typically find.

4.1 CONDITIONS

1. rot and insect damage
2. leaning
3. bowing or buckling
4. excessive holes, notching, or mechanical damage
5. sagging top plate/concentrated loads
6. lack of fire stopping
7. sagging lintels

Deduction Versus Observations Results In Opinion Versus Fact

Recognize that in most cases you can't see everything. Most of your analysis is going to be by deduction rather than direct observation. Therefore, an element of doubt is built in. Make it clear to your client where you are not reporting a fact, but offering an opinion based on indirect and incomplete evidence.

4.1.1 ROT AND INSECT DAMAGE

Causes

Rot may be caused by –
1. Condensation
2. leakage through the walls or roof
3. wood/soil contact

Implications

Since wood frame walls are an integral part of the structure, damage by rot or insects damage can

1. weaken the structure,
2. cause localized deflection, and
3. lead to ultimate collapse.

Strategy

How Condensation Forms

Condensation typically occurs in exterior walls. It is the result of warm moist air from the house leaking into the walls during the winter months. As the warm moist air cools in the wall, the moisture falls out of it. Cold air can't hold as much moisture as warm air. Those of us in cold climates know this from being able to see our breath on a cold winter day.

As the air loses its moisture, the moisture accumulates in the walls. Air/vapor barriers are intended to stop the warm moist air from leaking into the walls. These are never perfect, and some air will always leak in. In the Insulation and Interior Module, we'll talk more about condensation problems and how to identify them.

Condensation Leads To Rot

Rot requires temperature between 40°F and 115°F, and air environment with spores, and a moisture content in the wood of over 20%. When condensation accumulates in walls, these conditions can easily be met.

*Worst Damage
At Bottom
Of Wall*

The majority of condensation damage is usually at the sole plates and the bottom of the studs because condensation runs down the wall cavities by gravity and accumulates at the sole plate. The end grain of the stud sits on the bottom plate and wicks up moisture that collects on the bottom plate.

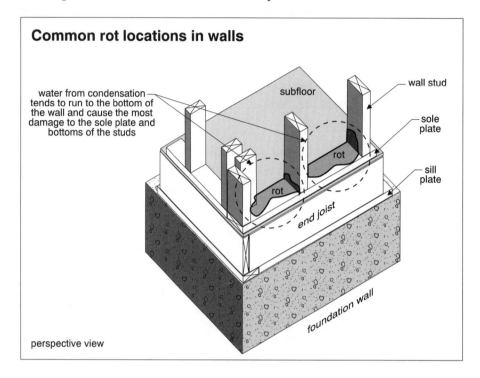

Common rot locations in walls

water from condensation tends to run to the bottom of the wall and cause the most damage to the sole plate and bottoms of the studs

subfloor

wall stud

sole plate

rot

sill plate

rot

end joist

foundation wall

perspective view

*Mechanism
Reverses
In Hot
Climates*

This process can take place in reverse in hot humid climates. Hot moist outdoor air (over 100°F with 90% relative humidity) leaking into the walls will be cooled if the house has air conditioning. The inside face of the wall will be much cooler than the outside face. Condensation may form in the walls.

*Roof Or
Wall
Leakage*

Water leakage into the wall assembly from a faulty roof or gutter system, through siding or through openings in the walls will cause rot damage as well. Gaps around windows are a common water entry point.

Studs, sheathing, siding and interior finishes may be damaged, along with top plates, lintels, sole plates, rim joists, joist ends and beam ends.

*Water Is The
Big Enemy
Of Houses*

Home inspectors consider water to be their worst enemy. In almost every facet of the inspection, you're looking for how water can get into parts of the house where we don't want it.

*Roof And
Exterior
Inspections
Help With
Wall Inspection*

Your Roofing inspection will help to identify areas where the roof may be allowing water into the wall systems. Your Exterior inspection will include looking at gutters and downspouts, siding, trim, flashings, etc., where water may get into the wall system. Your Interior inspection should also identify damage from leakage or condensation that may affect walls.

Check Underside Of Subfloor

The majority of the damage is likely to be done near the bottom of wall cavities where the water gets trapped at the sole plates. You won't usually be able to see these details, although if a basement or crawlspace is unfinished, you can often see evidence of leakage around the perimeter of the house on the underside of the subfloor.

Doors and Windows Wood/Soil Contact

Watch below doors and windows for moisture damage to walls and floors. Leakage and condensation can team up to do considerable damage here. We've talked a couple of times already about the danger of having wood in direct contact with soil. Rot is almost a certainty here unless the soil is exceptionally dry. Also, the direct wood/soil contact provides easy access for wood-boring insects to enter the structure. Many destructive insects such as subterranean termites actually live in the soil and only venture into the wood to collect food. Direct wood/soil contact makes insects' lives easier and the life of the house a good deal shorter.

Six To Eight Inch Clearance From Soil

The bottom of any wood frame wall around the perimeter of a house should be at least 6 inches above finished grade level. Where the exterior siding may be attacked by rot, it should be at least 8 inches above grade.

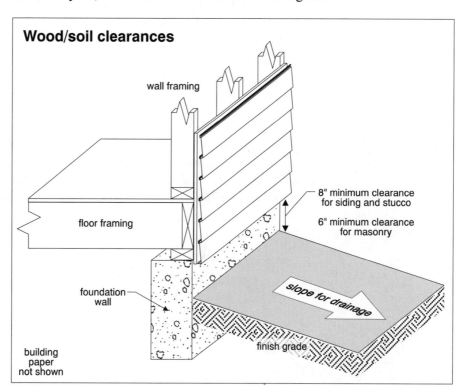

While the most severe damage occurs at sills and the bottom of studs, wall sheathing can also be damaged by rot and insect attack. Sections of sheathing at the bottom of wall sections are usually most severely damaged. Where there is wood/soil contact, sheathing deterioration is very likely.

4.1.2 LEANING

Wood frame walls should be plumb.

Causes

When walls are out of plumb, it is usually a result of –

1. racking of the building, or
2. foundation movement.

Racking may be the result of inadequate diagonal bracing and/or interior finishes and exterior sheathings which do not provide resistance to racking.

Racking can be the result of the removal of interior walls and floors. Open concept renovations must consider the possible racking forces on a building. Partition walls are effective stiffeners in most structures.

Implications

Walls that lean are inherently unstable and may collapse. Leaning walls may remove the necessary endbearing for joists and beams. Leaning walls usually require further investigation and corrective action.

Strategy

Racking may be the result of poor initial construction, earthquake, or strong winds. Racked structures usually show distress in many areas. Doors and windows often do not operate properly, floors may be sloped, and walls are visibly out of plumb both from the inside and out. Structures which have racked are unlikely to be stable, unless they have been reinforced. You can use a mason's level or plumb bob to verify and quantify the amount of racking. Be wary of "open concept" issues with few interior partitions.

Foundation Movement

As foundations settle, they may lean in or out at the top. In either case, the walls above them may follow the foundations and will no longer be plumb. There is also a risk that the connection between the foundation and wall will be broken, and the wall may no longer be held firmly in place. Foundation movements may be very serious and have serious implications for the floors, walls and roofs above. Where you've identified foundation movement, look for walls that are out of plumb above.

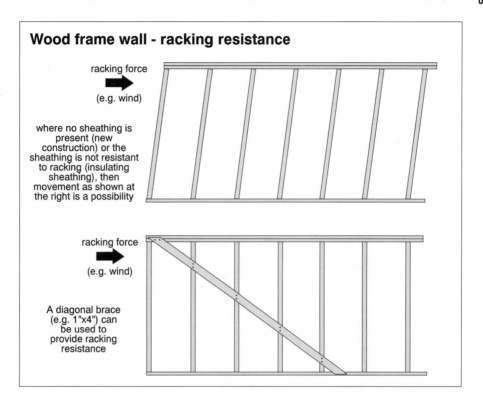

Wood frame wall - racking resistance

racking force

(e.g. wind)

where no sheathing is present (new construction) or the sheathing is not resistant to racking (insulating sheathing), then movement as shown at the right is a possibility

racking force

(e.g. wind)

A diagonal brace (e.g. 1"x4") can be used to provide racking resistance

4.1.3 BOWING OR BUCKLING

Causes

Bowing or buckling is caused by several things:

1. Loadbearing walls may buckle because they are too tall (overspanned) for their size and spacing of studs,
2. Bracing interior finishes, sheathing or girts may be missing.
3. Concentrated loads on the walls may exceed the capacity of the studs, or
4. Studs may be weakened by mechanical damage, excessive notching or holes, rot, insect damage, poor connections, etc.

Buckling and Racking

Loadbearing wood frame walls are subject to buckling and racking. They must be braced to prevent this. Most interior finishes including drywall, and most exterior sheathings including waferboard provide this bracing. However, walls may have neither exterior sheathing nor interior finishes. For example, when a house is framed with wood frame bearing walls in the basement or crawlspace

Girts

these bearing walls are often unfinished. The studs require **girts** which are horizontal blocks installed near the midpoint of the wall. The girts are typically made of the same material as the studs.

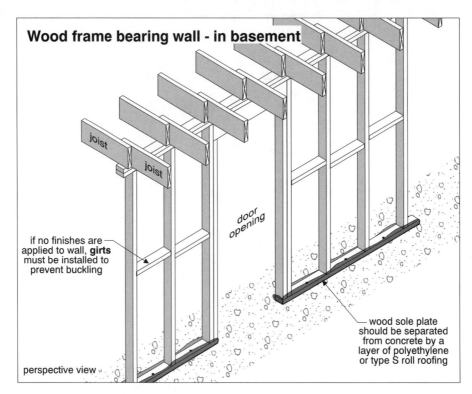

Wood frame bearing wall - in basement

joist

joist

door opening

if no finishes are applied to wall, **girts** must be installed to prevent buckling

wood sole plate should be separated from concrete by a layer of polyethylene or type S roll roofing

perspective view

Implications   Walls that are bowing or buckling may lead to collapse and should be further investigated. Corrective action is often necessary.

Strategy   Look for bearing walls that are bowing inward or outward. Occasionally, the bowing may be localized and may be the result of warped and/or poor quality lumber. This also shows up on partitions. Where the movement is a result of warped studs, there is usually very little pattern to the movement and it's usually localized. Warping can be in opposite directions in adjacent studs, which creates a dramatic visual effect. You may not know whether it's a buckling problem or just warped studs, but before calling for a structural investigation, you should know whether it's a loadbearing wall.

Warped Or Bowing?   If drywall has no cracks or crushing, you're probably looking at warped studs. If, however, there is cracking plaster or drywall, bowing or buckling could be taking place. Remember, houses are often decorated to help sell them. Repaired plaster or drywall will mislead you.

If you're in a basement with a loadbearing wood frame wall, ensure that bracing is provided by interior finishes or girts. You shouldn't be able to walk through bearing walls.

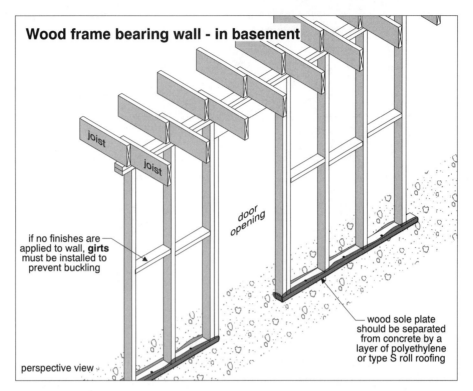

Wood frame bearing wall - in basement

joist

joist

door opening

if no finishes are applied to wall, **girts** must be installed to prevent buckling

wood sole plate should be separated from concrete by a layer of polyethylene or type S roll roofing

perspective view

Look At Whole Picture
Use all of the evidence at your disposal, not just one or two pieces. If walls have bowed or buckled significantly, you will usually see movement in the areas above as well. Floors may slope down toward the buckled wall, exterior siding may be out of plumb and plaster or drywall in walls above may show unusual cracks. A mason's level or plumb bob will help quantify the problem.

Tall Studs Vulnerable
When walking into rooms with very high ceilings, typical of older Victorian homes, you should be looking for bowing or buckling. The longer studs are more susceptible to bowing and buckling.

4.1.4 EXCESSIVE HOLES, NOTCHING OR MECHANICAL DAMAGE

We have discussed the rules for cutting and notching studs.

Causes
This damage is a result of –

1. poor original construction practice
2. careless home "improvement"

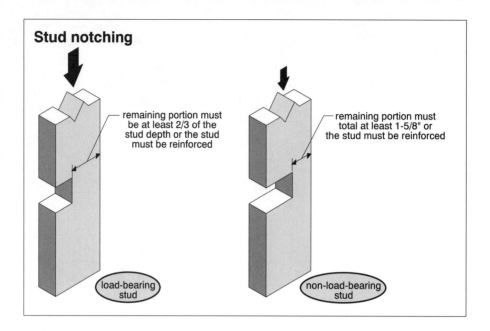

Stud notching

remaining portion must
be at least 2/3 of the
stud depth or the stud
must be reinforced

remaining portion must
total at least 1-5/8" or
the stud must be reinforced

load-bearing
stud

non-load-bearing
stud

Implications   While you won't often see the direct evidence, excessive holes or notching may result in bowing, buckling or leaning walls. The weakened studs may be able to carry their loads most of the time, but when particularly heavy snow or wind loads are experienced, failure may occur quickly. New families with different lifestyles bring new loads to houses and put them in new places. Cracks may develop when people move in, although the damage had been done many years ago.

Strategy   We've talked about looking for bowing, buckling and leaning walls already. If the studs are visible, look for evidence of this mechanical damage. However, in most cases, you won't be able to see it.

In some cases, walls are neither drilled nor notched intentionally, but are simply cut accidentally. Damaged wood may have been used in the original framing, or poor quality wood may split, often around knots, under normal loads. Cracks in plaster or drywall may suggest damaged studs behind.

Cutting And   When warped studs are used to build a partition wall, it's common to straighten
Straightening   the studs before the drywall is installed. This is often done by cutting part way
Partition   through the stud on a diagonal, near the midpoint. The weakened stud can be
Studs   pushed back into a vertical position. Very often, the diagonal cut is nailed through to close the slot, which straightens out the stud. If you see this practice, make sure you're looking at a partition wall and not a loadbearing wall. In some cases, shims are driven into the cut to help straighten the stud.

Reinforce   If loadbearing studs are straightened in this method, the stud must be reinforced. A
Loadbearing   sistered stud is often nailed across the weakened section. The best practice is to
Studs   replace the stud, of course.

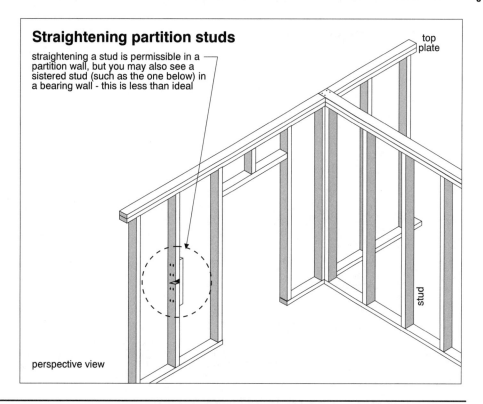

Straightening partition studs

straightening a stud is permissible in a partition wall, but you may also see a sistered stud (such as the one below) in a bearing wall - this is less than ideal

top plate

stud

perspective view

4.1.5 SAGGING TOP PLATE OR CONCENTRATED LOADS

Top plates may deflect between studs as a result of

Causes

1. an undersized (single) top plate,
2. unexpected concentrated loads (such as a column),
3. splices in the midspan of top plates, or
4. top plates being cut or notched for pipes.

Implications   This is a localized problem, which can be corrected easily. However, if undetected (which is often the case), this can result in significant settlement of the wall or floor system immediately above. In a worse case, the top plate would collapse altogether, allowing the column or floor system above to fall between the studs. Such catastrophic failure rarely occurs. More typically, you'll get a series of cracks and a sag in the floor or wall above, which prompt people to investigate.

Strategy   Be wary of large openings in bearing walls, or bearing walls which have been replaced with a beam and columns. Whenever one loadbearing wall sits on another, the loads are uniformly transferred from the upper wall to the lower wall.

Concentrated Loads   When the upper wall is substantially replaced with a lintel and jack studs, or a beam and two columns, the loads are concentrated. It is a mistake to rest a column which has a considerable load on a top plate of a wood frame bearing wall. A second column should be inserted directly below the upper column to carry loads continuously down. Studs can be sistered to create built-up columns below concentrated loads.

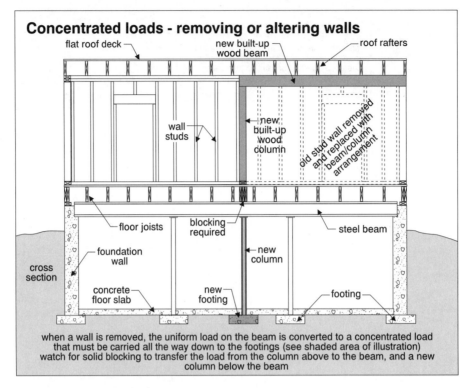

Concentrated loads - removing or altering walls

when a wall is removed, the uniform load on the beam is converted to a concentrated load that must be carried all the way down to the footings (see shaded area of illustration) watch for solid blocking to transfer the load from the column above to the beam, and a new column below the beam

Concentrated Loads On Subfloors

Let's review lintels and jack studs.

A lintel in an opening in a bearing wall is supported by jack studs under each end. The weight at the bottom of the jack studs may be considerable. In platform construction, walls sit on the subfloor. The subfloor is supported by joists. If the jack stud sits on a piece of subfloor that is spanning between two joists, deflection of the subfloor should be expected. The solution involves adding solid blocking below the subfloor under the jack studs to transmit the loads down to joists, beams, studs or sill plate below.

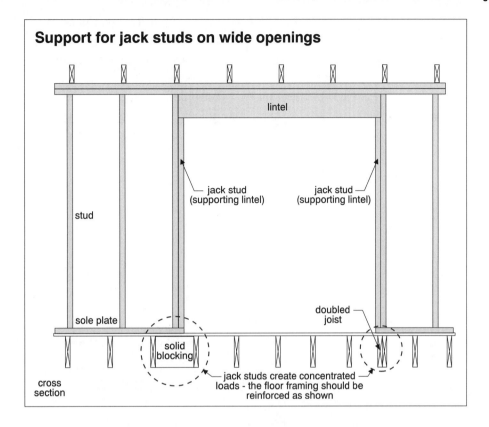

Support for jack studs on wide openings

lintel

jack stud
(supporting lintel)

jack stud
(supporting lintel)

stud

sole plate

doubled
joist

solid
blocking

cross
section

jack studs create concentrated
loads - the floor framing should be
reinforced as shown

Concentrated loads are a common cause of localized wall and floor failures.

Offset
Bearing
Walls

While the problem that results from offsetting bearing walls is actually a floor failure, the cause lies in the way the walls are built. We've been talking about problems caused by concentrated loads. The **offset bearing wall** is a variation on this.

Common
Offset
Situations

A loadbearing wall should rest directly on the loadbearing wall or beam below it. As a practical matter, this is often not done because it doesn't fit the room layout. For example, in a side hall home, the living room is wider than the front hall and stairway on the first floor. The basement beam running straight from the front of the house to the back may be directly below the hall/living room wall, or may be offset.

At the rear of the first floor, the kitchen and dining room are often side by side. These rooms are usually of similar width. If the beam in the basement is directly below the hall/living room wall, it won't be below the kitchen/dining room wall, and vice versa.

The second floor may have two bedrooms at the front of similar size. The second floor bearing wall between the bedrooms will be near the middle of the house, but the first floor bearing wall will be offset toward the hallway side, so the living room can be larger. The first and second floor bearing walls often don't line up.

*Two Feet
Of Offset
Allowed*

Many authorities allow an offset of up to two feet in bearing walls supporting floors above. In our experience, this often results in floor unevenness. What appears to be a hump often shows up on the floor separating the offset walls. The hump appears to be immediately above the bearing wall or beam below. In reality,

*May Be
Too Much*

it is the offset bearing wall above deflecting the floor beside the lower bearing wall or beam. The hump may, in part, be caused by the tails of joists kicking up as they are bent down by the wall above, about two feet away from their bearing point.

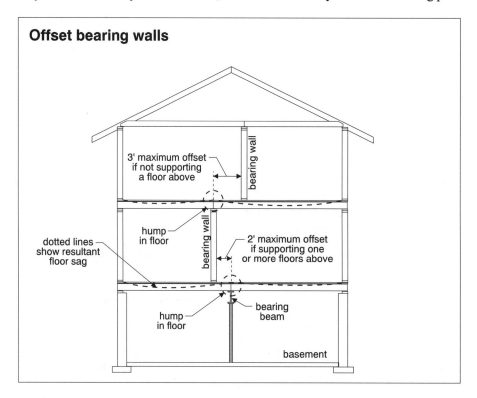

Offset bearing walls

Hump Or Sag

The offset bearing wall sag and hump configuration is usually not serious and no remedial action is necessary. However, you'll have to evaluate each case.

*Complicating
The Pattern*

The pattern is often complicated by doorway openings in the bearing walls. For example, a wide opening in the upper wall will put no load on the floor joists below the opening. As a result, there'll be no floor sag as you go through this opening and no hump above the bearing wall below. However, at either side of the opening, there will be a concentrated load from the jack studs supporting the lintel. These concentrated loads will exert considerable forces on the floor joists beneath. These joists at either end of the opening may deflect considerably.

This absence of deflection across the opening, but exaggerated deflection at either end of the opening may create a dramatic effect. A lot of people see a hump in the opening as you walk through. The hump is actually created by the sagging joists at either side of the opening. The amount of sag is related to the width of the opening, the load on the jack studs, the size of the floor joists and the amount of offset.

4.1.6 LACK OF FIRE STOPPING

Common On Balloon Framing

This problem is more prevalent on balloon frame construction than platform framing. Because balloon frame wall construction is continuous from the foundation up to the roof, a natural chimney can be created in each stud cavity. Good practice dictates that fire stops (e.g., horizontal wood blocks) be provided at each floor level.

Platform framing may require fire stops where pipes or chimneys run up through the building.

Causes

Lack of fire stopping is usually an original installation issue. Occasionally it is removed during home "improvements."

Implications

• A house may burn very quickly
• There may be more noise traveling through the building vertically than one would expect.
• In exterior wall situations, there can be considerable heat loss through the convective loops created by these passages.

Strategy

With balloon frame construction, try to look up the wall cavities between the studs from the basement or crawlspace. You should not be able to see from one floor level to the next. While wood blocking is the most common fire stopping, thermal insulation also constitutes fire stopping. This will only be found in exterior walls, typically.

4.1.7 SAGGING LINTELS

Causes

Lintels that sag may be a result of –

1. missing or undersized lintels,
2. inappropriately supported lintels (jack studs missing, too short, damaged or not well connected),
3. concentrated loads on lintels, or
4. the use of cedar shims (easily crushed) to fill gaps.

Implications

This is a localized framing problem and while the ultimate failure may be collapse of the lintel, most often the result is pyramid shaped cracking of the finishes above the lintel on both sides of the wall.

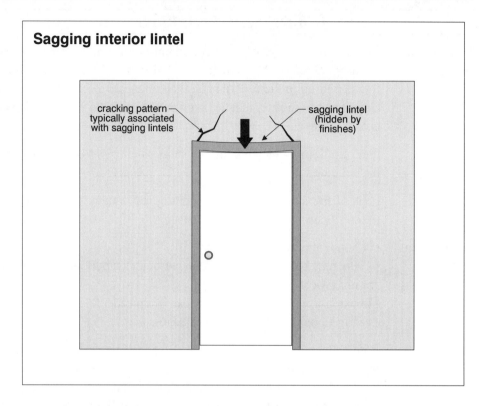

Sagging interior lintel

cracking pattern typically associated with sagging lintels

sagging lintel (hidden by finishes)

Strategy

Look for distress that is concentrated around the tops of door or window openings. Where the lintel is the problem, there will be no difficulty with the bottom part of the wall around the opening.

Sight along the top of the opening for sag. While cracks may accompany sagging lintels, cracks are often caused by other things. Cracks on the interior that radiate up from the top corners of openings may also result from normal shrinkage of wood framing members or footing/foundation movement.

General Strategies

Check Doors And Windows

In any wall system, door and window openings provide many of the clues. Although the Standards require you to only operate a representative sample of windows and interior doors (one per room), you may want to operate more for your structural inspection. Remember that the Standards ask you to operate every exterior door.

Trimmed Doors

Look for doors and windows that are difficult to operate, have clearly been shaved so that they will operate, or have frames out of plumb or out of level. Do not leap to conclusions, since window and door problems alone do not indicate structural difficulties. They are, however, a piece of the puzzle.

Analyzing Wall Cracks

Cracking in walls is difficult to analyze definitively. Cracks on interior finishes are doubly difficult because they are often patched to improve cosmetics, or as part of normal decorating. Wallpaper and paneling also masks cracks that would be visible in painted plaster or drywall surfaces.

Cracks Are Clues, Not Answers

The majority of cracks that show only on interior finishes, particularly around doors and windows, are cosmetic only and not important structurally. However, when analyzing structural movement, you should document all these cracks to see whether they fit a pattern of movement throughout the building. A crack by itself doesn't mean much, but a crack may be what tips you off to look for a pattern of movement throughout.

Structure
MODULE

QUICK QUIZ 4

☑ INSTRUCTIONS

- You should finish reading Study Session 4 before doing this quiz.

- Write your answers in the spaces provided.

- Check your answers against ours at the end of this Section.

- If you have trouble with this Quiz, re-read the Session and try the Quiz again.

- If you do well, move on to Field Exercise 1.

1. Give three causes of rot.

_____

_____

_____

2. Where is condensation damage likely to be worst?

    a.   above windows

    b.   at the tops of walls

    c.   at corners of walls

    d.   at midpoints of walls

    e.   at bottoms of walls

3. What is the biggest enemy of houses? (one word)

_____

4. How far above grade should a wood frame wall with wood siding stop?

   _____

5. Exterior walls on completed houses are rarely subject to racking because they have _____ and/or _____ .

6. Open concept homes are more likely than conventional homes to:

   a. settle
   b. rack
   c. shift
   d. sag
   e. rot

7. Three reasons for walls bowing or buckling are:

   _____

   _____

   _____

8. Longer studs are more susceptible than conventional length studs to:

   a. settling
   b. rotting
   c. leaning
   d. leaking
   e. bowing or buckling

9. Wall framing problems are often tough to identify because wall framing details are usually concealed.
   True ☐   False ☐

10. Offset bearing walls: (two answers)

   a. are an asset
   b. are a serious structural problem
   c. are common
   d. often result in minor structural problems
   e. must always be parallel to joists

11. Missing fire stopping: (three answers)

   a. is more common on balloon frame than platform construction
   b. is a fire hazard
   c. is tough to see on most inspections
   d. is only found in masonry houses
   e. is never found in masonry houses

12. Interior wall cracks radiating up from the top of windows may mean: (three answers)

    a.   sagging lintels

    b.   foundation settlement

    c.   over-spanned joists

    d.   a lack of wall sheathing

    e.   shrinkage of framing members

If you had no trouble with the Quiz, you are ready for Field Exercise 1.

Key Words:

- **Rot and insect damage**
- **Leaning**
- **Bowing or buckling**
- **Holes and notches**
- **Top plate**
- **Concentrated loads**
- **Lintels**
- **Condensation**
- **Racking**
- **Girts**
- **Loadbearing walls**
- **Partition walls**
- **Offset bearing walls**

Structure
MODULE

FIELD EXERCISE 1

☑ INSTRUCTIONS

By now you are familiar with Field Exercises. We are going to ask you to go out and look at some houses. You are going to want to look at the inside and outside of the homes.

It is fine to use houses that you have used in other Field Exercises. Depending on where you live, you may have trouble finding masonry walls or wood frame walls. Do the best you can, and if you cannot find examples of a certain type, you will know that they are not common in your area.

Allow yourself 15-30 minutes per house for this Exercise.

Look at as many masonry walls as you can:

Part A

1. How many of each did you see?

    a. brick _____
    b. stone _____
    c. concrete _____
    d. cinder block _____
    e. clay tile _____
    f. glass block _____

2. Did you see any header courses?

    _____

3. Did you see any soldier courses?

    _____

4. Did you see any cracks? If so:

a.   How many were there?

_____

b.   Did they go top to bottom, side to side, and/or through the wall, inside to outside?

_____

c.   What direction did they run?

_____

d.   What direction of movement is suggested by the crack pattern?

_____

e.   Was the movement in more than one direction?

_____

f.   Are there other conditions that also suggest movement, such as wall leaning, bowing or bulging, openings out of square, rooflines displaced, etc?

_____

g.   Was there any evidence that the movement was continuing? (e.g., patches that have re-opened)

_____

h.   Can you tell why the movement took place? (e.g., footing or foundation settlement)

_____

i.   What are the implications? Is the house stable?

_____

_____

j.   What would you tell your client to do?

_____

_____

5. Did you see any other problems?

    a. leaning, bowing or bulging walls _____
    b. mortar missing or deteriorated _____
    c. wavy brick walls _____
    d. excessive corbelling _____
    e. hollow brick or block on its side _____
    f. patching _____

Part B

Look at some wood frame walls (remember houses with masonry exterior walls will probably have wood frame interior walls).

6. Could you tell if the walls were platform or balloon framed?
    Where did you look?

    _____

    _____

7. What stud sizes did you see?

    _____

8. What stud spacings did you see?

    _____

9. Did you see any top plates?

    _____

10. If so, could you tell if they were single or double?

    _____

11. Did you see any of these problems?

    a. rot or insect damage
    b. leaning
    c. bowing or buckling
    d. excessive holes, notches or mechanical damage
    e. sagging top plates
    f. excessive offset on bearing walls
    g. sagging lintels

All finished with the Exercise? Then you are ready for Study Session 5.

Structure
MODULE

STUDY SESSION 5

1. You should have finished Sessions 1, 2, 3 and 4, and completed Field Exercise 1 before starting this Session.

2. This Session covers masonry veneer walls. After completing this Session you should be able to –

   • List five ways to identify masonry veneer walls
   • Describe in two sentences the vented rain screen principle
   • List thirteen common problems

3. This Session should take you about one hour to complete.

4. Quiz #5 is at the end of this Session.

5. If you have not done so yet, read Section 6.3 of the Structure chapter of **The Home Reference Book** before starting this Session. All done? Great! Let's get started.

Key Words:
- *Masonry veneer*
- *Single wytheing*
- *Metal ties*
- *Brick ties*
- *Steel studs*
- *Vented rain screen*
- *Pressurized cavity*
- *Weep holes*
- *Flashing*

- *Bowing or leaning*
- *Mortar missing or deteriorating*
- *Efflorescence*
- *Too close to grade*
- *Corbelling*
- *Bricks on their sides*
- *Lintels*
- *Stone/brick deterioration*

► 5.0 MASONRY VENEER WALLS

Brick or stone veneer walls are wood frame walls with a masonry siding. The siding is so heavy and thick (typically 2¾ to 3½ inches thick), it must be supported on the foundation. Veneer walls may suffer a combination of the problems we've talked about for masonry and wood frame walls.

Not Slices

Veneer walls aren't the ½ inch or 1 inch thick slices that people glue on. They are single wythe masonry walls laid up in mortar and secured to the wall behind, typically with metal ties.

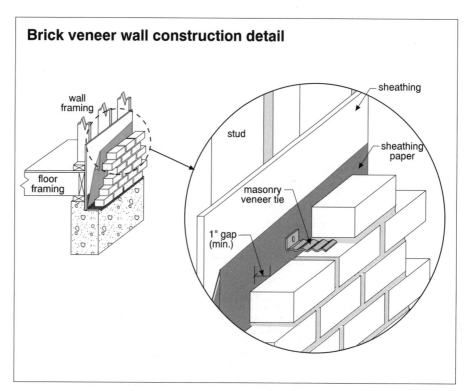

Brick veneer wall construction detail

Special Features

There are some issues unique to masonry veneer walls.

1. Brick and wood expand and contract in different directions and at different rates. Clay brick walls get slightly taller after they have been built. Wood frame walls shrink after they have been built, as the wood dries.

2. Brick is brittle and wood is much more flexible.

3. Masonry should not rest on wood (although this is permitted under some circumstances). In veneer walls, we have the two materials side by side with the wood frame providing lateral support for the masonry. The wood frame doesn't carry the vertical load (weight) of the masonry.

4. The masonry does not carry the live or dead loads of the structure. Roof loads for example, are transferred through the stud walls to the foundation.

5. Brick veneer is not watertight. Wind-driven rains will drive water through most masonry walls. The air gap and sheathing paper behind the brick protect the wall. Other types of wood frame walls rely on their siding materials to keep them dry.

These issues create some interesting conditions in wood frame, brick veneer construction.

Design Considerations Brick veneer walls should allow for differential movement between the brick and wood frame, and should protect the wood frame walls from moisture, since we can't rely on the brick. Early brick veneer walls did not address these issues. Incidentally, some people think brick veneer is a relatively new construction technique. There are lots of wood frame, brick veneer houses built in the latter half of the 1800s.

Brick Ties Masonry is secured to stud walls with metal ties. In old construction, these metal ties were nails driven part way into studs. As the brick wall was laid up, the heads of the nails were embedded in the mortar joints.

Modern Brick Ties Modern **brick ties** are typically 1 inch wide "L" shaped galvanized steel straps. The straps are nailed to the studs (ideally with large head nails). The tabs are bent out to form an "L" and the strap is embedded in the mortar. The part of the strap embedded in the mortar is corrugated to provide a good bond between the strap and the mortar.

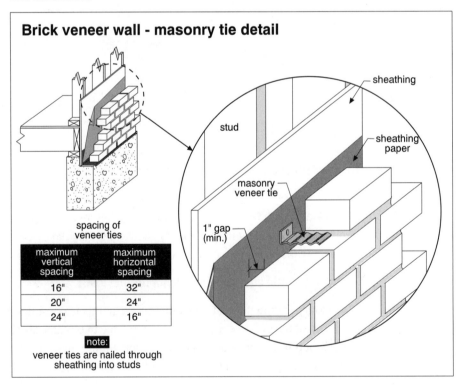

Brick veneer wall - masonry tie detail

sheathing

stud

sheathing paper

masonry veneer tie

1" gap (min.)

spacing of veneer ties

maximum vertical spacing	maximum horizontal spacing
16"	32"
20"	24"
24"	16"

note:
veneer ties are nailed through sheathing into studs

*Tie
Pattern
Not Visible*

These ties can be installed in a number of patterns. One typical pattern is to use the ties on every stud (therefore, every 16 inches horizontally) and every 32 inches as you go up each stud. In most cases, you aren't going to know where the ties are, how they were installed, how many were used, or whether they are in good condition. You will, however, know that if the masonry veneer is pulling away from the wood wall, that the ties are not working.

*Brick Veneer
Steel Stud
Walls*

There have been problems with masonry veneer walls secured to steel stud framing. Many of the difficulties have to do with how the tie is secured to the steel studs. You can't nail into steel studs. Screws were used often with conventional brick ties. As a steel screw goes through the thin sheet metal of a steel stud, the only thing holding the screw to the stud is the metal contact between the screw thread and the steel wall of the stud. It's easy to overtighten the screw and remove enough metal so that the steel stud does not hold the screw well. Further, any rust that occurs at the screw/stud connection will weaken the support and allow the tie to pull out.

*Watch For
Veneer
Walls
Pulling
Away*

While there are ties available now that provide better securement to the studs, you should look very carefully at the integrity of a brick veneer wall if you know the framing is steel studs. There are a number of issues with steel studs that involve thermal bridging, heat loss and condensation. Under adverse conditions, these issues may promote rusting of the studs and brick ties.

5.0.1 VENTED RAIN SCREEN PRINCIPLE

*Building
Paper Or
Housewrap*

We talk about this in **The Home Reference Book**. Let's review it. The goal is to keep the wood frame wall dry. The basic protection for the wood frame wall is the building paper over the sheathing. Some modern sheathings integrate the building paper. Modern housewraps such as TYVEK® replace conventional building paper. Where sheathing is not used, a double layer of building paper may be employed to keep the wall dry.

*Rain Screen
Slows Water
Entry And
Drains It*

Wind-driven rain will pass through masonry walls, mostly at the junctions between the mortar and the bricks, although depending on the brick and the mortar, the rain can also pass right through the body of either one. Rather than trying to create a watertight barrier to stop this from happening, the vented rain screen principle reduces the moisture penetration and collects the water and drains it out.

Let's look first of all at how it reduces the water driving through. Moisture passes through a brick wall if there is a driving force. This force is the wind. If the pressure of the wind is much greater on the outside face of the brick than on the inside, moisture will be driven through. The **vented rain screen principle** reduces the pressure difference across the masonry with a simple trick.

The Trick

The veneer is built 1 inch away from the wood frame wall. Holes in the bottom of the brick veneer allow the wind to drive into the cavity behind the brick. As the wind pushes in, it pressurizes this cavity. It's kind of like blowing up a balloon.

Pressurized Cavity

As the cavity behind the brick becomes pressurized, it decreases the pressure differential across the brick. This means that less water drives through the brick. Well designed rain screens have the cavity broken up into compartments so the wind can effectively pressurize the windward side of the building. You won't be able to see whether this was done.

Getting Rid Of The Water

Now that we've reduced the amount of water that gets through the brick, the next step is to get rid of the water. The majority of the water that penetrates the brick will run down the back face of the brick. Any water that finds its way to the frame wall (along a brick tie or a piece of mortar that bridges the 1 inch gap, for example) will run down the outside of the sheathing paper.

Flashing And Weep Holes

At the bottom of the wall cavity, a metal or plastic **flashing** collects the water and carries it outside through the **weep holes**. The flashing should extend about ¼ inch out beyond the face of the wall, run under the brick, and up the face of the stud wall about 6 inches. The sheathing paper overlaps the flashing so any water running down the sheathing paper will be directed over the flashing, rather than behind it.

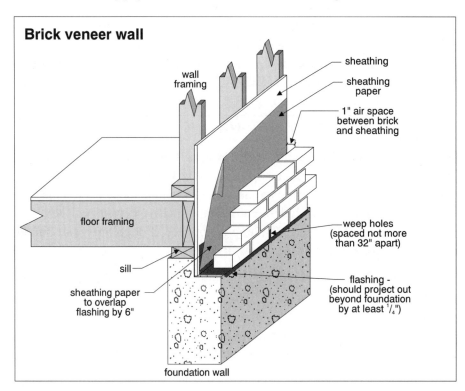

Brick veneer wall

- sheathing
- sheathing paper
- 1" air space between brick and sheathing
- weep holes (spaced not more than 32" apart)
- flashing - (should project out beyond foundation by at least ¼")

wall framing

floor framing

sill

sheathing paper to overlap flashing by 6"

foundation wall

The holes in the brick veneer that allow the wind to enter and pressurize the wall also allow water to flow out. These **weep holes** are really air pressurization holes and water drainage holes.

Rope Wicks

Some masonry veneer walls have rope wicks instead of open weep holes to allow water to drain out of wall cavities. Wind cannot push through these wicks and pressurize the wall cavity. If you see rope wicks, the wall cannot act as a vented rain screen. It may or may not perform adequately.

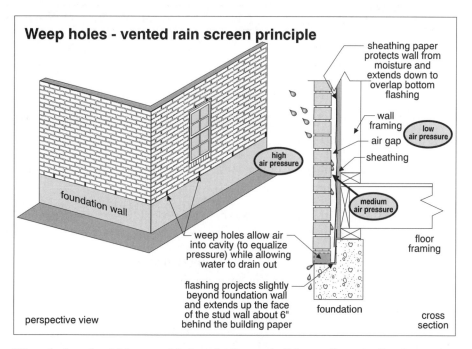

Weep holes - vented rain screen principle

sheathing paper protects wall from moisture and extends down to overlap bottom flashing

wall framing

air gap

sheathing

low air pressure

high air pressure

medium air pressure

foundation wall

weep holes allow air into cavity (to equalize pressure) while allowing water to drain out

flashing projects slightly beyond foundation wall and extends up the face of the stud wall about 6" behind the building paper

floor framing

foundation

perspective view

cross section

Weep Holes At Bottom Of Every Wall Section

Weep holes should be provided at the bottom of the wall, typically about every fourth mortar joint, and should also be provided anywhere water may collect in the wall. For example, where a wall has a door or window opening, flashings and weep holes should be provided above to allow water to escape.

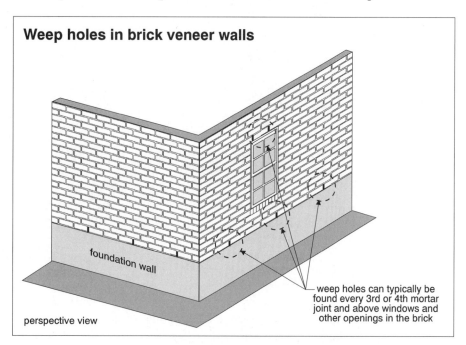

Weep holes in brick veneer walls

foundation wall

weep holes can typically be found every 3rd or 4th mortar joint and above windows and other openings in the brick

perspective view

Flashings Missing Or Joints Leak

We don't usually get to see the flashing details. They are often missing or adjacent pieces of flashing material are not sealed. Water may leak through the top of the foundation wall at joints in the flashing.

Let's look at how we can identify veneer walls.

5.0.2 IDENTIFYING MASONRY VENEER WALLS

We've already discussed identifying masonry walls. Some of the characteristics of veneer walls include –

1. the presence of **weep holes** (mostly but not always),

2. the presence of **wood studs** inside (often visible through electrical switch or outlet boxes from the inside, for example,

3. the **absence of header bricks** (bricks turned end ways to lock the two wythes of the masonry wall together),

4. the **absence of masonry arches** (brick veneer construction most often employs steel lintels, although there are some exceptions), and

5. a **single wythe of brick supported on a metal angle** fastened to the exterior of the foundation. This indicates the brick veneer has been added to a building. The foundation wasn't wide enough to carry the brick, so a shelf was attached to the face of the foundation to support the brick. This situation is relatively rare.

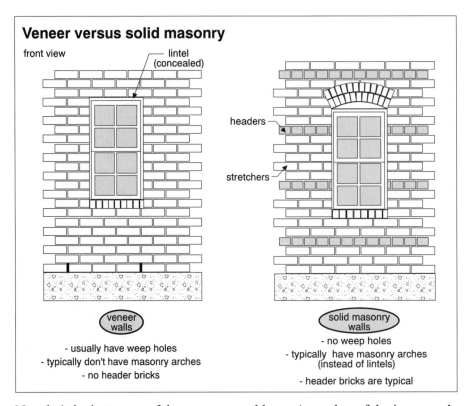

Veneer versus solid masonry

front view — lintel (concealed)

headers
stretchers

veneer walls
- usually have weep holes
- typically don't have masonry arches
- no header bricks

solid masonry walls
- no weep holes
- typically have masonry arches (instead of lintels)
- header bricks are typical

Now let's look at some of the common problems. A number of the issues we've already addressed with masonry and wood frame walls will be applicable here. The key is to keep in mind the brick or stone wall is not loadbearing, but is only acting as a siding.

5.1 CONDITIONS

Common masonry veneer wall problems include –

1. cracked
2. bowing or leaning
3. mortar missing or deteriorating
4. stone/brick deterioration (including spalling)
5. weep holes missing or obstructed
6. flashings missing or ineffective
7. efflorescence
8. too close to grade
9. wavy brick walls
10. excess corbelling
11. bricks on their sides
12. sagging lintels or arches
13. prior repairs

There may also be wood frame wall problems including –

1. rot and insect damage
2. leaning or racking
3. bowing or buckling
4. excessive holes, notches or mechanical damage
5. sagging top plate
6. lack of fire stopping
7. sagging lintels

The wood frame section of the wall is not usually visible.

5.1.1 CRACKED

The discussion of brickwork cracks in 3.1.1 of this Section applies here. Although the veneer walls are not loadbearing, if the foundations move, the veneer walls will move as well. Since this is a rigid, brittle wall system, foundation movement will usually be telegraphed through the veneer.

Metal Angle Supporting Masonry

There is one type of cracking that is unique to brick veneer. When the brick veneer is supported on a metal angle fastened to the foundation wall, the brick veneer can move if this support angle rusts, deflects or pulls away from the foundation. In this case, there can be considerable cracking and movement of the brick veneer, with no foundation movement or wood frame wall movement. In most cases, this is readily visible from the outside. Where brick veneer has been added, carefully inspect the integrity of the angle and sight up the wall carefully for evidence of cracking, leaning or bowing. While unusual, it's possible for the foundation wall to move or deteriorate due to the load imposed.

5.1.2 BOWING OR LEANING

The bowing wall discussions in 3.1.2 of this Section apply here.

Causes   The most common causes of bowing or leaning brick veneer walls are

1. foundation movement,
2. failure of brick ties,
3. shrinkage of wood framing, and
4. excess corbelling.

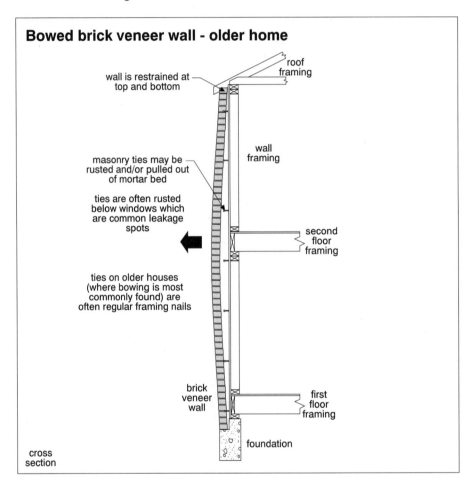

Bowed brick veneer wall - older home

roof framing

wall is restrained at top and bottom

wall framing

masonry ties may be rusted and/or pulled out of mortar bed

ties are often rusted below windows which are common leakage spots

second floor framing

ties on older houses (where bowing is most commonly found) are often regular framing nails

brick veneer wall

first floor framing

foundation

cross section

5.1.3 MORTAR MISSING OR DETERIORATING

Again, the earlier discussions apply. See 3.1.3 in this Section.

5.1.4 DETERIORATION OF THE BRICK OR STONE ITSELF

Again, we talked in Section 3.1.4 about deterioration of the masonry units. This includes spalling and cracking.

Causes   The common causes include

1. sandblasting
2. masonry too close to grade
3. excessive wetting
4. freeze/thaw action

5.1.5 MISSING OR OBSTRUCTED WEEP HOLES

Causes
1. Poor original construction,
2. amateurish home (improvements), or
3. ill-informed efforts to conserve energy.

Implications
1. Moisture leakage into the building,
2. deterioration of the masonry wall,
3. deterioration of the base of the wood frame wall.

Strategy   Once you have identified the wall as masonry veneer, look for weep holes. Very old wall systems did not have weep holes. Weep holes may be

1. open vertical joints (no mortar in every 4th of 5th joint) in the bottom or lower rows of masonry and above openings,

2. plastic screens fitted into open mortar joints (in the same pattern as above), or

3. rope wicks protruding out through the bottom of the wall and over door and window openings.

The rope wicks are useful in drawing moisture out of the wall, but are not a true vented rain screen system, since they do not allow pressurization of the wall cavity.

Young Buildings   Where weep holes are missing and the wall is relatively young, write this up as a deficiency and check for the possible implications. If problems have shown up, corrective action should be recommended. If the problems have not manifested themselves, you may recommend corrective action or monitoring of the situation.

Mature Buildings   If there are no weep holes in a building over 25 years old and there is no deterioration, just recommend monitoring. The building maybe all right because –

1. the building is well enough protected from driving rain, the masonry wall is tight enough that only a small amount of water enters the system, and/or

2. the moisture is escaping from the wall without doing any damage.

5.1.6 MISSING OR INEFFECTIVE FLASHINGS

Causes
Implications

We've talked about these in the Exterior Module. Flashings include those over and around openings, at changes in material and direction, or at the bottom of walls where the weep holes are. The causes of most flashing problems are original installation work and the implications are water entering the wall system.

5.1.7 EFFLORESCENCE

Causes

We talk about these salt deposits in Section 3.1.5. They are the result of moisture moving through the walls and are rarely a serious problem.

5.1.8 TOO CLOSE TO GRADE

Causes

In Section 3.1.6 we said that most brick should be 6 inches above grade, to protect it from moisture problems. Efflorescence and spalling can result if brick is too close to grade.

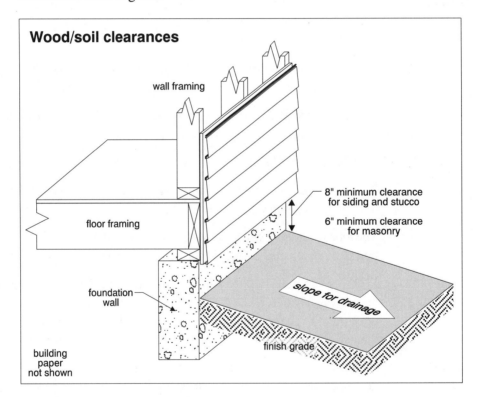

Wood/soil clearances

wall framing

floor framing

8" minimum clearance for siding and stucco

6" minimum clearance for masonry

slope for drainage

foundation wall

finish grade

building paper not shown

5.1.9 WAVY BRICK WALLS

We talked about these in 3.1.7 of this section.

5.1.10 EXCESS CORBELLING

Watch for corbelled brick that exceeds 1 inch in total. Refer to 3.1.8 in this section to review corbelling.

5.1.11 BRICKS ON THEIR SIDES

Bricks with cores removed are much weaker on their sides. Refer to 3.1.9 in this section for more details.

5.1.12 SAGGING LINTELS

Materials

The lintels for brick veneer walls are typically steel angles. The lintels for the wood frame wall inside are most often wood. There is usually no connection between the lintel supporting the brick veneer and the wood lintels supporting the wood framing inside.

Causes

Lintel sag may result from

1. undersizing
2. rust
3. increased loads

As we discussed earlier, arches are not used as often as lintels in masonry veneer walls. Rusting of the lintels because of a flashing problem, for example, results in expansion of the steel and horizontal cracks may radiate out from the top corners of the opening and, in some cases, a vertical crack above the middle. This rusting and cracking may or may not be associated with sagging lintels. Rust weakens steel, and if the lintel is weakened enough, it will sag.

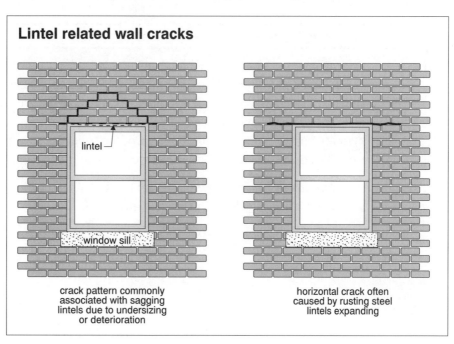

Lintel related wall cracks

lintel

window sill

crack pattern commonly
associated with sagging
lintels due to undersizing
or deterioration

horizontal crack often
caused by rusting steel
lintels expanding

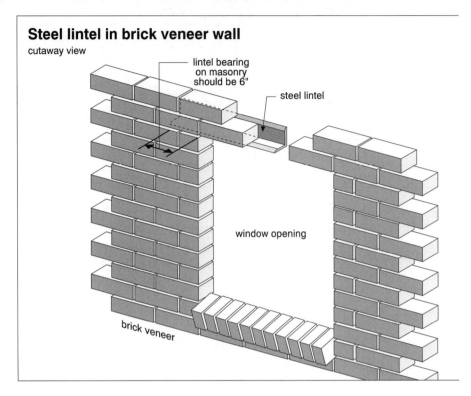

Steel lintel in brick veneer wall
cutaway view

lintel bearing on masonry should be 6"

steel lintel

window opening

brick veneer

Strategy	Look around lintels for cracking, and sight along the undersides for sag. Watch for rust at exposed sections. Mortar joints may be missing mortar at the lintel. There are often weep holes above lintels, especially on wide openings. These help water escape. Where there are no weep holes, it is important that the lintel not be caulked to the brick over the opening. This will trap water in the brick veneer at the lintel leading to rust.

5.1.13 PRIOR REPAIRS

Causes	Prior repairs in brick walls may indicate deterioration or rearrangement of the home. Doors and windows are often moved or blocked off. Where localized deterioration of the masonry has taken place (for example, where a downspout was disconnected and water damaged the brick) localized repairs are common. The masonry veneer is not a loadbearing part of the structure, so you're only looking to see that the wall can support its own weight.
Implications	
General Strategy	As with other masonry walls, you'll want to take a macro look from far away and a micro look from up close at masonry veneer walls.

Structure
M O D U L E

QUICK QUIZ 5

☑ INSTRUCTIONS

- You should finish reading Study Session 5 before doing this Quiz.

- Write your answers in the spaces provided.

- Check your answers against ours at the end of this Section.

- If you have trouble with this Quiz, re-read the Session and try the Quiz again.

- If you do well, move on to Study Session 6.

1. In masonry veneer walls:

    a. the masonry is roughly 1 inch thick
    b. the masonry is supported primarily by the wood framing
    c. header courses are found every 7th row
    d. weep holes are often found
    e. metal ties are never used

2. Brick veneer walls are watertight.
    True ☐   False ☐

3. Briefly describe the vented rain screen principle for a brick veneer wall. (Point form is fine. Hint: Use the words "cavity," "pressure," "drainage," "flashing" and "weep holes" in your discussion.)

    _____

    _____

    _____

4. Give five techniques to help differentiate masonry veneer walls from

solid masonry walls.

_____

_____

_____

_____

_____

5. List 13 common masonry veneer wall problems. Think of the masonry veneer part only.

_____

_____

_____

_____

_____

_____

_____

_____

_____

_____

_____

_____

_____

6. List seven common veneer wall problems. Think of the wood frame part only.

_____

_____

_____

_____

_____

_____

_____

7. Rusting steel lintels over windows cause what kind of masonry crack patterns?

    _____

8. The masonry veneer is a loadbearing part of the structure.
    True ☐   False ☐

If you had no trouble with the Quiz, you are ready for Study Session 6.

Key Words:

- *Masonry veneer*
- *Single wytheing*
- *Metal ties*
- *Brick ties*
- *Steel studs*
- *Vented rain screen*
- *Pressurized cavity*
- *Weep holes*
- *Flashing*

- *Bowing or leaning*
- *Mortar missing or deteriorat-*
- *Efflorescence*
- *Too close to grade*
- *Corbelling*
- *Bricks on their sides*
- *Lintels*
- *Stone/brick deterioration*

Structure
M O D U L E

STUDY SESSION 6

1. You should have completed Sessions 1 to 5 and Field Exercise 1 at this point.

2. At the end of this Session, you should be able to –

   • Explain in one sentence the functions of arches and lintels.
   • List five materials used in arches and lintels.
   • List nine common lintel problems.

3. This Session may take you about 45 minutes to complete.

4. The last Quick Quiz in this Section is at the end of this Session.

5. Read Sections 6.6 and 6.7 of **The Home Reference Book** if you haven't already.

Key Words:

• *Arches*

• *Lintels*

• *Endbearing*

• *Missing*

• *Cracks*

• *Mortar Deterioration*

• *Wood supporting masonry*

• *Masonry deterioration*

• *Sagging, leaning or rotating*

• *Rust*

• *Rot or insect damage*

► 6.0 ARCHES AND LINTELS

Function

Arches and lintels transfer the loads of walls over openings to the wall systems on either side. They must be strong enough and stiff enough to carry the vertical loads without deflecting and must be durable enough to withstand weathering, since they are exposed to the elements.

Materials

Arches are most often the same masonry as is used in the wall face (e.g., stone, brick or concrete), although architectural detailing sometimes dictates the use of different materials. For example, stone arches in brick walls are common.

Lintels are typically steel, wood, or a large single piece of masonry.

Interior And Exterior

Openings in interior and exterior bearing walls require lintels or arches. Arches and lintels are both common on exterior masonry walls. Lintels are almost exclusively used in interior wood walls and exterior wood frame walls with siding. Lintels are more common with masonry veneer although arches are sometimes used. Separate lintels are used for the exterior masonry and for the interior wood framing on a masonry veneer wall.

Masonry Loads

Arches and lintels in masonry walls have a different set of loads than in wood frame walls. In a masonry wall, the arch or lintel carries the weight of the masonry immediately above the opening. However, if you draw two lines up toward each other from the top corners of the opening at 45° angles, you'll end up with a triangle. This triangle of material is all that is carried by the arch or lintel above an opening in a masonry wall, no matter how much brick is above it. Therefore, if you have a ten story masonry building, the size of the lintel over a first floor window would be same as the size of the lintel over a tenth story window.

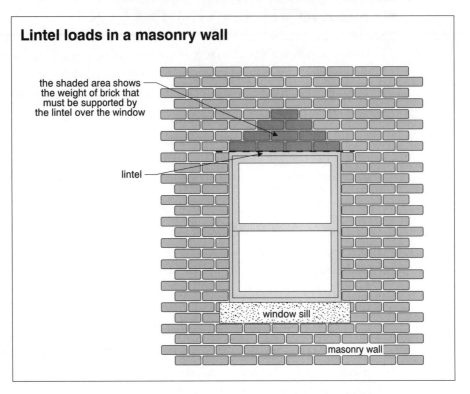

Lintel loads in a masonry wall

the shaded area shows the weight of brick that must be supported by the lintel over the window

lintel

window sill

masonry wall

Wood Frame Walls Are Different

A lintel in a wood frame wall sees all of the vertical loads above that opening. You have to draw two **vertical** lines up from the corners of the opening and pick up all the loads that fall in that area to figure out how much load there is on that lintel. A lintel on the first floor of a ten story wood frame building may have to be significantly larger than the lintel on the top floor (although you can't build ten story wood frame buildings, for other reasons).

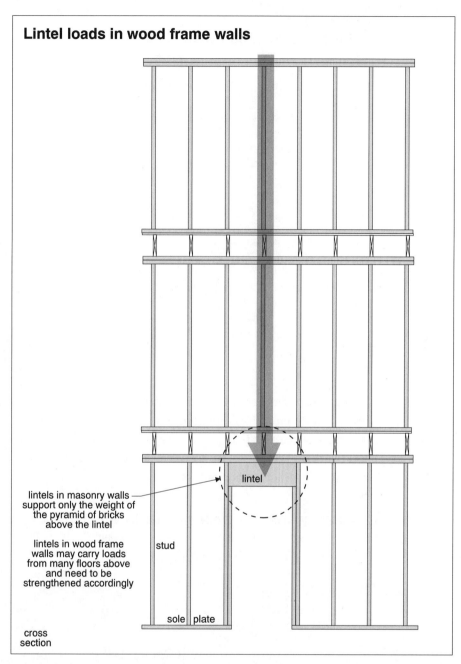

Lintel loads in wood frame walls

lintels in masonry walls support only the weight of the pyramid of bricks above the lintel

lintels in wood frame walls may carry loads from many floors above and need to be strengthened accordingly

lintel

stud

sole plate

cross section

Endbearing   Lintels in masonry walls should typically have six inches of full and level end-bearing. Lintels in wood frame walls typically have 1½ inches of endbearing (on the jack studs below).

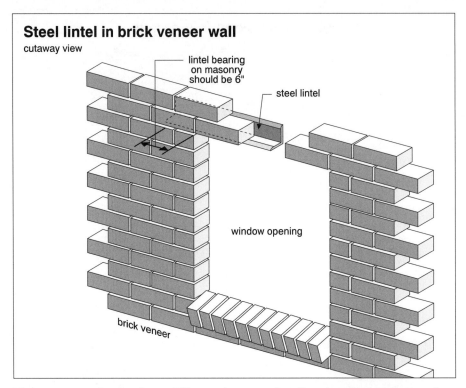

Steel lintel in brick veneer wall
cutaway view

lintel bearing on masonry should be 6"

steel lintel

window opening

brick veneer

Various types of arches have different shapes and endbearing. Arches impose large lateral thrusts on walls beside openings. Lintels do not. Since our inspection is looking at success or failure, we're not going to be analyzing arch design in any case. With arches we'll look for vertical movement (sag) and horizontal movement (outwards) of walls beside openings.

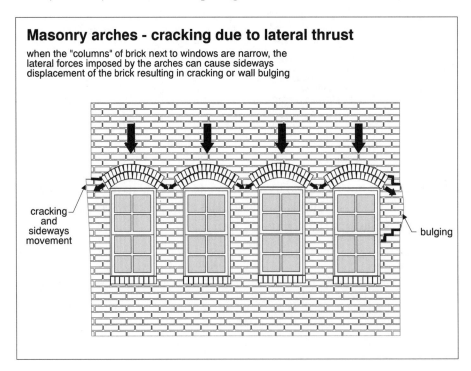

Masonry arches - cracking due to lateral thrust
when the "columns" of brick next to windows are narrow, the lateral forces imposed by the arches can cause sideways displacement of the brick resulting in cracking or wall bulging

cracking and sideways movement

bulging

Let's look at some of the problems with arches and lintels.

6.1 CONDITIONS

Common problems include –

1. missing
2. cracks
3. mortar deteriorating or missing
4. wood supporting masonry
5. stone or brick deterioration
6. sagging, leaning or rotating
7. endbearing
8. rust
9. rot/insect damage

6.1.1 MISSING

Causes Missing arches or lintels are usually the result of amateurs adding a window or door.

Implications On a masonry wall, the implications are a cracking pattern that forms a triangle over the opening. Even if all the bricks fell out of this triangle, the brick wall would eventually stabilize as it created its own arch. The window may be damaged, the wall may leak and/or the window may become loose.

In a wood frame wall, the implications may be more severe. Wall, floor and roof systems may drop over the opening.

Strategy Every opening wider than a few inches should have an arch or a lintel. Steel lintels are sometimes difficult to see and wood lintels are rarely visible. However, you will see the effect of the arch or lintel missing.

6.1.2 CRACKS

Causes Some of the cracks that occur around openings are simply because the wall as a whole is moving, and the window openings are weak points where stresses are concentrated. However, cracks may also be the result of arch or lintel failures. This may be because

1. the arch or lintel itself is undersized (overspanned),

2. the arch or lintel is deteriorating (mortar is missing, metal is rusting, or wood is rotting),

3. of an unexpected concentrated load,

4. of insufficient material beside the arch to resist the lateral thrust.

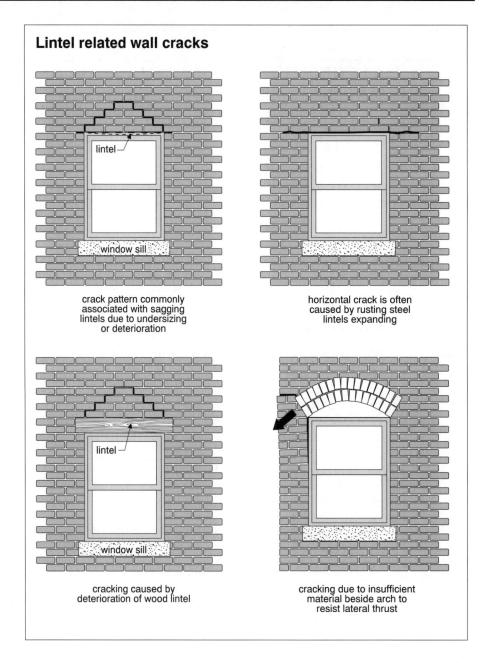

Lintel related wall cracks

crack pattern commonly
associated with sagging
lintels due to undersizing
or deterioration

horizontal crack is often
caused by rusting steel
lintels expanding

cracking caused by
deterioration of wood lintel

cracking due to insufficient
material beside arch to
resist lateral thrust

Implications   The implications can be

1. cosmetic,
2. water leakage into the wall system,
3. localized masonry failure
4. wall, floor and roof collapse.

Strategy   Where cracks occur in or around arches or lintels, use the same kind of reasoning that you used in looking at wall cracks in general.

- Are the cracks localized or extensive?
- What directions of movement do they indicate?
- How big are they?
- How old are they?
- Do they form a triangle over the opening? If so, it is probably a localized arch or lintel issue.
- Are the cracks horizontal and radiating out from the top of the opening? If so, it is probably a rusting lintel.
- Is there displacement of the wall associated with the cracking? If so, repairs may be urgent.

6.1.3 MORTAR DETERIORATING OR MISSING

We've talked about this in other wall discussions.

6.1.4 MASONRY RESTING ON WOOD

Again, we've touched on this before. We don't generally want masonry bearing on wood. However, you will find particularly in older homes, wood lintels supporting stone or brick. Where this is visible, check the integrity of the wood closely. Watch for rot and crushing, particularly at endbearing points. Watch also for sag and rotation of wood lintels.

6.1.5 STONE OR BRICK DETERIORATION

Again, this is similar to what we've talked about in the other wall sections.

6.1.6 SAGGING, LEANING OR ROTATING LINTELS OR ARCHES

Causes   Material deterioration, overspanning (undersizing) or overloading.

Implications   Localized or widespread failure above, depending on whether it's a masonry or wood frame wall.

Strategy   As mortar deteriorates in the arches, it is common for masonry units in the arches to slip out of position, or for the whole arch to bow outward. Rotating arches or lintels indicate the need for immediate repair.

Rusting lintels may pitch forward, causing the wall above to rotate outward. Again, immediate repairs are called for.

Sagging lintels may lose their endbearing or fail suddenly. Replacement of the lintel is called for. In most cases, you won't be able to tell whether the lintel is sagging because it was undersized, the load increased, or the lintel weakened.

6.1.7 ENDBEARING

*Six Inches
Or 1½ Inches*

Lintels should be considered small beams and require appropriate endbearing. Steel lintels resting on masonry require 6 inches of continuous endbearing, ideally (although various code authorities have different numbers on this). Numbers as low as 4 inches are found. Check what is accepted in your area. Again, the acid test is, "Is it working?" Wood lintels typically require 1½ inches of endbearing.

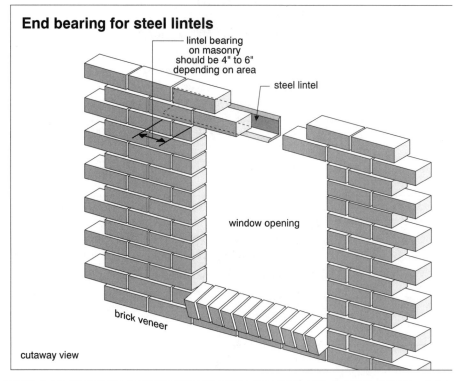

End bearing for steel lintels

lintel bearing on masonry should be 4" to 6" depending on area

steel lintel

window opening

brick veneer

cutaway view

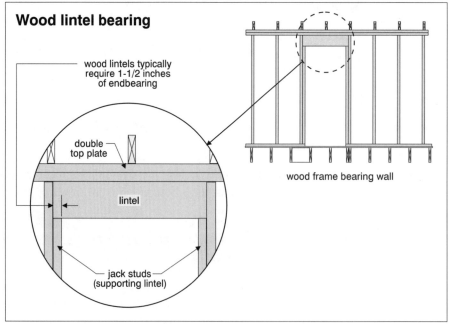

Wood lintel bearing

wood lintels typically require 1-1/2 inches of endbearing

double top plate

lintel

jack studs (supporting lintel)

wood frame bearing wall

6.1.8 RUST

Rusting is a common problem with steel lintels.

Cause It may be caused by –

1. Moisture penetration into the walls above the lintel
2. poor weep hole and flashing details
3. failure to keep exposed lintel surfaces painted

Implications Failure of the structural components above.

Strategy The top edge of the exposed flange of lintels should not be caulked. This will trap water inside the wall. This is a common mistake made by homeowners. When caulking windows, this gap seems to cry out for caulking. The underside of the lintel flange can be caulked to the top of the window or door.

Look for evidence of rusting and the horizontal cracks radiating out from the opening as we've discussed.

6.1.9 ROT AND INSECT DAMAGE

Wood lintels are subject to rot and insect damage as are all other wood components. Be particularly suspicious of wood lintels exposed on the face of the wall. These are often found in older masonry buildings.

In some cases, solid masonry walls have a brick arch supporting the outside wythe of brick and a wood lintel supporting the inner wythe. In most cases, this won't be visible to you. However, failure of this wood lintel due to rot or insect damage can cause movement of the inner wythe of brick. This is usually accompanied by moisture and deterioration of the interior finishes, but this is not always apparent. Cracking around and above openings on exterior surfaces of masonry walls that are otherwise unexplained may be the result of failure of a wood lintel supporting the inner wythe of the masonry wall.

Structure
MODULE

QUICK QUIZ 6

☑ INSTRUCTIONS

• You should finish reading Study Session 6 before doing this Quiz.

• Write your answers in the spaces provided.

• Check your answers against ours at the end of this Section.

• If you have trouble with this Quiz, re-read the Session and try the Quiz again.

• If you do well, move on to Field Exercise 2.

1. Briefly describe the functions of arches and lintels. (Hint: use the words "loads," "transfer" and "openings" in your discussion.)

_____

_____

_____

2. What materials are used for arches?

_____

_____

3. With wood frame walls, the lintel size is independent of the number of stories above.
   True ☐ False ☐

4. With masonry wall, the lintel size is independent of the number of stories above.
   True ☐ False ☐

5. End bearing for lintels in masonry should be at least ___ inches.

6. End bearing for lintels in wood frame walls should be at least ___ inches.

7. List nine common arch and lintel problems.

    _____   _____   _____

    _____   _____   _____

    _____   _____   _____

8. Masonry resting on wood is a less than ideal arrangement.
    True ☐   False ☐

9. The top of the exposed edge of a steel lintel should be caulked.
    True ☐   False ☐

10. Wood lintels on the exterior face of a building are particularly prone to
    _____ problems.

If you had no trouble with the Quiz then, you are ready for Field Exercise 2.

Key Words:

- **Arches**
- **Lintels**
- **Endbearing**
- **Missing**
- **Cracks**
- **Mortar Deterioration**
- **Wood supporting masonry**
- **Masonry deterioration**
- **Sagging, leaning or rotating**
- **Rust**
- **Rot or insect damage**

Structure
MODULE

FIELD EXERCISE 2

☑ INSTRUCTIONS

Again, we are going to ask you to go out and look at some houses.
Again, we will be looking at both the inside and outside of the house.
You will be looking for masonry veneer walls, arches and lintels. The arches
and lintels may be in masonry veneer walls, masonry walls or wood frame
walls. Again, you may have trouble finding examples of all of these.
Do what you can.

Try to look at 10 different houses at least. Allow yourself about 15 minutes
per house.

1. Try to identify walls as masonry veneer. Hints:

    a. are there weep holes?

    _____

    b. are there headers?

    _____

    c. are there stud walls inside?

    _____

    d. are there masonry arches?

    _____

2. Did you see any of these conditions on masonry walls?

    a. cracks

    b. bowing or leaning

    c. masonry deteriorating

    d. mortar deteriorating or missing

    e. weep holes missing or obstructed

    f. flashings missing or ineffective

    g. efflorescence

    h. masonry too close to grade

    i. wavy walls

    j. excess corbelling

    k. bricks or blocks on their sides

    l. sagging lintels or arches

    m. prior repairs

3. For the cracks, follow this step-by-step approach:

    a. how many cracks are there?

_____

    b. are they continuous through the building components?

_____

    c. are the cracks horizontal, vertical, diagonal or random pattern?

_____

    d. what part(s) of the building is/are moving?

_____

    e. are there other indications of stress such as racking, leaning, bulging etc?

_____

    f. is it still moving?

_____

    g. why has it moved?

_____

    h. what are the implications?

_____

    i. what would you recommend to your client?

_____

4. Did you see any of these in the wood frame components?

    a. rot and insect damage
    b. leaning/racking
    c. bowing or buckling
    d. excessive notches, holes or mechanical damage
    e. sagging top plates
    f. lack of fire stopping
    g. sagging lintels

5. Look for arch movement in masonry walls.

    a. are there cracks?

    _____

    b. are the cracks localized or extensive?

    _____

    c. where are they in the arch?

    _____

    d. how big are the cracks?

    _____

    e. how many are there?

    _____

    f. how old are they?

    _____

    g. what direction do they go? (are they triangular above the window?)

    _____

    h. what has moved? How far? In which direction?

    _____

    i. is the arch near the end of a wall? (there may not be enough masonry to resist the lateral thrust)

    _____

6. Look at steel lintels.

    a. Can you see how much end bearing they have?

_____

    b. Can you see any rusting?

_____

    c. Can you see any sag or rotation?

_____

7. Look at wood lintels. (These may be hard to find. Look inside buildings as well as outside. Homes being built or remodelled may be the only place you can have a look at these.)

    a. Can you see any rot or insect damage?

_____

    b. Can you see how much end bearing there is?

_____

    c. Do you see any sag or rotation of the lintel?

_____

When you have finished the Field Exercise, look at the Inspection Tools section and the Inspection Checklist. Then you are ready for the Final Test!

► 7.0 INSPECTION TOOLS

1. **Flashlight**

   Used to examine dark areas, such as crawlspaces.

2. **Screwdriver/Awl**

   Used to probe suspect surfaces.

3. **Moisture Meter**

   Used to identify elevated moisture content in components.

4. **Tape Measure**

   Used to evaluate spans and spacing for wall studs, for example.

5. **Plumb Bob And/Or Mason's Level**

   Used to quantify bowing or out-of-plumb walls.

6. **Ladder**

   Used to closely examine suspect areas.

7. **Binoculars**

   Used to closely examine inaccessible areas.

► 8.0 INSPECTION CHECKLIST

Location Legend   N = North   S = South   E = East   W= West
B = Basement   1 = 1st story   2 = 2nd story   3 = 3rd story

LOCATION		LOCATION	
	SOLID MASONRY WALLS		**WOOD FRAME WALLS**
	• Cracks*		• Poor nailing
	• Bowing, leaning or bulging		•Top plates weak or sagging
	• Masonry deteriorating or spalling		• Bottom plates have poor bearing
	• Mortar deteriorating or missing		• Rot or insect damage
	•Wavy masonry		• Leaning, bowing, buckling or racking
	• Excess corbelling		•Excess holes or notches
	• Hollow units on their sides		• Mechanical damage/fire damage
	• Prior repairs		• Firestopping missing
	• Foundations weak or missing		• Lintels sagging
	• Lateral support is suspect		•Wood too close to soil
	• Efflorescence		• Sheathing missing or ineffective
	• Masonry too close to soil		• Girts missing
			• Offset excessive
	MASONRY VENEER WALLS		
	• Cracks*		**ARCHES**
	• Bowing, leaning or bulging		• Cracked
	• Masonry deteriorating or spalling		• Dropped, rotating or leaning
	• Mortar deteriorating or missing		• Masonry units moving
	•Wavy masonry		• Missing
	• Excess corbelling		• Mortar deteriorating or missing
	• Hollow masonry units on their sides		• Masonry deteriorating, spalling or missing
	• Efflorescence		• Efflorescence
	• Prior repairs		• Prior repairs
	• Foundations weak or missing		
	• Masonry or wood too close to the soil		**LINTELS**
	•Weep holes missing or ineffective		• Rot or insect damage
	• Flashings at weep holes missing or ineffective		• Sagging or undersized
	• Lintels sagging		• Rust
			• End bearing poor
			• Missing
			• Rotating or leaning
			•Wood supporting masonry
			• Mechanical damage or fire damage

*HELPFUL THINGS TO DO

1) Make a sketch.

2) Note these things:

- Length,
- Continuous through components?,
- Orientation and shape (horizontal, vertical, diagonal or random)
- What has moved ?
- In what direction?
- Are there other related conditions (e.g., leaning)?
- Is it still moving?
- Why did it move?
- What are the implications?
- Your recommendations.

► ANSWERS TO QUICK QUIZZES

Answers to Quick Quiz 1

1. False

2. 1. Transferring live and dead loads to the flooring or foundation system
   2. Resist racking
   3. Support interior and exterior finishes
   4. Hide electrical and mechanical systems
   5. Accommodate thermal insulation
   6. Provide sound insulation
   7. Provide privacy

3. 1. Dead loads from structural members
   2. Snow loads
   3. Wind loads
   4. Earthquake loads
   5. Live loads from people, furnishings and contents of homes

4. 1. Brick
   2. Stone
   3. Concrete block
   4. Cinder block
   5. Clay tile
   6. Glass block

5. a and d

6. 1. Header bricks
   2. Metal ties

7. e

8. Leaning outward

9. a

10. 1. Cracks
    2. Leaning, bowing, or bulging
    3. Mortar deteriorating or missing
    4. Wavy brick walls
    5. Excess corbelling
    6. Bricks (cored) installed on their sides
    7. Temporary repairs
    8. Deterioration of the masonry
    9. Efflorescence
    10. Too close to grade

11. 1. What kind of wall is it?
     2. What has moved?
     3. Which way has it moved?
     4. How far?
     5. Is it still active?
     6. Why has it moved?
     7. What are implications?
     8. What should be done about it?

12. 1. Number of cracks
     2. Continuity of cracks
     3. Type and orientation of cracks
     4. Amount and direction of movement
     5. Related problems
     6. Still active
     7. Cause
     8. Implications
     9. Recommended action

13. Sketch

14. False

15. True

Answers to Quick Quiz 2

1. 1. Inadequate lateral support
     2. Foundation movement
     3. Sagging or sloping floor systems
     4. Rafter spread
     5. Failure of ties
     6. Brick expansion

2. Leaking water at the window has rusted metal ties

3. c

4. These are typically tying the walls into the building and have been added as result of lack of lateral support.

5. 1. Weathering
     2. Poor quality mortar
     3. Poor job of laying the mortar
     4. Weather was too hot
     5. Weather was too cold
     6. Mortar set too long before being used
     7. Additives to the mortar weakened it

6. The walls may have been laid up too quickly or the mason may have skimped on the amount of mortar on the back part of the bricks.

7. Corbelling is staggering bricks so that higher bricks project out beyond bricks below. A wall can be corbelled one-third of its thickness before becoming unstable.

8. True

9. False

10. False

Answers to Quick Quiz 3

1. Balloon

2. b

3. True

4. False

5. both b and d

6. False

7. b

8. Horizontal wood braces installed between studs to prevent buckling. They are typically installed near the mid-point of the wall.

9. 1. Support the siding.
   2. Stiffen the walls
   3. Keep wind and water out of the building

10. 1. Interior finishes such as drywall, plaster or plywood
   2. Exterior sheathings
   3. Panel-type sidings
   4. Diagonal bracing

11. No sheathing is needed if the building is otherwise protected from racking and weather, and the siding needs no support.

12. In waferboard, the pieces are randomly oriented. In oriented strandboard (OSB), the wafers are aligned, at least on the faces of the panel.

13. False

14. False

15. c

16. 1. Partition walls have no structural elements below
2. Load bearing walls rest on foundations, beams or another wall system
3. Ends of floor or ceiling joists rest on load bearing walls but not partition walls
4. Load bearing walls often have a wall directly above. Non-load bearing walls are less likely to have this.
5. Door openings in load bearing walls have lintels. Openings in partition walls do not need lintels.

Answers to Quick Quiz 4

1. 1. Leakage
2. Wood-soil contact
3. Condensation

2. e

3. Water

4. Eight inches

5. Interior finishes and/or exterior sheathing

6. b

7. 1. The walls are too tall
2. Bracing is missing
3. Unexpected concentrated loads
4. Damaged studs

8. e

9. True

10. both c and d

11. both a, b and c

12. both a, b and e

Answers to Quick Quiz 5

1. d

2. False

3. The vented rain screen principle includes a one-inch cavity between the masonry wall and the wood frame wall. Weep holes in the masonry veneer allow air to pressurize the cavity, reducing the pressure differential across the brick. This helps to reduce the amount of moisture driven through the wall by wind pressure. The weep holes not only allow air into the cavity, but allow moisture to drain out. A flashing at the bottom of the cavity extends up behind the sheathing paper and out across the top of the foundation below the brick. Water is guided out of the wall through the weep holes.

4. Veneer walls have –

1. Weep holes
2. Wood studs behind the masonry
3. No header bricks
4. No masonry arches
5. A single wythe of bricks supported on a metal angle

5. 1. Cracked
2. Bowing or leaning
3. Mortar missing or deteriorating
4. Stone/brick deterioration or spalling
5. Weep holes missing or obstructed
6. Flashings missing or ineffective
7. Efflorescence
8. Too close to grade
9. Wavy brick walls
10. Excess corbelling
11. Bricks on their sides
12. Sagging lintels or arches
13. Temporary repairs

6. 1. Rot and insect damage
2. Leaning or racking
3. Bowing or buckling
4. Excess notches, holes and mechanical damage
5. Sagging top plate
6. Lack of fire stopping
7. Sagging lintels

7. Horizontal cracks usually radiating out from the corners of the window. Occasionally there are vertical cracks over the corners of the windows.

8. False

Answers to Quick Quiz 6

1. Arches and lintels transfer dead and live loads above around openings

2. Arches are often the same material as the walls and may be stone, brick or concrete.

3. False

4. True

5. Six inches

6. One and one-half inches

7. 1. Missing
2. Cracks
3. Mortar deteriorating or missing
4. Wood supporting masonry
5. Stone or brick deterioration
6. Sagging, leaning or rotating
7. End-bearing
8. Rust
9. Rot or insect damage

8. True

9. False

10. Rot

4

ROOF
FRAMING

Structure

M O D U L E

► TABLE OF CONTENTS

► 1.0 OBJECTIVES AND OVERVIEW

1.1 OBJECTIVES

During this section you will –
• learn the various components of roof structure
• learn what typically goes wrong
• learn how to identify the conditions that indicate non-performance
• discuss the implications of non-repair

Not The
Last Word
This program is not an in-depth Structure course and you should not assume that you have all the knowledge of a professional engineer, architect, designer, carpenter, mason, etc. after studying this material. This program does not qualify you to design or build homes. There are many places to go to learn more and we encourage you to continue expanding your knowledge.

Structure
MODULE

STUDY SESSION 1

1. This section includes the scope of the roof inspection and an introduction to inspecting roof structures.

2. At the end of this Session you should be able to –

   • List three situations where you would not fully inspect attics.
   • List seven basic roof shapes.
   • Define steep roofing in one sentence.
   • Define flat roofing in one sentence.
   • List six functions of roofs.

3. For more background, please read Section 7.0 of the Structure chapter of **The Home Reference Book**.

4. This section may take you about an hour to complete.

5. Quick Quiz 1 will help you make sure you have understood and remembered the material.

Key Words:
- *Access hatches*
- *Danger*
- *Damage to property*
- *Leaks*
- *Condensation*
- *Shed*
- *Gable*
- *Hip*
- *Gambrel*
- *Mansard*
- *Butterfly*
- *Flat*
- *Steep*
- *Insulation*
- *Anchorage*
- *Lateral support*
- *Micro*
- *Macro*
- *Sag*
- *Dishing*
- *Spreading*
- *Endbearing*
- *Connections*
- *Rot and insect damage*
- *Mechanical damage*
- *Fire damage*
- *Cracks*
- *Sagging*
- *Pull-down stairs*

► 2.0 SCOPE AND INTRODUCTION

2.1 SCOPE

The ASHI® Standards of Practice.

The following is the Structure section of the ASHI® Standards of Practice, effective January, 2000. The Purpose and Scope, General Limitations and Exclusions, and Glossary are included in the Footings and Foundations section.

3.0 STRUCTURAL SYSTEM

3.1 The *inspector* shall:

    A. *inspect:*

      1. the *structural components* including foundation and framing.

      2. by probing a *representative number* of structural components where deterioration is suspected or where clear indications of possible deterioration exist. Probing is NOT required when probing would damage any finished surface or where no deterioration is visible.

    B. *describe:*

      1. the foundation and *report* the methods used to *inspect* the under-floor crawl space

      2. the floor structure.

      3. the wall structure.

      4. the ceiling structure.

      5. the roof structure and *report* the methods used to *inspect* the attic.

3.2 The *inspector* is NOT required to:

    A. provide any *engineering service* or *architectural service.*

    B. offer an opinion as to the adequacy of any *structural system* or *component.*

INCLUSIONS AND EXCLUSIONS

What We'll Discuss

We'll discuss flat and steep or sloped roof framing systems. Steep roof framing systems might have an attic, a cathedral ceiling, or a combination, such as in a 1½ story house.

What We Won't Do

We are going to talk about wood frame systems only with rafters, joists or trusses. We will touch briefly on wood "I" joists, but otherwise won't deal with systems such as concrete or steel roof systems, post and beam, mill construction or heavy timber, or stress-skin panels.

Structure Only

We're going to be dealing with the skeletal part of roofing. We won't be talking about insulation and ventilation. We won't be talking about roof coverings or roof drainage and we won't be talking about interior finishes. These are dealt with elsewhere.

2.2 INTRODUCTION

Roofs can take on several shapes, depending on the architecture of the property. While there are an infinite number of variations, the majority of roofs are one or more of the following styles:

1. shed
2. gable
3. hip
4. gambrel (Dutch colonial)
5. mansard
6. butterfly
7. flat

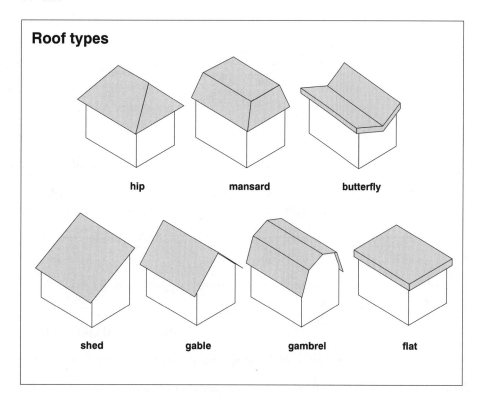

Roof types

hip   mansard   butterfly

shed   gable   gambrel   flat

Steep Roofing Vs Low-slope   Steep roofs are considered to be anything with a slope of more than 4 in 12. Low-sloped roofs have a slope of 2 in 12 to 4 in 12. Flat roofs have a slope of less than 2 in 12. Note: some roofers refer to flat roofs as low-slope, and anything over 2 in 12 as steep roofs.

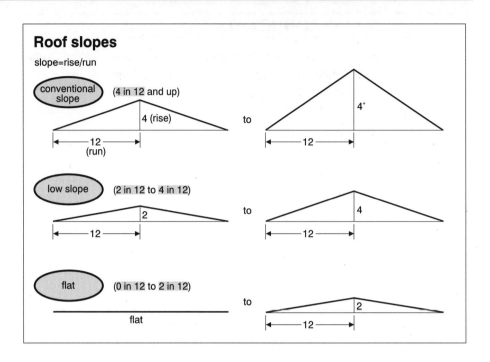

Roof slopes

slope=rise/run

conventional slope (4 in 12 and up)

4 (rise) to 4⁺

12 (run) 12

low slope (2 in 12 to 4 in 12)

2 to 4

12 12

flat (0 in 12 to 2 in 12)

flat to 2

12

FUNCTION

Roofs have several functions, some of which are apparent and some are not.

Live Loads
1. Roofs transfer the **live loads** such as water, snow, wind, roof-mounted equipment and, foot traffic, to the exterior and (sometimes) interior walls.

Dead Loads
2. Roofs transfer the **dead load** of the roof coverings, as well as soffits, fascia and gutters to the walls.

Lateral Support
3. Roof framing provides **lateral support** to walls, tying the top of the building together.

Cosmetics
4. Roofs provide a good deal of the **architectural appeal** of a home.

Drainage
5. Roofs facilitate the **drainage** of roof water away from the building.

Insulation And Ventilation
6. Roofs should accommodate **insulation** and proper **ventilation** to keep the building comfortable and to prevent damage to the roof structure.

INSULATION AND VENTILATION

Increased Roof Loads Due To Insulation
Many old buildings see an increased snow load when insulation levels in the building are upgraded. Improved insulation means less heat loss from the building. Less heat loss from the building means less melting of snow on the roof. This leads to greater snow loads and may result in structural failures.

A Weakened Roof Structure Due To Increased Insulation
Increasing the insulation makes the attic colder. Making the attic colder means that the warm moist air leaking into the attic from the house will condense more quickly. More condensation in the attic leads to higher moisture levels in the attic wood. Higher moisture levels in the wood may lead to mold, mildew and rot. Rot weakens wood. So,increased insulation can weaken roofs.

Increased
Ventilation
Helps

Most contractors now know that if insulation levels in roofs are increased, ventilation levels have to be checked. Good ventilation flushes the warm moist air out of the attic before it can condense and deposit its moisture on the attic wood. Insulation and ventilation are normally thermal issues, but can have a structural impact, and can change the ability of a home to carry live loads.

These issues will be discussed in more detail in the Insulation and Interior Module.

ANCHORAGE

Lateral
Support

The roof structure must be secured to the rest of the building, not only to provide lateral support for the rest of the building, but to prevent the roof from moving or getting blown off during high winds. Where wood roof framing sits on wood frame walls, the roof framing is typically nailed to the walls. In earthquake or hurricane areas, the roof may be strapped to the building. If the exterior walls are masonry, a wood sill is usually bolted to the top of the masonry wall. The roof framing members are nailed to the sill. This is similar to how wood frame walls are secured to foundation walls.

Bolted To
Masonry

The bolts are typically ½ inch diameter, 6 to 12 inches long (although this varies widely) and installed every 6 to 8 feet. In many cases, you won't be able to see these bolts because they will be buried out at the roof edge under the insulation. This is a difficult area to access in many houses. Lower quality work often includes the use of concrete nails to fasten the sill to the masonry.

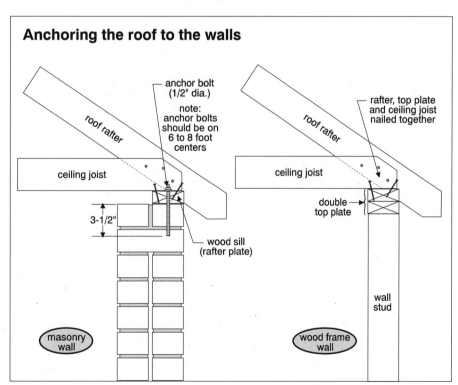

Anchoring the roof to the walls

roof rafter

anchor bolt (1/2" dia.)
note: anchor bolts should be on 6 to 8 foot centers

ceiling joist

3-1/2"

wood sill (rafter plate)

masonry wall

roof rafter

rafter, top plate and ceiling joist nailed together

ceiling joist

double top plate

wall stud

wood frame wall

GENERAL STRATEGY

Like many parts of the inspection, a look at the roof framing is required both from outside the building and inside. A **macro** and **micro** approach are necessary.

Macro

From far away, you're looking for things like –

1. a sag in the rafter or ridge system,
2. dishing in the field of the roof, and
3. spreading of the roof rafters (often visible at the soffits), or the top of the walls.

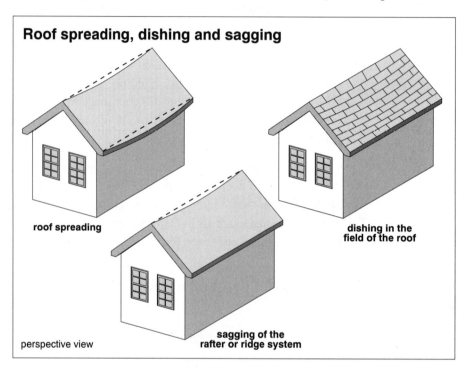

Roof spreading, dishing and sagging

roof spreading

dishing in the field of the roof

sagging of the rafter or ridge system

perspective view

Micro

The micro look will include identifying things such as –

1. poor endbearing
2. weak connections (especially in earthquake or hurricane areas)
3. rot or insect damage
4. mechanical damage
5. fire damage
6. cracks or sagging of the interior finishes

Find All
The Accesses
Into Attics

Many homes have more than one roof space. If they are all accessible, you should inspect all of them. Where only some are accessible, make sure you document what you could see and what you couldn't. Inspection reports often fail to point out that part of the roof space was not accessible.

Access hatches are usually in ceilings but may also be in walls, particularly in split level homes.

*Don't
Leave Dirt
Or Damage*

When opening attic access hatches, be gentle and be careful. You don't want to damage or soil the access hatch or the finishes around it. It's very common for home inspectors to leave considerable visible evidence that they have been up in the attic. Dirty finger prints on the access hatch or the surrounding areas are common. Little bits of insulation on the floor below are another give-away that someone has been up in the attic recently. Damaged paint around the edges of access hatches and damage around screw or nail heads are other indicators.

Many inspectors avoid these problems by –

• wearing latex gloves
• lifting off the attic access with a flashlight or other tool that won't leave fingerprints on the cover
• wiping up after themselves

*Small
Vacuums*

Some inspectors carry portable battery powered vacuums to clean up. Others place drop cloths below attic access hatches before opening them. The goal is to leave things as you found them. If you don't, people will ask you to clean, redecorate or repair, and worse still, may not recommend you to others.

*Falling
Insulation*

When opening an attic access hatch, be careful that insulation doesn't tumble down on you. It's not unusual for insulation to be blown in through a roof vent from above. This covers the attic access hatch with loose insulation. If you're the first one to open the hatch after the insulation is blown in, you can have insulation come down on you and into the house. This will waste a lot of your time and make you look foolish.

*Be Careful
With Pull-
Down
Staircases*

Pull-down stairs are very convenient, but can be very dangerous. As you start to pull down the stairs, be prepared for them to come more quickly than they should. Many of these stairs are poorly secured, have broken cables or springs, split stringers, loose treads, and loose or missing bolts. Some inspectors will pull down the staircases but use their own ladder to go up through the hole. You may include the staircase as an item that you inspect and report to your client. We touch on this in the Insulation and Interior Module.

*Do You
Walk The
Entire Attic?*

Whether you go through the attic from one end to the other and into all corners is a business decision. The more you see, the less risk there is of undetected problems coming back to haunt you. Also, the more you see, the better service you're providing your client. There is often mechanical equipment such as air conditioning fans and coils in the attic. You are expected to inspect these.

*Insulation
Covers
Joists*

One of the yardsticks we use to decide if we will walk through attics is whether or not the insulation levels cover the ceiling joists. You do not want to step between ceiling joists or trusses. Most ceiling finishes will not support your weight. You can damage the home and injure yourself by stepping on ceiling finishes.

Cut Or Damaged Wood Members

Some people say that if the insulation covers the ceiling joists or bottom chords of the trusses, you can feel for the joists or chords with your feet and still walk safely through the attic. This is true most of the time, but if the ceiling joists are covered with insulation, you won't know if you're stepping on one that is cracked, rotted or completely cut. This may result in you falling through the attic.

Electrical Connections

Similarly, you won't know whether someone has left an exposed electrical connection on top of a joist. Open junction boxes mounted to the top of ceiling joists are very common. Fishing around with your foot and stepping on one these is, of course, extremely dangerous.

Report What You Did

Use common sense to decide how much of the attic or roof space you're going to inspect and tell your client what you did. We don't walk or crawl on joists we can't see.

High Temperatures

During the summer months, attic areas can be extremely hot. Most would say that you have to inspect accessible attics even though they may be hot and uncomfortable.

When The Attic Has A Floor

Some attics have floors or partial floors laid on the ceiling joists. While this makes it easier to move through the attic, be careful walking on these floors. They are often poorly secured and may move under foot. Again, use common sense and look at what you're standing on.

Structure
M O D U L E

QUICK QUIZ 1

☑ INSTRUCTIONS

• You should finish reading Study Session 1 before doing this Quiz.

• Write your answers in the spaces provided.

• Check your answers against ours at the end of this Section.

• If you have trouble with the Quiz, re-read the Session and try the Quiz again.

• If you do well, move on to Session 2.

1. The Standards require you to inspect the roof structure.
    True ☐   False ☐

2. The Standards require you to describe the roof structure.
    True ☐   False ☐

3. The Standards require you to enter every attic space.
    True ☐   False ☐

4. The Standards require you to report how you inspected the attic.
    True ☐   False ☐

5. Under what three conditions are you not required to enter the attic space?

    _____

    _____

    _____

6. Give at least two examples of how you might damage the property while entering an attic space.

   _____

   _____

7. It is a good idea to start the inspection of the roof from a distance (other side of the street). What kinds of things are you looking for with respect to the roof structure? List at least 2.

   _____

   _____

8. List at least 4 things that you are looking for inside the attic with respect to the roof structure.

   _____

   _____

   _____

   _____

9. Why might pull-down attic staircases be dangerous?

   _____

   _____

10. Why might the loads on the roof structure increase when you add attic insulation?

    _____

    _____

    _____

If you had no trouble with the Quiz, you are ready for Study Session 2!

Key Words:

- *Access hatches*
- *Danger*
- *Damage to property*
- *Leaks*
- *Condensation*
- *Shed*
- *Gable*
- *Hip*
- *Gambrel*
- *Mansard*
- *Butterfly*
- *Flat*
- *Steep*
- *Insulation*
- *Anchorage*
- *Lateral support*
- *Micro*
- *Macro*
- *Sag*
- *Dishing*
- *Spreading*
- *Endbearing*
- *Connections*
- *Rot and insect damage*
- *Mechanical damage*
- *Fire damage*
- *Cracks*
- *Sagging*
- *Pull-down stairs*

Structure
MODULE

STUDY SESSION 2

1. You should have completed Study Session 1 and Quiz 1 before starting this session.

2. This Section introduces our discussion of rafters and roof and ceiling joists. By the end of this Session, you should be able to –

- List five functions of rafters, roof joists and ceiling joists.
- Define in one sentene each rafters, roof joists and ceiling joists.
- Describe in one sentence each hip, valley and jack rafters, and ridge boards and ridge beams.

3. This Session may take 45 minutes to complete.

4. Complete Quick Quiz 2 when you are done.

Key Words:

- *Rafters*
- *Roof joists*
- *Ceiling joists*
- *Roof spreading*
- *Splices*
- *Endbearing*
- *Heel*
- *Toe*
- *Hip rafter*
- *Valley rafter*

- *Jack rafter*
- *Horizontal projection*
- *Ridge board*
- *Ridge beam*
- *Gable walls*
- *Gable overhangs*
- *Dormers*
- *Eaves*
- *Flat roofs*
- *Cathedral roofs*

► 3.0 RAFTERS, ROOF JOISTS AND CEILING JOISTS

Functions

The functions of rafters, roof joists and ceiling joists include –

1. carry the live loads of wind, rain, snow and people
2. carry the dead loads of roof sheathing, roof coverings and roof-mounted equipment
3. support the dead loads of insulation and ceiling finishes
4. laterally support the walls of the building, preventing racking and wall or roof spreading
5. create an attic space, a ventilation space and support for soffits and fascia

Definitions

Rafters

Rafters are found on steep roofs (slope of more than 2 in 12). Rafters are typically 2 by 4's, 2 by 6's, 2 by 8's or 2 by 10s. The rafters support the sheathing and typically run from the roof peak down to the eaves. The rafters carry the dead load of the sheathing and roofing material, and the live loads above. Rafters may also carry the ceiling loads below on cathedral ceilings.

Roof Joists

Roof joists are found on low-slope roofs (slope of 2 in 12 or less). Their functions are similar to rafters. Roof joists may span continuously from one side of the house to another or may be supported on an interior bearing wall. They may carry ceiling loads.

Ceiling Joists

Ceiling joists are horizontal members used with rafters and roof joists. They carry the dead loads of the interior finishes and insulation. In some cases, they also carry storage, although they are typically not designed to carry the same loads as floors.

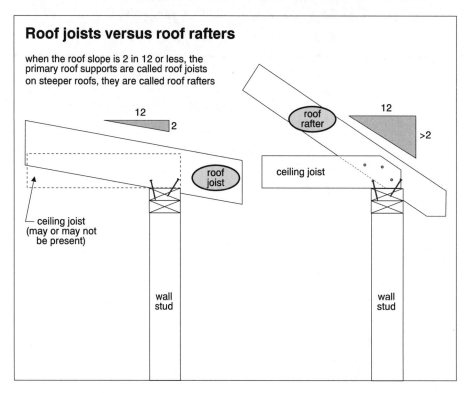

Roof joists versus roof rafters

when the roof slope is 2 in 12 or less, the
primary roof supports are called roof joists
on steeper roofs, they are called roof rafters

12

2

roof
rafter

12

>2

roof
joist

ceiling joist

ceiling joist
(may or may not
be present)

wall
stud

wall
stud

*Close The
Triangle*

Ceiling joists often tie the bottoms of opposing rafters together. This closes the triangle formed by the two rafters and prevents rafters from spreading. Ceiling joists may also support knee walls, ridge posts or struts, for example, helping to transmit live loads down to bearing walls.

Installation Basics

Materials

Rafters and roof joists may be anywhere from 2 by 4s to 2 by 10s. Ceiling joists may be similarly sized although 2 by 4s and 2 by 6s are the most common.

Spacing

Rafters, roof joists and ceiling joists may be spaced 12 inches, 16 inches, 20 inches, or 24 inches on center. Traditionally, 16 inch centers are common. In modern construction, 24 inches is more common.

Splices

Rafters or roof joists that are spliced need to be supported. These members should be continuous much like floor joists and wall studs. Splices should be reinforced. Sistering rafters or joists is one way to strengthen them.

Ceiling joists are often not continuous from one side of the building to the other. If they tie the rafters together at the bottom (a common situation) their splices should be very strong. It's common to find that the ceiling joists are spliced over a central bearing wall in the middle of the attic floor. Each pair of ceiling joists has to be securely tied together to act as a single tension member. When the roof is loaded, the rafter bottoms will try to spread apart. The ceiling joists have to resist this outward force.

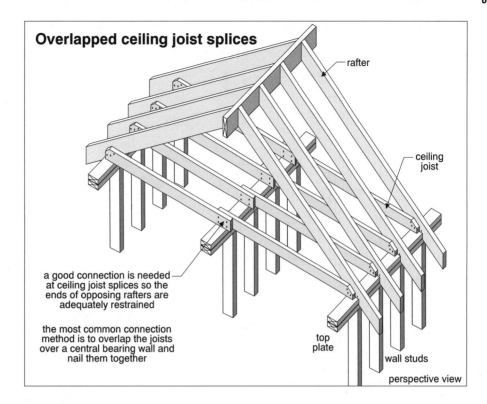

Overlapped ceiling joist splices

rafter

ceiling joist

a good connection is needed at ceiling joist splices so the ends of opposing rafters are adequately restrained

the most common connection method is to overlap the joists over a central bearing wall and nail them together

top plate

wall studs

perspective view

In some cases, the ceiling joists are overlapped and nailed. In other cases, plywood plates 2 to 3 feet wide are laid over the ceiling joists and secured to each joist. This not only ties opposing joists together, but helps distribute loads across more than one pair of ceiling joists.

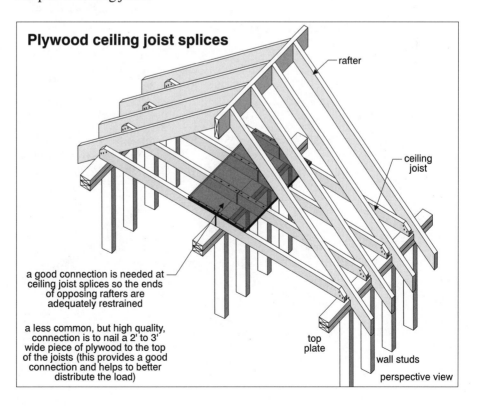

Plywood ceiling joist splices

rafter

ceiling joist

a good connection is needed at ceiling joist splices so the ends of opposing rafters are adequately restrained

a less common, but high quality, connection is to nail a 2' to 3' wide piece of plywood to the top of the joists (this provides a good connection and helps to better distribute the load)

top plate

wall studs

perspective view

Endbearing   A typical endbearing of 1½ inches is required for rafters, roof joists and ceiling joists.

Rest On Heels   Sloped members should rest on their **heels** rather than their **toes**. Toe bearing
Not Toes   is poor framing practice which creates a weak situation.

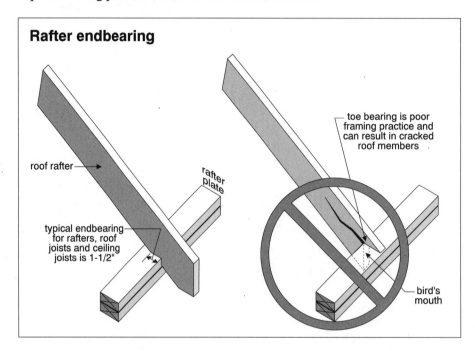

Hip And   **Hip** and **valley** rafters accommodate changes in direction and support
Valley Rafters   shortened rafters. These are usually called **jack** rafters.

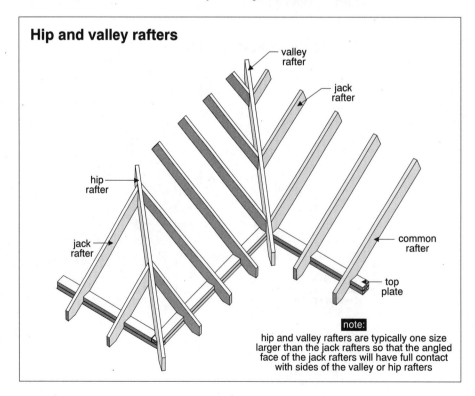

One Size Larger

Hip and valley rafters are typically one size larger than the common rafters. This ensures that the angled face of the jack rafters will be fully supported by the side surface of the hip or valley rafter. Where hip and valley rafters are undersized, the bottom of the jack rafters will project below the bottom of the hip or valley rafter. In some cases, the jack rafters lose their securement and slide off hip or valley rafters.

Rafter And Joist Sizing

The appropriate size for rafters and joists is determined by the live and dead loads they will see (including the weight of the roofing material), the spans, the spacing, the species and grade of wood, and whether or not they will be supporting a ceiling.

Horizontal Projection

The **span** of a rafter is not its **length.** The span is the **horizontal projection** from one support to another.

Supports At Ends Of Spans

Supports for rafters can take many forms. The span ends at each support member. For rafters, support members include

1. walls,
2. the roof peak (whether or not there is a ridge beam or a ridge board),
3. knee walls or struts,
4. purlins, and
5. collar ties.

For example, a 20 foot wide building with a roof peak down the middle and collar ties at the midpoint of each rafter has 5 foot spans for any given rafter section. This is independent of the slope of the roof, since the horizontal projection determines the span.

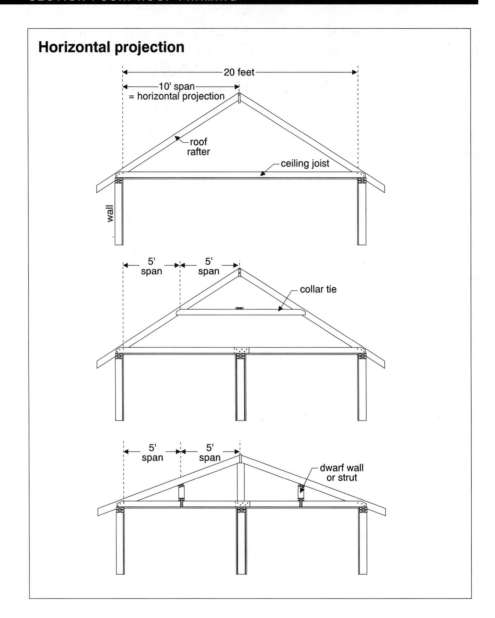

Horizontal projection

Ridges

Ridge Boards vs. Ridge Beams

A **ridge board** and a **ridge beam** are quite different. They are similar only in that they are both located at the ridge and are sandwiched between opposing rafters.

Ridge Beam

A **ridge beam** actually supports the rafters at the ridge, transferring live loads to posts or gable end walls. A ridge beam is typically needed if the roof slope is less than 4 in 12. (A wall can also be used.) The ridge beam should be at least a 2 by 6, and is often one size deeper than the rafters. The beam should be supported by posts no smaller than 2 by 4's every 4 feet. Where the posts are longer than about 8 feet, they have to be laterally braced to prevent buckling. (Engineered ridge beams may have much longer spans.)

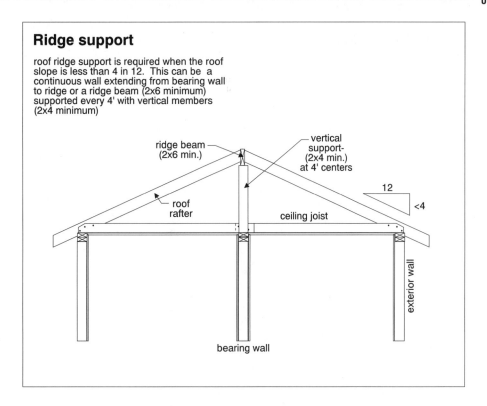

Ridge support

roof ridge support is required when the roof
slope is less than 4 in 12. This can be a
continuous wall extending from bearing wall
to ridge or a ridge beam (2x6 minimum)
supported every 4' with vertical members
(2x4 minimum)

ridge beam
(2x6 min.)

vertical
support-
(2x4 min.)
at 4' centers

roof
rafter

ceiling joist

12

<4

exterior wall

bearing wall

Rafters Won't Spread	Where ridge beams are used, there is no risk of spreading rafters. It's not necessary to tie the bottom of opposing rafter pairs together. Ridge beams are often used on asymmetric roofs where the slope on one side is much different from the other, the wall heights are different on either side, or dormers interrupt the roof slopes.
Ridge Board	If the slope of the roof is 4 in 12 or more, and the bottoms of opposing rafters are tied together by ceiling joists, a ridge beam is not required. A **ridge board** is used instead. A ridge board does not support the rafters at the ridge. They are typically a nominal 1 inch board and are usually one size deeper than the rafter size (so that rafters cut on an angle will have full bearing on the board). Ideally the rafters should oppose each other directly but many authorities will allow the rafters to be offset by their width.
Function	Ridge boards –

- make is easier to build the roof
- transfer loads between nearly opposing rafter pairs

Ridge boards don't carry much live load. Loads from an opposing rafter are offset (with apologies to the engineers) by the other rafter.

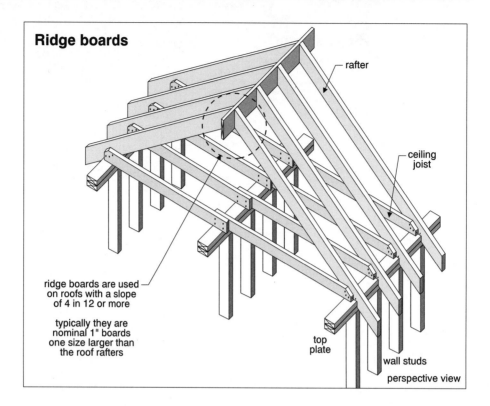

Ridge boards

rafter

ceiling joist

ridge boards are used on roofs with a slope of 4 in 12 or more

typically they are nominal 1" boards one size larger than the roof rafters

top plate

wall studs

perspective view

Ridge Board Not Needed   The ridge board can be omitted if the rafters oppose each other directly.

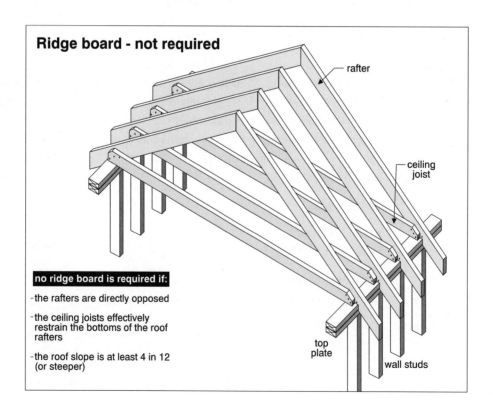

Ridge board - not required

rafter

ceiling joist

no ridge board is required if:

- the rafters are directly opposed

- the ceiling joists effectively restrain the bottoms of the roof rafters

- the roof slope is at least 4 in 12 (or steeper)

top plate

wall studs

Gable Walls

Gable ends are simply walls extending up to the underside of the roof sheathing. They are often framed like conventional walls, although sometimes the studs are installed flat. This means that their wide face is parallel to the end wall of the building.

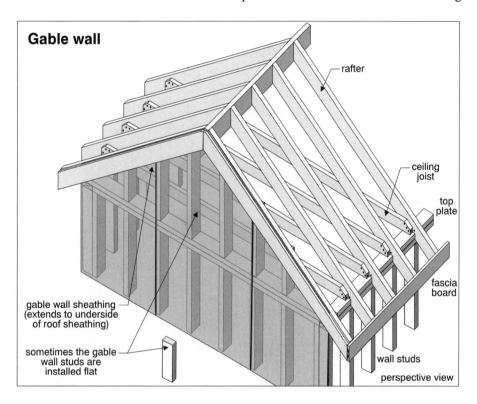

Gable wall

rafter

ceiling joist

top plate

fascia board

gable wall sheathing (extends to underside of roof sheathing)

sometimes the gable wall studs are installed flat

wall studs

perspective view

Brace For Hurricanes

We have found during hurricanes that unbraced gable end walls are vulnerable to heavy winds. Strong winds damage buildings if they can get inside through openings. Window and door openings, including garage doors, can allow wind to get inside a building and tear it apart.

Gable end walls become openings for the wind if they fail. If the wind knocks down a gable wall, the wind pressure fills the attic. The attic space becomes like a wind sock which may blow the roof off the house or blow the roof apart. If you're in a high wind area, check with local authorities for recommended practices for bracing gable ends.

Gable Overhangs

Lookout Rafters For Gables

It's a common architectural feature to have the roof overhand the walls. This also keeps walls drier during rains. We find fewer wall, window and door problems below wide roof overhangs. At the lower ends of rafters, this is usually just accomplished by extending the rafters beyond the walls. It's not quite so easy at gable ends. There are two common strategies used at gable ends.

Small
Overhangs

If the overhang is less than 16 inches, a 1-inch board the same width as the rafters may simply be scabbed on to the outside of the wall along the top. Horizontal braces (typically 2 by 4's on edge) run at right angles from the gable wall out to a rake rafter. The braces are attached to the 1 inch board at one end and to the rake rafter at the other. The roof sheathing helps support the rake rafter.

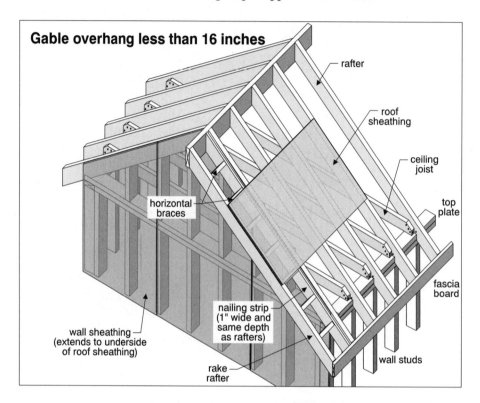

Gable overhang less than 16 inches

rafter

roof
sheathing

ceiling
joist

top
plate

horizontal
braces

fascia
board

nailing strip
(1" wide and
same depth
as rafters)

wall sheathing
(extends to underside
of roof sheathing)

wall studs

rake
rafter

Overhangs Of
More Than
16 Inches

Where the overhang is larger, the outboard or **rake rafter** needs better support. Typically, the braces are extended across the top of the gable wall and nailed to the first rafter inboard of the gable wall. The rake rafter is end nailed onto the braces. The braces are usually 24 inches on center and are sometimes called **lookouts**.

The rake rafters are often supported at the top by the ridge board or ridge beam which is extended beyond the end of the gable wall.

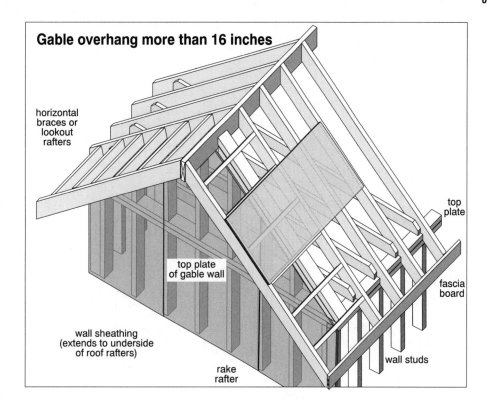

Gable overhang more than 16 inches

horizontal
braces or
lookout
rafters

top
plate

top plate
of gable wall

fascia
board

wall sheathing
(extends to underside
of roof rafters)

wall studs

rake
rafter

There are other ways to frame overhang details, but these are common.

Dormers

*Opening In
Roof Framing*

Think of a **dormer** in a rafter system as a stair opening in a floor joist system. The headers at either end of the dormer are usually doubled and the trimmers along either side are usually doubled. In very large dormers, these systems have to be engineered. Poorly framed dormers allow the roof system around them to sag. This is usually visible standing on the ground outside the home. The framing details are not usually visible unless the dormer is an unfinished attic.

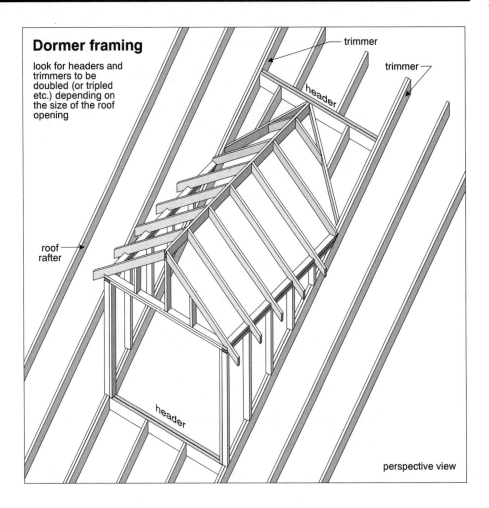

Dormer framing

look for headers and trimmers to be doubled (or tripled etc.) depending on the size of the roof opening

trimmer

trimmer

header

roof rafter

header

perspective view

Eaves

At the lower edge of the roof, the overhang may be non-existent, small or quite large, in some cases, up to several feet. This is an architectural detail and has some impact on roof drainage, keeping walls dry and controling the amount of sunlight that hits the walls. The **soffit**, traditionally made of wood, is attached to the underside of the overhang. It may be horizontal or follow the undersides of the rafters to create a sloped soffit.

Open Eaves   Some older buildings have no soffits and the rafters are visible from below. Some people refer to these as **open eaves**.

The **fascia** is traditionally a vertical wood board fastened to the ends of the rafters. Gutters are mounted on the surface of the fascia in many cases. Gutters should be secured to rafters rather than just to the fascia.

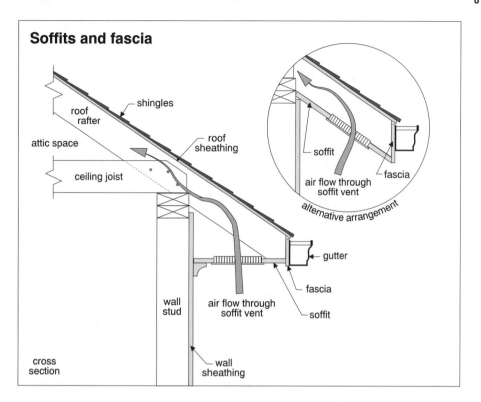

Soffits and fascia

Soffits and fascia diagram with labels: shingles, roof rafter, attic space, ceiling joist, roof sheathing, soffit, fascia, air flow through soffit vent, alternative arrangement, gutter, wall stud, air flow through soffit vent, soffit, wall sheathing, cross section

Soffit
Vents

Soffits are often fitted with ventilation holes to facilitate removal of heat and moisture from the attic. Modern soffits and fascia may be aluminum or vinyl, for example.

Flat Roofs And Cathedral Roofs

May Be No

Flat roofs have roof joists that may or may not have ceiling joists. Where there are

Ceiling Joists

no ceiling joists, the roof joists support the ceiling finishes below. Cathedral roofs usually use the rafters to carry the ceiling finishes.

Poor Venting

One of the chronic problems with both flat and cathedral roofs is a lack of ventilation. Where insulation is between the roof joists or rafters, there should be a space above to allow moist air and heat to be removed from the roof space. In many cases, this is not present, or not continuous.

Convection
Helps

Cathedral roofs should work somewhat better than flats because of convection. The warm moist air escapes out through the top of the roof system while cool dry air is being drawn in from below. However, it doesn't always work this way. Rotted structural members resulting from condensation in flat and cathedral roofs is a common problem in the northern United States and Canada.

Notches And Holes

The rules for notches and holes in roof framing members are the same as the rules for notches and holes in floor joists.

Structure
M O D U L E

QUICK QUIZ 2

☑ INSTRUCTIONS

- You should finish reading Study Session 2 before doing this Quiz.

- Write your answers in the spaces provided.

- Check your answers against ours at the end of this Section.

- If you have trouble with this Quiz, re-read the Session and try the Quiz again.

- If you do well, move on to Session 3.

1. List five functions of roof framing members.

_____

_____

_____

_____

_____

2. Define rafters, roof joists and ceiling joists.

_____

_____

_____

3. Ceiling joists are often not continuous from one side of the building to the other. In this case they are spliced over a central bearing wall. Why do they have to be securely tied together?

_____

_____

4. Define hip rafter, valley rafter and jack rafter.

_____

_____

_____

5. How is the span of a rafter measured?

_____

6. What is the difference between a ridge board and a ridge beam?

_____

7. What is a typical, chronic problem with flat and cathedral roofs?

_____

If you had no trouble with the Quiz, you are ready for Study Session 3.

Key Words:

- **Rafters**
- **Roof joists**
- **Ceiling joists**
- **Roof spreading**
- **Splices**
- **Endbearing**
- **Heel**
- **Toe**
- **Hip rafter**
- **Valley rafter**

- **Jack rafter**
- **Horizontal projection**
- **Ridge board**
- **Ridge beam**
- **Gable walls**
- **Gable overhangs**
- **Dormers**
- **Eaves**
- **Flat roofs**
- **Cathedral roofs**

Structure

M O D U L E

STUDY SESSION 3

1. You should have completed Study Session 1 and 2 at this point.

2. This Session covers the common conditions encountered with rafters, roof joists and ceiling joists. After completing this Session, you should be able to –

• List eight common problems with rafters, roof joists and ceiling joists.
• List three causes of sagging rafters or ridges.
• List five causes of rafter spread.

3. This Session is a bit longer than the others and may take 1 hour to complete.

4. Quick Quiz 3 will help you check that you have learned the material in this Session.

Key Words:
• *Sagging rafters*
• *Sagging ridge*
• *Sagging sheathing*
• *Rafter spread*
• *Heel bearing*
• *Toe bearing*
• *Pyrolysis*

3.1 CONDITIONS

Problems commonly encountered with rafters, roof joists and ceiling joists include

1. sagging rafters or ridges
2. rafter spread
3. poor endbearing
4. weak connections
5. weak framing at openings
6. rot or insect damage
7. mechanical damage or splitting
8. fire damage

3.1.1 SAGGING RAFTERS AND/OR RIDGE

Causes

Sagging may be caused by –

1. rafters overspanned or undersized
2. too many layers of roofing materials
3. excessive loads, including
   a. snow drifts (especially on multi-level houses)
   b. water accumulating on flat roofs
   c. roof-mounted equipment and solar collector panels
   d. removal of collar ties or other intermediate supports
   e. ineffective intermediate supports, including
      (i) collar ties
      (ii) ridge posts
      (iii) purlins
      (iv) knee walls
      (v) poor connections for example at hip and valley rafters, for example

Implications

The implications of sagging ridge or rafters may be simply cosmetic, or may lead to roof collapse. In some cases, the roofs sags to a given position and is stabilized, perhaps by intermediate supports. Although the roof continues to show a sag, it may be quite stable. Don't jump to conclusions looking from the outside.

Strategy

Not Sagging Sheathing

Remember to look from far away and up close. You're looking for a dishing in the roof surface or a sag at the ridge. Be careful not to confuse sagging sheathing with rafter or roof joist sag. Sagging sheathing is a repetitive pattern between rafters or roof joists. Sagging rafters or roof joists will be on a large scale across the roof surface.

Rafters Pulling Away From Ridge

Look at the ridge for evidence of rafters pulling away from a ridge board or slipping off the ridge. On gable ends, you can often see the tops of the rake boards moving apart, indicating movement of the rafters.

Hip And Valley Rafter

The connections between jack rafters and hip or valley rafters is a weak point on most roofs. Watch for evidence of movement of the jack rafters relative to hip or valley rafters.

*Lower Roof
Level Sees
Snow Drifts*

Rafter sag in cold climates on a lower roof in a multi-level roof house is often a result of the weight of the drifting snow which builds up on a low roof against a wall. Check low roofs carefully for sag.

*Expect
Some Sag*

Some ridge sag may be normal, particularly on roofs with rafters. Usually the support at the ends of the ridge is sturdier than the support in the middle. Consider a typical gable roof. The end of the roof is supported by a gable end wall. At all other areas, the ridge is supported by opposing rafters. Once the loads are applied, there will be a natural curve to the ridge that is often noticeable. What is considered **normal**. takes some experience and may depend on age and how wide the house is.

3.1.2 RAFTER SPREAD

*Like A
Ladder*

Rafter spread is the result of vertical loads (live and dead) on the rafters. Since the rafters are at an angle to these applied loads, the bottom of the rafter wants to slip out. This situation is similar to a ladder leaning against a wall. If the feet of the ladder were on flat, sheer ice, it would slide out from under you. Something has to keep the ladder from sliding out (friction or a contour in the ground). Similarly, unless the bottoms of opposing rafters are restrained or tied together, the rafters may slip out.

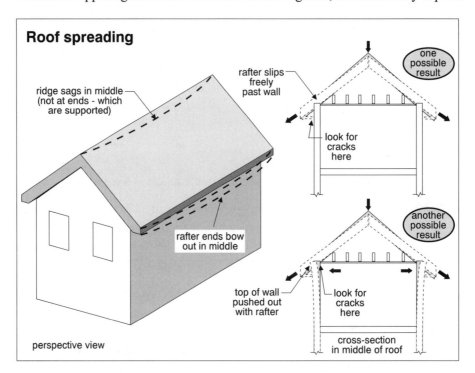

Causes

Rafter spread may be the result of failing to use ceiling joists to effectively tie opposing rafter bottoms together because –

1. the ceiling joists run perpendicular to rafters
2. the ceiling joists are not well connected to the rafters
3. the ceiling joist splices are not well made and ceiling joists are pulling apart
4. other methods of tying the rafters to the structure are ineffective
5. ceiling joists were removed to create cathedral ceilings

Implications   Rafter spread can result in –

- the rafters, soffits and fascia sliding out away from the walls
- the walls themselves may be pushed outward if the rafters are well secured to the walls.

Strategy   Sometimes it's difficult to know whether the problem is a result of original construction or some change that has taken place to the property. This is not of great importance to you as an inspector. The key thing is to pick up the problem.

Macro And Micro

Leaning Walls

Look at the roof surface from the ground outside. A sagging ridge may indicate rafter spread. A dishing roof surface may also mean rafter spread. Make sure the top of exterior walls are plumb and not leaning outward. Look near the middle of walls rather than the ends.

Gap Between Wall And Soffit

Watch for a gap between the soffit and the exterior wall. You can see this from the ground. The gap is usually wider near the midpoint of the wall and closes at the corners. Rafters usually only spread where they are not restrained by gable end walls or hips.

How Are Rafters Restrained?

Check in the attic whether the ceiling joists tie opposing rafter bottoms together. If they do not, rafter spread is more likely. Where ceiling joists are perpendicular to rafters, 1 by 4s may be used to tie the bottoms of rafters to several ceiling joists. While the approach varies dramatically, usually at least three or four ceiling joists are involved, and about every 3rd rafter is secured.

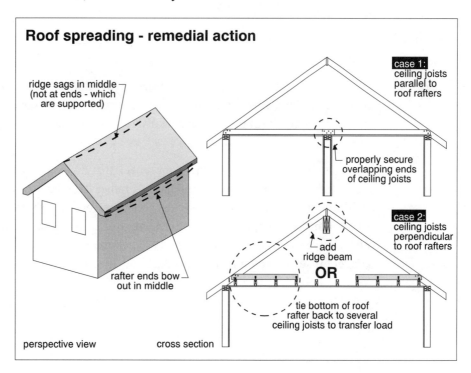

Roof spreading - remedial action

ridge sags in middle (not at ends - which are supported)

case 1: ceiling joists parallel to roof rafters

properly secure overlapping ends of ceiling joists

case 2: ceiling joists perpendicular to roof rafters

add ridge beam

OR

rafter ends bow out in middle

tie bottom of roof rafter back to several ceiling joists to transfer load

perspective view   cross section

Ceiling
Cracks

Cracks in interior ceilings running parallel to the outside wall and within a foot or two of the wall may indicate rafter spread. These cracks may be the result of one or two ceiling joists being pulled outward as the braces joining the rafter bottoms to the ceiling joists move outward.

Cracks At
Wall/Ceiling

Watch also for a crack at the wall/ceiling intersection along exterior walls. This may indicate the exterior walls are being pushed outward by the rafters.

Triangle
Broken

Where ceiling joists or rafters are cut to accommodate attic access hatches, dormers, skylights or chimneys, localized rafter spread may occur because of the discontinuity in the ceiling joists or rafters.

Ridge Beam
Prevents
Spread

If the house has a ridge beam, the rafters will not spread since they are supported at the top. Rafters can only spread if the connection at the peak is allowed to drop. A ridge beam working properly will not allow this to happen.

3.1.3 POOR ENDBEARING

Generally speaking, 1½ inch endbearing is required.

Causes

Poor endbearing may the result of –

1. poor installation,
2. building movement,
3. roof sag, or
4. rafter spread.

Implication

Where bearing is not adequate, the ends of wood members may crush, and rafters and/or joists may fall off their support.

Strategy

While it's difficult to get a look at endbearing, (usually because it's difficult to get to the wall/rafter intersection and because this area is usually covered with insulation), it may be worth the trip, especially if you see some misalignment of the house walls.

Heel
Bearing
Not Toe
Bearing

If you can get a look at the connections, check that the bottom of sloped framing sloped framing members rest on their heels rather than their toes. While 1½ inch endbearing is all that is required, it must be 1½ inch on the **bottom edge** of a rafter. **Bird's mouths** as they are sometimes called, should always be cut in the bottom of rafters, never in the top. Where rafters are bearing on their toes, watch for splits parallel to the grain running up from the bird's mouth.

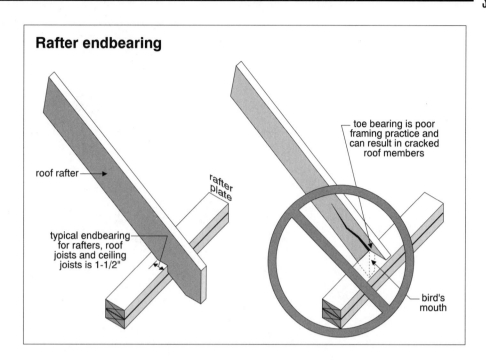

Rafter endbearing

roof rafter

rafter plate

typical endbearing for rafters, roof joists and ceiling joists is 1-1/2"

toe bearing is poor framing practice and can result in cracked roof members

bird's mouth

Angle Bearing Often Weak

Also watch where rafters are cut on an angle to bear against an opposing rafter, a ridge board or a ridge beam. The rafter face must be flush against the opposing member. If the cut is at the wrong angle and there is a point bearing, the wood is likely to crush and the rafter will drop. This applies at valleys and hips as well.

3.1.4 WEAK CONNECTIONS

Causes

Weak connections are caused by –

1. poor installation techniques
2. concentrated loads
3. rusting fasteners
4. amateurish renovation work
5. warping wood members
6. vibration

Strategy

Check for evidence of movement at all connections. Watch for nails that have pulled out and wood that has slid against an adjacent piece. Look also at hip and valley rafters for the full length of the cut face of the jack rafter resting flush against the hip or valley rafter. Look for movement around openings for dormers, skylights, access hatches, chimneys and any other interruption in the framing pattern.

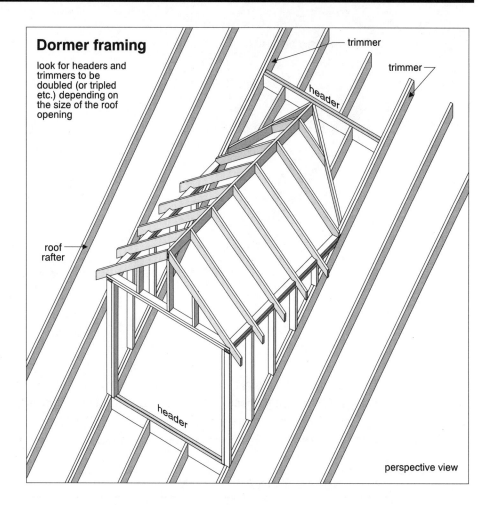

Dormer framing

look for headers and trimmers to be doubled (or tripled etc.) depending on the size of the roof opening

trimmer

trimmer

header

roof rafter

header

perspective view

Condensation Causes Rust	High humidity levels are often experienced in attics, resulting in condensation problems. This can not only rot wooden members but can rust metal fasteners.
Joist Hangers	Where joist hangers have been used in roof framing, watch for the same conditions as we talked about for joist hangers on floor framing. This includes the wrong size or type of joist hanger, not enough nails, the wrong type of nails, the joists or rafter not sitting in the base of the hanger, etc.

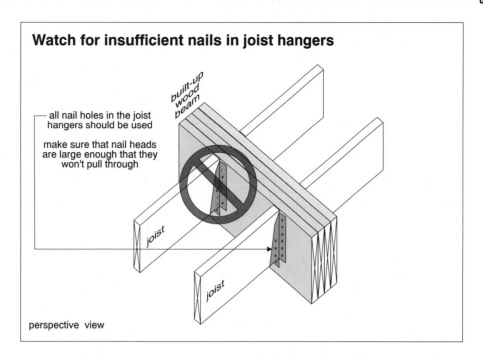

Watch for insufficient nails in joist hangers

built-up wood beam

— all nail holes in the joist hangers should be used

make sure that nail heads are large enough that they won't pull through

joist

joist

perspective view

3.1.5 WEAK FRAMING AT OPENINGS

This is a result of –

Causes
1. poor installation,
2. rot, often due to flashing leakage at the openings, or
3. weak connections.

Strategy   Check around openings and watch for localized sag in roof surfaces or ceilings around dormers, skylights and other openings. This is easiest to see from a distance. You can usually spot this from the ground.

When in the attic area, check for evidence of leakage and rot in the framing members immediately below the openings. Flashing leaks are common roofing problems.

Where trimmers can be seen, make sure they have been at least (doubled) where more than one rafter has been cut, and make sure connections are secure. Headers should also be doubled if more than one rafter has been cut. This rule may vary depending on your area. Some authorities will allow two cut rafters with a double trimmer and single header. Find out what is allowed in your area. A performance-based inspection (rather than code-based) of these components is suggested.

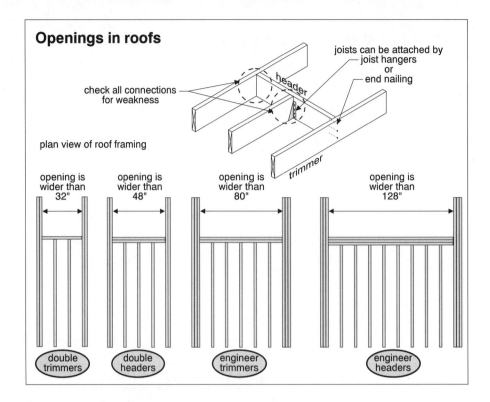

Cracks in ceilings below openings may indicate movement of framing members.

3.1.6 ROT OR INSECT DAMAGE

Wood roof framing members are vulnerable to rot and insect damage.

Causes   Rot may result from –

1. leakage
2. condensation
3. ice dams

Insects are more likely to attack wet or rotted wood and although subterranean termites may enter a house from the ground below, they do make their way to roof framing members. There are also other wood-boring insects often found in roof framing.

Strategy   Look for mold and mildew that may indicate rot. Look for darkening of both framing members and sheathing. Check around any flashed openings including plumbing stacks, roof vents, chimneys, etc., for evidence of leakage.

Leakage will cause rot and make this area more susceptible to insect attack. Check around the perimeter of the roof. Gutter and downspout backup, ice dam problems and water collecting from leaks above, make these areas susceptible to damage.

Condensation vs. Leakage   You can sometimes differentiate between condensation and leakage by looking for an overall trend. Condensation is usually much more wide spread and results in more uniform damage to the roof area than leakage. Leaks tend to run down sloped roof surfaces, rather than along them horizontally.

Although condensation is usually more uniform, there are a few situations where it can be quite localized. A bathroom exhaust fan discharging into the attic can cause severe condensation.

In cold climates, condensation can form almost immediately after opening the attic hatch. A sudden burst of warm moist air from the house, hitting the roof sheathing will form a condensation pattern near the hatch. Don't be fooled!

Condensation damage is more likely on lower sloped roofs and flat roofs. As we've discussed, condensation is more likely to develop on well insulated and poorly ventilated roofs. Condensation damage is much more common with plywood or waferboard than on plank sheathing. The gaps in planks seem to allow enough natural ventilation to reduce condensation and rot problems.

Note: Rot and insect damage apply to all wood framing members. We won't repeat this discussion for other components, but will refer back to it.

3.1.7 MECHANICAL DAMAGE OR SPLITTING

Causes
1. Low quality wood
2. wood which has failed under load, due to
   a. overspanning
   b. undersizing
   c. concentrated loads
3. amateurish installation or renovations, including excessive notching and holes
4. animal activity (pest damage)

Strategy   Check each visible framing member for integrity. Is the whole piece there, are there sections missing? Are there splits, cracks or checks that obviously weaken the member? Where visible, check particularly closely at bird's mouths for splitting. Check also where nails have been driven close to the edge of boards (a common situation with toe-nailing). This often leads to splitting of the wood at the critical fastener point.

Crushing   Crushing is another form of damage. This is common where end-bearing areas are too small, loads are excessive and concentrated, or the wood has been weakened by rot or insect attack.

Wood failures are often the result of a combination of problems.

Note: Mechanical damage and splitting is common to all wood roof framing components. We won't repeat the discussion here, but will refer to it as we talk about the other components.

3.1.8 FIRE DAMAGE

Fire damage may result from;

1. a fire in the house itself, or
2. a chimney fire.

Strategy   Check carefully around chimneys and electrical boxes for evidence of charring. Pay particular attention to recessed lights. Early recessed lights, in particular, were subject to overheating and may have started a fire.

Animals Chew Wires   Animals chewing on electrical wires will sometimes start an electrical fire in the attic. A smoldering fire may not involve the whole house and may self-extinguish. Watch for localized damaged of this sort.

Pyrolysis   Also, watch for charring that may be the result of **pyrolysis**. This phenomenon results from overheating wood repeatedly over time. The auto-ignition temperature of wood (the temperature at which it will burst into flames spontaneously) is typically around 500°F. Prolonged exposure to high temperatures (well below the auto-ignition temperature) can lower the auto-ignition temperature to 200°F to 300°F. This makes the wood far more susceptible to fire and it may eventually burn when exposed to temperatures that wouldn't normally start a fire.

Any charred wood should be examined carefully. Is it from a one time incident? Is it an ongoing process that may worsen, for example, every time a fireplace is used? Treat charred wood with caution. Further investigation may be necessary.

Note: Fire damage is a condition which may be found on any wood
       framing component

Structure
M O D U L E

QUICK QUIZ 3

☑ INSTRUCTIONS

•You should finish reading Study Session 3 before doing this Quiz.

•Write your answers in the spaces provided.

• Check your answers against ours at the end of this Section.

•If you have trouble with this Quiz, re-read the Session and try the Quiz again.

• If you do well, move on to Study Session 4.

1. Give 3 causes of sagging rafters.

   _____

   _____

   _____

2. How might you tell the difference between sheathing sag and rafter sag from the exterior of the house?

   _____

   _____

3. Give 5 causes of rafter spread.

   _____   _____   _____

   _____   _____

4. Explain why a ridge beam helps prevent rafter spread.

_____

_____

5. Proper endbearing is required for rafters and ceiling joists. Generally speaking, what is the minimum recommended endbearing?

_____

_____

6. Where rafters have been cut to accommodate a skylight, for example, the roof loads must be transferred to adjacent rafters. How is this done?

_____

_____

7. Give two examples of how you might differentiate between a roof leak and a condensation problem in an attic.

_____

_____

If you had no trouble with this Quiz, you are ready for Study Session 4.

Key Words:
- *Sagging rafters*
- *Sagging ridge*
- *Sagging sheathing*
- *Rafter spread*
- *Heel bearing*
- *Toe bearing*
- *Pyrolysis*

Structure

MODULE

STUDY SESSION 4

1. You should have finished Sessions 1, 2, and 3 at this point.

2. At the end of this Session, you should be able to –

   • Identify collar ties, knee walls and purlins.
   • Understand the typical conditions that are encountered.
   • Identify typical problems.

3. This Session may take you approximately 45 minutes to complete.

4. Quick Quiz 4 and Field Exercise #1 are at the end of this Study Session.

Key Words:
• **Collar ties**
• **Knee walls**
• **Purlins**
• **Dwarf walls**
• **Struts**
• **Strongbacks**

▶ 4.0 COLLAR TIES

Function

Compression

Collar ties are typically 2 by 4s on edge that run horizontally across the mid-height of attics to reduce the spans of the rafters on either side. Collar ties are intermediate supports that prevent rafter sag. They are primarily compression members that carry the live and dead loads that rafters see. They are usually being squeezed from each end rather than pulled.

Tension

Under some circumstances, collar ties can be in tension (pulled). Collar ties can help prevent rafter spread. However, that is not their primary function and they are not ideally located to perform this task.

Location

Collar ties are ideally half way up the rafter span. You get the most benefit from collar ties by making the rafter spans equal on either side of the collar tie. If the collar tie is close to the peak, the span of the rafter below the collar tie is much longer than the rafter span above the collar tie. This means that the long rafter span on the lower section might still sag.

Similarly, putting the collar tie close to the bottom leaves a long rafter span from the peak down to the collar tie.

Mid-span Is Best

If you put the collar tie in the middle, you end up with equal and short rafter spans. This is the ideal location for collar ties. If the goal were to have the collar tie in tension, keeping the rafters from spreading, the ideal location would be at the bottom of the rafters. This task of tying the rafters together to prevent spread is often performed by ceiling joists. Ceiling joists are in tension when resisting rafter spread. While they look similar and are in a similar orientation, collar ties have a very different job than ceiling joists.

A collar tie performs the same task as a knee wall or a purlin. It keeps rafters from sagging. The collar tie uses the opposing rafters to prevent sagging whereas purlins and knee walls use the bearing walls or ceiling joists below to resist rafter sag.

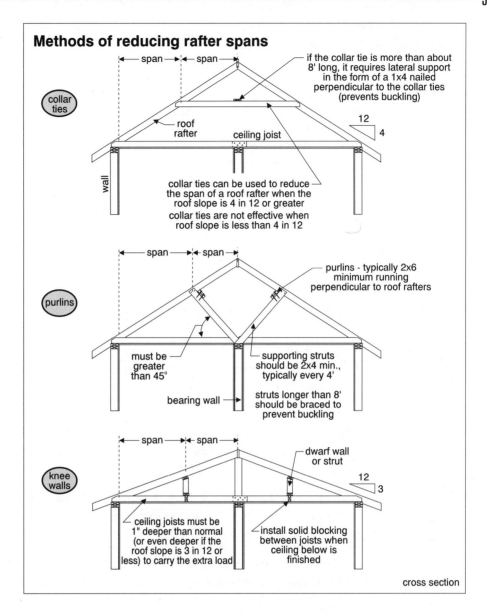

Methods of reducing rafter spans

collar ties

span — span

if the collar tie is more than about 8' long, it requires lateral support in the form of a 1x4 nailed perpendicular to the collar ties (prevents buckling)

roof rafter

ceiling joist

12
4

wall

collar ties can be used to reduce the span of a roof rafter when the roof slope is 4 in 12 or greater

collar ties are not effective when roof slope is less than 4 in 12

purlins

span — span

purlins - typically 2x6 minimum running perpendicular to roof rafters

must be greater than 45°

supporting struts should be 2x4 min., typically every 4'

bearing wall

struts longer than 8' should be braced to prevent buckling

knee walls

span — span

dwarf wall or strut

12
3

ceiling joists must be 1" deeper than normal (or even deeper if the roof slope is 3 in 12 or less) to carry the extra load

install solid blocking between joists when ceiling below is finished

cross section

Materials

As mentioned, the most common material for collar ties is a 2 by 4. Since the collar tie is a compression member, the mode of failure is **buckling**. The buckling will occur in the narrow dimension. A 1 by 8 is not nearly as good at resisting buckling as a 2 by 4. Generally, a 2 by 4 is the minimum size allowed for a collar tie.

Resisting Buckling

Longer collar ties are more susceptible to buckling. It's easier to push on each end of a yardstick and have it bend than push on each end of a 6 inch ruler and have it bend. If the collar tie is longer than 8 feet, lateral bracing should be provided near the midpoint. This is most often accomplished with 1 by 4's nailed across all the collar ties near their middle.

How Many Collar Ties Are Needed?   Collar ties are ideally provided on every rafter pair. Since we're doing a performance based inspection, we're not going to be worried about what the rules say, but whether they work.

Minimum Slope 4 in 12   Collar ties are only effective on steep roofs. If the slope is less than 4 in 12, collar ties are at too shallow an angle to the rafters to be effective.

4.1 CONDITIONS

Problems that you may encounter with collar ties include –

1. missing
2. buckling
3. rot or insect attack
4. mechanical damage or splitting
5. fire damage

Implication   The implication of missing or ineffective collar ties is sagging of the rafters.

4.1.1 MISSING

Causes   Collar ties may be missing because of –

1. original installation
2. renovations that remove the collar ties. Collar ties are often removed when attics are finished as living spaces and/or ceilings are converted from flat to cathedral

Strategy   The performance issue is whether or not the rafters are sagging. If there is no rafter sag, collar ties are not an issue. If the rafters are sagging, you might look to see whether collar ties have been removed.

You can also check the rafter span, size and spacing to get an idea whether the rafters need intermediate support, although this goes beyond the Standards of Practice.

4.1.2 BUCKLING

Causes   Buckling may be due to excess loads from such things as –

• too many layers of roofing material
• a replacement roofing material which is much heavier than the original
• drifting snow
• equipment on the roof
• heavy wind storms such as may be associated with hurricanes
• wrong sized lumber (1 by 10s don't make good collar ties)
• collar ties longer than 8 feet with no braces
• ties weakened due to rot, insect, mechanical damage or fire damage
• not enough collar ties.

Strategy   It should be easy to see buckling collar ties in the attic because they run right through the middle. However, you may only see the buckling collar ties during the winter, when the roof has a large live load. This is a problem that may be quite noticeable in the winter, but barely noticeable in the summer when the rafter rebounds as the load lightens. Sighting along collar ties is the best way to identify buckling.

4.1.3 ROT AND INSECT DAMAGE

We talked about this at the beginning of this section. Please refer back to 3.1.6.

4.1.4 MECHANICAL DAMAGE AND SPLITTING

This was discussed earlier. Please refer back to 3.1.7.

4.1.5 FIRE DAMAGE

This was discussed in 3.1.8. Please refer back to that section.

► 5.0 KNEE WALLS AND PURLINS

Function   **Knee walls** and **purlins** perform basically the same function as collar ties. They are designed to reduce the rafter span and prevent rafter sag. They carry the dead loads from the rafters, sheathing and roof covering down to the soil through walls, floors, foundations and footing systems. They also carry the live loads from wind, snow, water, equipment, foot traffic, etc.

Knee walls may also support interior finishes and insulation.

Knee Wall Materials   These walls are also called **dwarf walls**, **struts** or **strongbacks**. They are the same as conventional 2 by 4 stud walls elsewhere in the house. There is a top plate, studs and a bottom plate. Knee walls may be vertical or up to 45° off vertical. If offset, they are often called **struts** or **stongbacks**.

Single Top Plate   There is often a single top plate. This is okay if the studs line up with the rafters they are supporting. Think of knee walls as small bearing walls supporting rafters.

Purlin Materials   Purlins are 2 by 4s or 2 by 6s, typically. The purlin should be the same size as the rafter, at least. Think of purlins as small beams that run under the mid-point of all the rafters.

Purlin Posts   Purlins are supported by 2 by 4 posts or struts. If the purlins are 2 by 4s, the posts are usually every 4 feet. If the purlins are 2 by 6s, the posts are usually every six feet. If the posts are longer than 8 feet, they should be braced to prevent them from buckling. Purlin posts can also be up to 45° off vertical.

*What They
Rest On*

Knee walls and struts ideally rest on bearing walls. Sometimes they bear close to, but not directly on, bearing walls. Where the walls or posts rest on joists, the joists should be the next size larger than they otherwise would be.

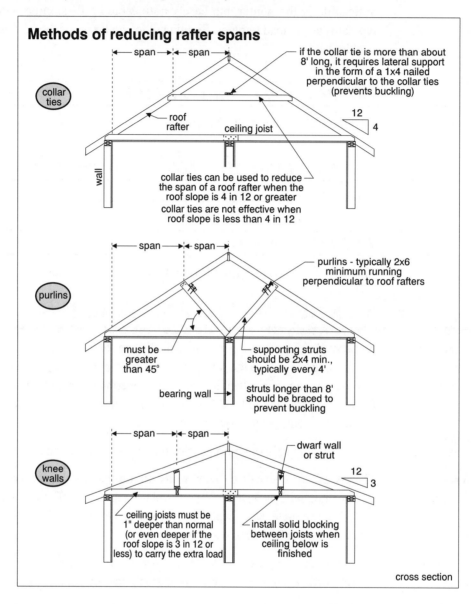

Methods of reducing rafter spans

collar ties

span — span

if the collar tie is more than about 8' long, it requires lateral support in the form of a 1x4 nailed perpendicular to the collar ties (prevents buckling)

roof rafter

ceiling joist

wall

12
4

collar ties can be used to reduce the span of a roof rafter when the roof slope is 4 in 12 or greater

collar ties are not effective when roof slope is less than 4 in 12

purlins

span — span

purlins - typically 2x6 minimum running perpendicular to roof rafters

must be greater than 45°

bearing wall

supporting struts should be 2x4 min., typically every 4'

struts longer than 8' should be braced to prevent buckling

knee walls

span — span

dwarf wall or strut

12
3

ceiling joists must be 1" deeper than normal (or even deeper if the roof slope is 3 in 12 or less) to carry the extra load

install solid blocking between joists when ceiling below is finished

cross section

The concentrated loads exerted by knee walls or purlins and posts may cause sagging and cracking of ceilings below. As mentioned earlier, when dealing with house structures, you have to think vertically. Follow loads up or down through the house from one floor to the next. You'll often be rewarded with a very clear explanation of a pattern of movement and/or cracks that has puzzled others.

5.1 CONDITIONS

Problems that are common with knee walls and purlins include –

1. knee walls or struts buckling, bowing or leaning
2. sagging rafters
3. sagging top plate
4. sagging purlins
5. weak connections
6. rot and insect attack
7. mechanical damage and splitting
8. fire damage

5.1.1 BUCKLING, BOWING OR LEANING

Studs in knee walls or struts (posts) supporting purlins may buckle, bow or lean because of –

1. excess load
2. overspanning (too tall and/or too slender), or
3. poor connections allowing slippage.

Strategy   Look at these vertical or near vertical members for bowing. Are they straight? Have they slipped out of position at the top or at the bottom? Were they originally vertical and no longer vertical?

Look for roof sag resulting from this movement.

5.1.2 SAGGING RAFTERS

Rafters may sag as a result of knee wall or purlin problems because –

1. the rafter span is too great
2. the knee wall or purlins are moving because the joists below them are deflecting
3. the knee walls or struts for the purlins may be bowing, buckling or leaning
4. the knee walls or struts may have slipped out of position

Strategy   From outside, watch for evidence of rafter sag. This can also be picked up inside from within the roof space. Sighting along the rafters can help although if significant, it should be visible from most angles.

Watch for ceiling cracks, especially below the bottom of knee walls or struts for purlins.

Check the connections for evidence of movement. Have the walls, posts or purlins shifted?

5.1.3 SAGGING TOP PLATE ON KNEE WALLS

Single top plates are common on knee walls. This is okay as long as the rafters line up with the studs below.

Cause A common cause of sagging top plates is failure to line up the rafters and the knee wall studs.

Strategy Sight along the top plate, looking for deflection. From the exterior of the building, a repeated sagging pattern might be noticed. It is easy to confuse this problem with sagging sheathing which we'll discuss later. Again, don't draw any conclusions until you've had a look inside the roof space.

5.1.4 SAGGING PURLINS

Purlins may sag because –

Causes
1. they are overspanned
2. they are undersized
3. they are seeing more load than was intended
4. they were installed on their side

Strategy A 2 by 6 purlin should be installed so that the rafters rest on the 2 inch surface of the purlin, not the 6 inch surface. Purlins laid flat to the underside of the rafters are less effective. If you think of floor joists (the purlin is like a floor joist) it's easy to see how the purlin is strong when the load presses against the edge but is weak when the load presses against the flat side. Think of a purlin as a yardstick. Which way is it easier to bend?

Again, the sagging purlins will show up as sagging rafters from the outside. Make sure your inspection includes a look both inside and out. When in the attic, look to see whether the rafters are sagging. If the sag is not there, but in the purlins (where the purlin spans from one post or strut to the next), the pattern will be different, although you may not pick it up from the outside.

Sight along the purlins as well as sighting along the rafters. This should tell you which are sagging.

5.1.5 WEAK CONNECTIONS

Causes   Weak connections may be caused by –

1. poor installation
2. rust of the fasteners
3. rot at the connections

Strategy   Check all visible connections for movement. Metal gusset plates may work loose or may not have been secured well originally. Watch for rotation of framing members. This may suggest weak connections.

5.1.6 ROT AND INSECT DAMAGE

We've talked about this in 3.1.6.

5.1.7 MECHANICAL DAMAGE OR SPLITTING

We talked about this in 3.1.7.

5.1.8 FIRE DAMAGE

We talked about this in 3.1.8.

Structure
MODULE

QUICK QUIZ 4

☑ INSTRUCTIONS

- You should finish reading Study Session 4 before doing this Quiz.
- Write your answers in the spaces provided.
- Check your answers against ours at the end of this Section.
- If you have trouble with this Quiz, re-read the Session and try the Quiz again.
- If you do well, move on to Field Exercise #1.

1. What is the main function of a collar tie?

   _____

   _____

2. What is the ideal location for a collar tie?

   _____

3. Why is lateral support required on long collar ties and how might this support be provided?

   _____

   _____

4. What is the minimum roof slope required for collar ties to be effective?

   _____

5. What is the difference between a knee wall and a purlin?

_____

_____

6. What can cause sagging of the top plate on a knee wall?

_____

_____

If you had no trouble with the Quiz, you are ready for Field Exercise 1.

Key Words:

- **Collar ties**
- **Knee walls**
- **Purlins**
- **Dwarf walls**
- **Struts**
- **Strongbacks**

Structure
MODULE

FIELD EXERCISE 1

☑ INSTRUCTIONS

You should complete everything up to Quick Quiz 4 before doing this Exercise.

In this Exercise you will inspect the roof structure of 8 to 10 houses. The roof structure must be rafters rather than trusses.

Allow yourself roughly 1/2 an hour for each house. You will need daylight.

For each house do A, B and C below.

Part A - Exterior Inspection

For this section you will be inspecting the roof from the exterior. Step back from the house and observe the roof plane. Look for rafter or ridge sag. Continue around the house and note irregularities in the roof structure such as rafter spreading.

Part B - Gaining Access

The next step is to gain access to the attic space. Identify all attic hatches. Open the hatch, being careful not to damage the finish. At this point, you have to decide whether you will enter the attic space or inspect the attic from the hatch. Is there clear access? Is there anything that would be dangerous about entering the attic? Is it possible that you could damage the house by entering the attic? Decide and document how you inspected the attic and why, if appropriate.

Part C - Interior Inspection

List all the structural components you can. Refer back to the Study Sessions if you see a component that you don't recognise.

Were you able to identify any problems discussed in the text? If so, make a list.

N.B.

As we discussed earlier, some ridge line sag is normal. After comparing many ridge lines you will be able to differentiate between normal sag and excessive sag. You should probably drive around the neighborhood and look quickly at many ridge lines to get a feel for this.

Now, let's go on to Study Session 5.

Structure
M O D U L E

STUDY SESSION 5

1. You should have finished Study Sessions 1 to 4 and Field Exercise 1, before starting this Session.

2. This Session covers roof trusses.

3. At the end of this session, you should –

   • Be able to identify different types of Trusses.
   • Know the functions of Trusses.
   • Know the basics of Truss construction.
   • Know the typical conditions encountered with Trusses.
   • Be able to identify problems involving Trusses.

4. This Session may take you 1 hour to complete.

5. Quick Quiz 5 is at the end of this section.

Key Words:

- *Trusses*
- *Gusset plates*
- *Chords*
- *Webs*
- *Fink truss*
- *Howe truss*
- *Bracing of compression webs*

- *Lateral support*
- *Sag*
- *Truss uplift*
- *Endbearing*
- *Notches and holes*

► 6.0 TRUSSES

Functions   The functions of trusses are the same as rafters, roof joists and ceiling joists.

These include –

1. supporting the dead loads, such as sheathing, roof coverings and roof-mounted equipment
2. supporting the live loads, including wind, snow, rain and people on the roof
3. supporting ceiling finishes and insulation
4. laterally supporting exterior walls
5. creating attic space and ventilation space
6. supporting soffits and fascia

Materials   The most common materials (and the only ones we'll be dealing with) are wood with metal or plywood **gusset plates**. Gusset plates are connectors that join chords and webs in trusses.

Chords   Trusses have top and bottom **chords** that form the perimeter triangle. There are typically two top chords and one bottom chord, although this can vary, depending on the truss. A parallel chord truss, for example, has one top and one bottom chord. A scissor truss, designed to create a cathedral ceiling, has two bottom chords and two top chords.

Roof sheathing is typically fastened to the top chords and ceiling finishes are typically attached to the bottom chords. These chords are typically made of 2 by 4s, 2 by 5s, or 2 by 6s.

Webs   **Webs** are the internal components of trusses. Webs typically run from the top chord to the bottom chord. They may be vertical or at an angle to the vertical. Some webs are in compression and others are in tension. It's not easy to visually determine which webs are being squeezed and which are being pulled.

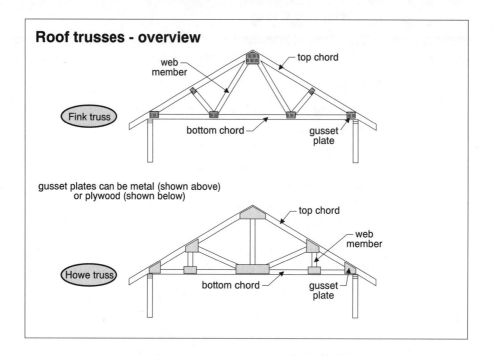

Roof trusses - overview

web member

top chord

(Fink truss)

bottom chord

gusset plate

gusset plates can be metal (shown above) or plywood (shown below)

top chord

web member

(Howe truss)

bottom chord

gusset plate

Bracing Of Compression Webs

The webs are wood members, often 2 by 3s or 2 by 4s. Tension webs are stretched stretched and are not inclined to buckle. Compression webs, however, are squeezed from either end and are prone to buckling. As a result, compression webs are often braced with 1 by 4s, running along several trusses. The braces are fastened to the midpoints of all the compression webs to prevent them from buckling. Many truss manufacturers staple paper signs to their trusses with the words "brace here" to help with proper assembly. You can see these signs and if there are no braces, you'll know something was left out.

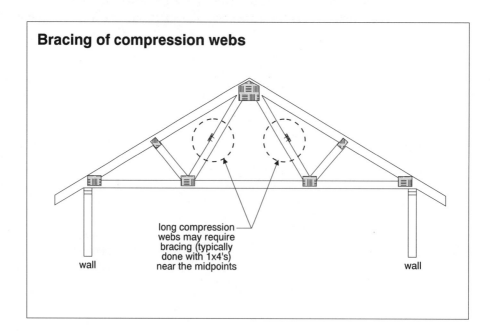

Bracing of compression webs

long compression webs may require bracing (typically done with 1x4's) near the midpoints

wall

wall

Trusses Need Lateral Support — Trusses require lateral support to prevent rotation or sideways movement. Diagonal bracing is often used during construction to keep the trusses in place until the sheathing and ceiling finishes are installed. The drywall below and plywood, waferboard, strand board or plank sheathing on top, provide adequate stiffening and lateral support for most trusses.

Spacing — It is common to find trusses spaced 24 inches on center. This has some implications for both sheathing and drywall. It's common to find that the sheathing sags

Sheathing Sag — between trusses. This is because –

1. the sheathing wasn't thick enough, or
2. the sheathing has been weakened, often by rot resulting from condensation.

Drywall Sag — Drywall ceilings often sag below trusses. This is often in part because the trusses are 24 inches on center. It's good practice to strap the undersides of trusses with 1 by 4s, every 16 inches. This allows the drywall to be fastened every 16 inches rather than every 24 inches.

Condensation Causes Drywall Sag — Another cause of drywall sag during winter construction is condensation. The polyethylene vapor retarder (barrier) is typically fastened to the underside of the truss and drywall ceilings are put up before the insulation is in place. The insulation can't be put in until the drywall ceiling is there to support it.

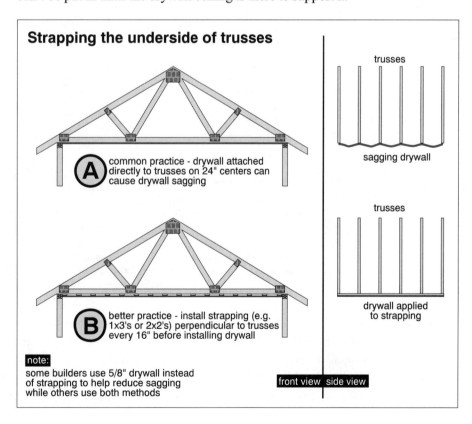

Strapping the underside of trusses

A common practice - drywall attached directly to trusses on 24" centers can cause drywall sagging

B better practice - install strapping (e.g. 1x3's or 2x2's) perpendicular to trusses every 16" before installing drywall

note: some builders use 5/8" drywall instead of strapping to help reduce sagging while others use both methods

trusses

sagging drywall

trusses

drywall applied to strapping

front view   side view

High
Humidity

The humidity level in buildings under construction is often very high, because of curing concrete, exhaust products from propane heaters, and moisture from drywall finishing activities. While the building temperature is usually kept above 50° to facilitate work, the attic area may be very cold. Before insulation is installed, the ceiling itself will also be cold.

Drywall
Gets Wet

The warm moist air in the house hitting the cold drywall and polyethylene vapor barrier above, often results in condensation. Moisture in the drywall causes it to sag between supports. The sag will be repetitive between the fasteners holding the drywall to the underside of the trusses or the strapping. Once the insulation is provided, the drywall becomes warm, and the problem does not reoccur. Sagging drywall ceilings are most often a cosmetic issue related to condensation resulting from winter construction, rather than an ongoing problem.

Shapes Of
Trusses

Several common truss shapes are illustrated below.

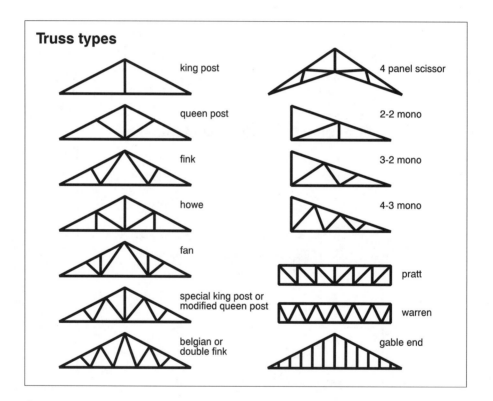

Truss types

king post

queen post

fink

howe

fan

special king post or
modified queen post

belgian or
double fink

4 panel scissor

2-2 mono

3-2 mono

4-3 mono

pratt

warren

gable end

Truss Spans
And Sizes

We can't tell in the field whether the spans are acceptable and whether the truss chords and webs are the right size. We have to rely on the designer. However, we can look at the performance of the truss. If there is movement, we can describe that, without knowing whether it's a design problem or some other difficulty. As in most areas, we identify non-performance rather than analyze the design.

6.1 CONDITIONS

Common truss problems include –

1. sag
2. truss uplift
3. buckled webs
4. weak connectors
5. rotation or lateral movement
6. poor end bearing
7. notches and holes
8. rot or insect damage
9. mechanical damage or splitting
10. fire damage

6.1.1 TRUSS SAG

Causes   Truss sag is usually caused by –

1. excessive loads
2. overspanning
3. weak connectors
4. cut or damaged webs or chords

Strategy   When looking at roof framing, be careful not to confuse truss sag with sheathing sag. The sagging of sheathing creates a repetitive wave pattern across the roof. A sagging truss will more often show up as a large dish in the roof.

Snow Drifting   As we've talked about before, you have to look inside and out. One of the common
On The   problem areas in truss roofs is where a higher roof is adjacent to a lower level roof.
Lower Roof   In snowy areas, snow will drift on the lower roof adjacent to a wall extending above the roof. The concentrated load created by this drifting snow may cause sagging or even break truss members in this area. Your roofing inspection should include a careful look at lower roof areas adjacent to higher parts of the building.

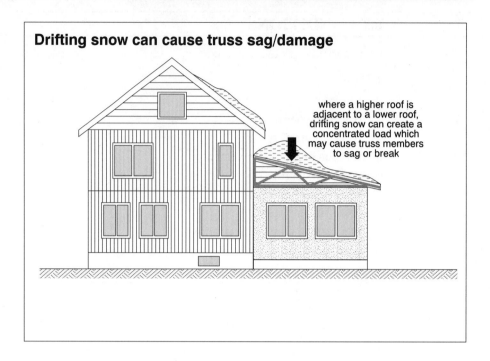

Drifting snow can cause truss sag/damage

where a higher roof is adjacent to a lower roof, drifting snow can create a concentrated load which may cause truss members to sag or break

6.1.2 TRUSS UPLIFT

Truss uplift is a cold weather problem that is not terribly serious from a structural standpoint, but is very disturbing to homeowners and can cause considerable cosmetic disruption.

Occurs In Winter In Cold Climates

Truss uplift occurs in the winter only. It occurs because the bottom chord of the truss arches up. The ends of the bottom chord rest on the outside wall, but the center portion rises. This usually creates a gap between the top of interior partitions near the center of the house and the ceiling. This gap can be well over an inch. In some cases, the partition wall is rigidly attached to the bottom chord of the trusses. In this case, the partition wall may be pulled up and a gap may appear between the bottom of the wall and the floor!

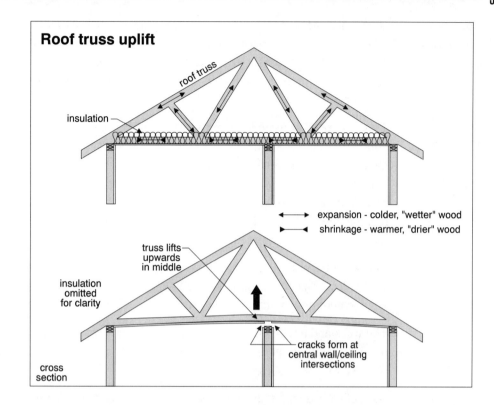

Roof truss uplift

roof truss

insulation

expansion - colder, "wetter" wood
shrinkage - warmer, "drier" wood

truss lifts
upwards
in middle

insulation
omitted
for clarity

cracks form at
central wall/ceiling
intersections

cross
section

Don't *Mistake It* *For Sagging* *Walls Or Floors*	These gaps always look like the wall is dropping (if the gap is at the wall ceiling intersection), or like the floor is dropping (if the gap appears at the wall/floor intersection). This is because we are prisoners of gravity, and think that all movement in a vertical plane is down. In this case, however, the movement is up. Either the ceiling is lifting off the wall or the wall is lifting off the floor. Close examination and perhaps a mason's level will allow you to verify this.
Causes	The cause of truss uplift is not perfectly understood. The explanation that makes the most sense to us goes like this.
Different *Temperatures*	The cause of the bottom chord arching up is thought to be related to the differential moisture content of the wood framing members in the truss. Let's look at the different environments the truss components see. In cold climates, the bottom chord of the truss is surrounded by insulation. As a result, it is kept relatively warm. The majority of the webs and the top chords are above the insulation and are in a much colder environment. But temperature differences alone do not explain truss uplift.
Relative *Humidity* *Is Key*	**Relative humidity** is an indication of the amount of moisture in the air relative to the amount the air could possibly hold when it is saturated. Warm air can hold a lot more moisture than cold air. If you take a bundle of air at 70°F and 40% relative humidity, and heat it up, the relative humidity will drop. The amount of moisture in the air stays the same. However, the air is capable of holding much more moisture; so at 90°F, the relative humidity might be only 20%.

Cooling The Air Causes Condensation

If you take the same bundle of 70° air at 40% relative humidity and cool it, the relative humidity increases. For example, if you drop the air temperature to about 40°, the relative humidity approaches 100% and you may get condensation. We haven't added moisture to the air. Simply cooling the air has changed the relative humidity.

Wood Reacts To Relative Humidity

This is important in understanding truss uplift because wood reacts to relative humidity not the absolute humidity, which is a measure of the actual moisture in the air. If the relative humidity is low, no matter what the temperature, wood will not tend to draw moisture out of the air. As a matter of fact, moisture will leave the wood and the wood will become dryer. If the wood is surrounded by air with a high relative humidity, moisture will travel from the air into the wood. Now let's look at our attic environment.

The bottom chord is in a warm environment. This means that the relative humidity will be low. The air surrounding the bottom chord might be close to 70° and the relative humidity might be 30 to 40%.

The webs and top chords are in a much colder environment, with a much higher relative humidity - perhaps 80%, for example. To put the whole picture together, we need to look at one other thing.

Wood Expands When Wet

Most of us are comfortable with the concept that wood swells. From the discussion, it's easy to see that the top chords and webs are going to see more moisture than the bottom chord. As a result, the top chords will get longer. They are tightly pinned at the bottom corners. The top chords get longer and the peak of the roof rises slightly. This pulls the webs up and they pull up on the bottom chord. The bottom chord can't rise at the wall corners because it's fixed at the outer edges. As a result, it lifts in the middle. As we discussed, it may lift off the partition walls in the middle of the building, or may lift the partition walls off the floor.

It's A Cyclical Problem

Truss uplift occurs in the winter. As the attic environment changes in the warmer months, truss uplift will reverse and the truss will settle back down. The problem repeats itself every winter and corrects itself every summer. The amount of truss uplift may vary depending on weather severity.

Which Trusses Are More Likely To Suffer Uplift?

Trusses with longer spans and lower slopes are more likely to suffer. Trusses in well insulated attics are more likely to lift.

Corrective Action

We can't prevent truss uplift. The more tightly we secure partitions to the bottom chord, the more the house is picked up.

The solutions lie in concealing the movement. One approach is to use a molding attached to the ceiling, but not to the partitions. As the ceiling is lifted up during truss uplift, the molding simply slides up the wall. This is sometimes successful in masking cosmetic deficiencies, although the moldings will sometimes scratch the wall surfaces, or the raised moldings will reveal paint of a different color or bare spots on wallpapered sections of the wall.

A more recent solution is to allow the ceiling drywall near the center partitions to float. The drywall is not attached to the trusses within roughly 18 inches of the partition walls. The edge of the ceiling drywall is secured to the wall with a 1 by 6 attached to the top plate, or a drywall clip fastened to the top of the wall. When the truss lifts, the edge of the ceiling drywall stays in place since it's not attached to the bottom chord near the partitions. The drywall bends up over 18 inches to the point where it's attached to the trusses.

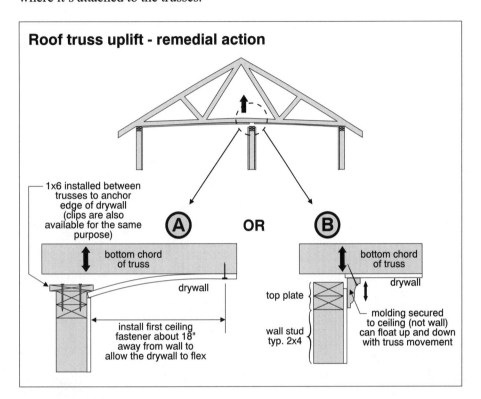

Roof truss uplift - remedial action

1x6 installed between trusses to anchor edge of drywall (clips are also available for the same purpose)

(A) OR (B)

bottom chord of truss

drywall

install first ceiling fastener about 18" away from wall to allow the drywall to flex

top plate

wall stud typ. 2x4

bottom chord of truss

drywall

molding secured to ceiling (not wall) can float up and down with truss movement

Strategy

When looking at truss roofs, understand that their advantage is their long uninterrupted spans and no need for interior bearing walls, but watch for the uplift problem particularly at interior partitions near the center of the truss span. Truss uplift is much easier to see in the winter, when the trusses have moved, than in the summer, when they have relaxed.

Look for gaps or evidence of movement at the wall/ceiling intersection and the wall/floor intersection. When you're in the attic, you can look for evidence of floating ceiling drywall near the center partitions. You'll have to remove some insulation to get a look at this.

Trusses most likely to lift are those with long spans, low-slopes and lots of insulation in the attic. Again, once you recognize the problem, you can set your client's mind at ease because it is not a serious structural issue. However, if you fail to identify it, you can expect a frantic phone call during the winter.

6.1.3 BUCKLED WEBS

Causes

Buckled truss webs may be a result of

1. missing braces on long compression webs
2. braces not well connected to compression webs
3. damaged compression webs
4. concentrated loads that exceed the strength of the trusses

Strategy

When looking at trusses, pay attention to all interior webs. You won't necessarily know which are in compression and which are in tension, but look for buckling, bending and poor connections.

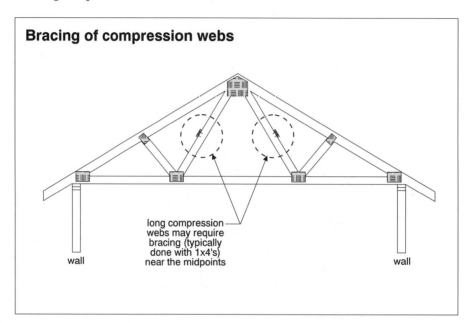

Bracing of compression webs

long compression webs may require bracing (typically done with 1x4's) near the midpoints

wall   wall

6.1.4 WEAK CONNECTIONS

Weak truss connections are a fairly common problem. It may be caused by –

1. gusset plates or connectors missing
2. connectors not applied in the right location
3. connectors not fully seated because of
   a. poor original assembly
   b. rough handling
   c. warping wood
   d. rotational or movement of truss components, due to racking
4. rusted connectors
5. rotted wood
6. cut, damaged or split wood at the connectors

While you may not get a look at all the connectors, this should be part of your focus when looking at trusses. Are the connectors in place, are they well secured? Is there evidence of slippage? Again, the more insulation you're willing to pull away, the more connections you'll see.

Most inspectors do not do a 100% inspection and do not pull a great deal of insulation away. Removing insulation to look at connectors goes beyond the ASHI® Standards.

6.1.5 ROTATION OR LATERAL MOVEMENT

This problem is most common during construction. Once ceiling finishes and sheathing are in place, it is unusual for trusses to move.

Cause   The cause of rotation or lateral movement is usually lack of support during construction.

Strategy   Look at the spacing of trusses. Is it the same between each pair of trusses? Is the spacing the same from top to bottom?

Multi-level Roofs   Rotation or lateral movement can be a problem in multi-level homes after the ceilings and roof sheathing are in place. Where one roof overlaps another, it is common not to sheath the underlying roof trusses. These trusses should be laterally braced. They often are missing this bracing.

6.1.6 POOR ENDBEARING

At the ends of trusses, the top and bottom chords meet. Trusses should rest on walls so that the top and bottom chord transmit their loads directly to the wall. If the truss is too far outboard, the bottom chord will sit on the wall, but the top chord will rest on the bottom chord out beyond the wall. This is not a desirable situation.

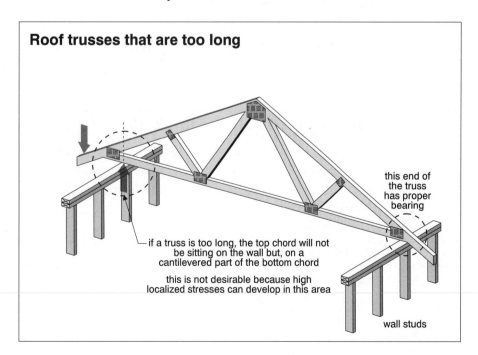

Roof trusses that are too long

this end of the truss has proper bearing

if a truss is too long, the top chord will not be sitting on the wall but, on a cantilevered part of the bottom chord

this is not desirable because high localized stresses can develop in this area

wall studs

Since trusses usually extend out beyond the walls, trusses too short to bear on the full wall plate are unusual.

*Parallel
Chord
Trusses*

Trusses may be supported by metal hangers, although this is not common. Parallel chord trusses are common on flat and cathedral roofs. Some trusses are designed to bear on their top chord. Some are designed to bear on their bottom chord. It's a mistake to install trusses upside down. You won't be able to tell by looking, other than to see signs of distress near the truss ends. There may be crushing, pulling apart, or bending of truss components.

Strategy

In most cases, you'll have a difficult time looking at the endbearing of trusses because they'll be surrounded by insulation, and they'll be out at the eaves of the roof where access is difficult. With flat and cathedral roofs, you may not see the trusses at all. Remember to document what you could and could not see.

6.1.7 NOTCHES AND HOLES

Notches and holes are not permitted in trusses unless the design allowed for them. This would be unusual.

Causes

Notches and holes are made by people working in the roof space.

Strategy

Wherever you see holes or notches in truss members (chords or webs), write this up for further evaluation. Simple sistering or other repairs common with joists and rafters may not work with trusses. It's possible that the truss design allowed for this, but you have no way of knowing.

Where members have been notched or drilled, look for evidence of movement indicating distress. Where you see buckling or sagging, you can be sure that the design did not contemplate these.

6.1.8 ROT AND INSECT DAMAGE

We've talked about this under 3.1.6.

6.1.9 MECHANICAL DAMAGE OR SPLITTING

We've talked about this under 3.1.7. Watch for trusses cut where they meet chimneys, vents or stacks. Field cutting and re-supporting often creates weaknesses and stress concentrations the designer didn't anticipate. When in doubt, recommend further evaluation.

6.1.10 FIRE DAMAGE

We've talked about this under 3.1.8.

Structure
M O D U L E

QUICK QUIZ 5

☑ INSTRUCTIONS

- You should finish reading Session 5 before doing this Quiz.

- Write your answers in the spaces provided.

- Check your answers against ours at the end of this Section.

- If you have trouble with this Quiz, re-read the Session and try the Quiz again.

- If you do well, it is time for Study Session 6.

1. On a roof truss, what is the difference between a chord and a web?

   _____

   _____

2. Why is it common to find sagging of roof sheathing on trusses.

   _____

3. Give 2 possible causes of truss sag.

   _____

   _____

4. On a house that has a truss roof structure, if you see a gap at the top of a partition wall between the wall and the ceiling, what might you suspect?

   _____

   _____

5. Why might a drywall ceiling sag below trusses?

_____

_____

6. There are many different kinds of trusses. List as many as you can.

_____

_____

_____

_____

_____

_____

_____

7. What is a common solution for truss uplift?

_____

_____

_____

8. Where are notches and holes commonly permitted in trusses?
Webs ☐   Chords ☐   Neither ☐

If you had no trouble with the Quiz, you are ready for Study Session 6.

Key Words:

- **Trusses**
- **Gusset plates**
- **Chords**
- **Webs**
- **Fink truss**
- **Howe truss**
- **Bracing of compression webs**

- **Lateral support**
- **Sag**
- **Truss uplift**
- **Endbearing**
- **Notches and holes**

Structure
M O D U L E

STUDY SESSION 6

1. You should have completed Study Session 5 before starting this Session.

2. This Session covers engineered wood roof systems.

3. At the end of this session, you should be able to –

- Identify a Wood "I" Joist.
- Know the basis of "I" Joist construction.
- Know the common conditions found with Wood "I" Joists.
- Identify typical conditions with "I" Joists.
- Know the function of Sheathing.
- Identify types of Sheathing.
- Identify common Sheathing conditions.

4. This Session may take you half an hour.

5. Quiz 6 and Field Exercise #2 are at the end of this Session.

Key Words:
- *Wood I Joists*
- *Bird's mouths*
- *Toe bearing*
- *Ridge beam*
- *Panel type roof sheathing*
- *Plank type roof sheathing*
- *Edge support for sheathing panels*
- *H clips*
- *Tongue and groove*
- *FRT plywood*
- *Delaminated plywood*

► 7.0 WOOD "I" JOISTS

Wood "I" joists are one example of an engineered wood system. There are several, but since wood I's are common, we'll mention some of the issues associated.

Function   These joists perform the same functions as rafters, roof joists and ceiling joists.

Materials   These "I" joists typically have solid lumber or laminated veneer lumber (LVL) top and bottom chords. The webs are typically plywood, waferboard, OSB (oriented *Engineered* strandboard), or metal. These systems are typically bottom bearing and can be *Systems* installed upside down or right side up. They typically require at least 1¾ inches of endbearing. There are several bearing details that may be appropriate. When used in a rafter type orientation, they cannot simply butt against an opposing "I" joist at the peak. They must rest on or against a ridge beam. Metal hangers are appropriate supports.

7.1 CONDITIONS

Some of the common problems on wood "I" joists used in roof framing include –

1. bird's mouths
2. toe bearing
3. no ridge beam

7.1.1 BIRD'S MOUTHS

While rafters can rest on bird's mouths as long as they bear on the heel, wood "I" joists cannot have bird's mouth cuts. Notching the bottom plate considerably weakens the joists.

Strategy   Watch for notched bottom chords and bird's mouth cuts.

7.1.2 TOE BEARING

The bottom edge of wood "I" joists must be supported at either end. Joists cannot be hung from the top chord only. It is not appropriate to notch the end of the joist so that some of the web and the top plate only rest on the bearing surface.

Strategy   Watch for "I" joists that bear on their toes at either the top or bottom.

7.1.3 NO RIDGE BEAM

Wood "I" joists must rest on a wall or a ridge beam. They cannot lean against each other at the peak the way rafters can. This is an installation issue.

Strategy Check that there is a ridge beam present.

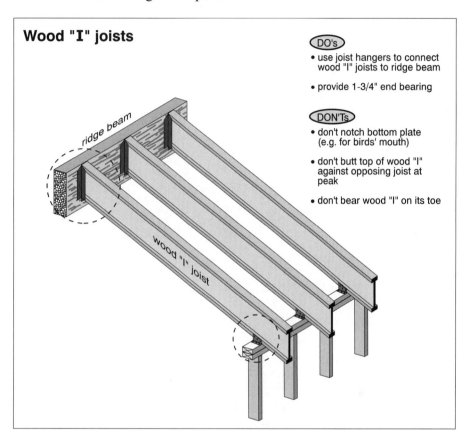

Wood "I" joists

DO's
- use joist hangers to connect wood "I" joists to ridge beam
- provide 1-3/4" end bearing

DON'Ts
- don't notch bottom plate (e.g. for birds' mouth)
- don't butt top of wood "I" against opposing joist at peak
- don't bear wood "I" on its toe

ridge beam

wood "I" joist

► 8.0 ROOF SHEATHING

Functions Sheathing is designed to carry the dead load from the roof covering and roof-mounted equipment to rafters, roof joists or trusses.

Sheathing carries the live loads from wind, water, snow and people to roof framing members.

Sheathing provides lateral bracing for roof framing members, including rafters, roof joists and trusses. Sheathing often provides a nailing surface for roof coverings.

Materials Wood plank roof sheathing is typically 1 by 4, 1 by 6 or 1 by 8. Joints may be butted or tongue-and-grooved. If tongue-and-grooved, the tongues should face up the roof and the tongues should face down, so water doesn't collect in the grooves.

Plank roofing may be solid or spaced. Spaced sheathing is common with wood, slate, tile and concrete roof coverings, for example. Asphalt shingles need solid sheathing.

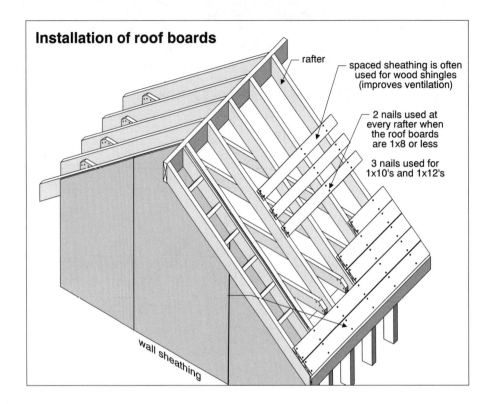

Installation of roof boards

rafter

spaced sheathing is often used for wood shingles (improves ventilation)

2 nails used at every rafter when the roof boards are 1x8 or less

3 nails used for 1x10's and 1x12's

wall sheathing

Plywood roof sheathing, typically in 4ft. by 8ft. sheets, is common. Thicknesses range from $\frac{3}{8}$ to $\frac{3}{4}$ inch. Plywood roof sheathing should be installed with the long dimension perpendicular to rafters or trusses (the long dimension is laid across the roof.)

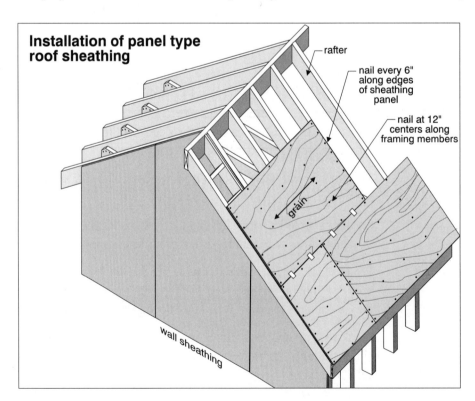

Installation of panel type roof sheathing

rafter

nail every 6" along edges of sheathing panel

nail at 12" centers along framing members

grain

wall sheathing

Waferboard and OSB are also typically laid in 4 by 8 sheets across the roof. Thicknesses are similar to plywood, but vary with load, span, roof covering material, etc.

Like
Subflooring
On Flat Roofs

Sheathing on flat roofs is usually thicker than sloped roofs because the snow loads and or water loads may be greater. The thickness and strength of sheathing for flat roofs is often the same as subflooring.

No Sheathing
Necessary

In some situations, sheathing is not used. Where the roof covering is concrete tile, some manufacturers recommend a wood batten system without sheathing. Battens are typically 2 inch by 2 inch. There is often a moisture barrier (plastic sheet) laid on top of the rafters to collect and drain any water that may make it through the roof coverings. The tiles are often hung on the battens and may also be nailed, screwed, clipped or wire tied to battens.

Where there is no sheathing, the possibility of lateral movement and rotation of individual wood members is greater. The battens do not provide as much lateral support as planking or plywood sheathing.

Edge Support
For Panel
Sheathing

Plywood waferboard and OSB requires support at all edges unless they are very thick. Local construction guides and codes spell out when edge support is needed. Most panel sheathing rests on the rafters or trusses at either end and/or intermediate supports. At top and bottom edges, support may be provided by –

1. "H" clips (see illustration)
2. 2 by 2 blocking
3. tongue and groove joints in the panels

Gaps Between
Panels

Gaps of roughly $\frac{1}{8}$ inch should be provided between each panel to allow sheathing to expand without buckling.

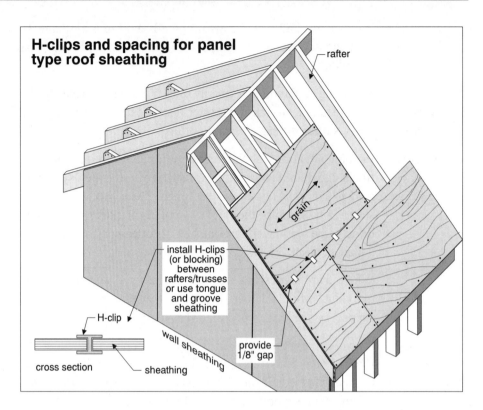

H-clips and spacing for panel type roof sheathing

- rafter
- grain
- install H-clips (or blocking) between rafters/trusses or use tongue and groove sheathing
- H-clip
- cross section
- sheathing
- wall sheathing
- provide 1/8" gap

Waferboard And OSB

We've talked about the differences between waferboard and oriented strandboard. Waferboard is made up of randomly oriented wood wafers or chips. Oriented strandboard may be of different types, but the grain of the wafers or strands is oriented at least through part of the panel. In the strongest type of oriented strandboard, the strands in all plies are oriented. In a somewhat weaker version, the strands in the top and bottom layers only are oriented. Interior layers have randomly oriented strands.

Vertical Joints Staggered

In both plank and panel sheathing, vertical joints should not run continuously up one rafter or one truss. Adjacent vertical joints should be staggered to improve the strength.

Sheathing Spans

Many older buildings had rafters spaced at 16 inches on center. Many modern homes have trusses spaced at 24 inches on center. Although many authorities have allowed $^3/_8$ inch plywood and $^7/_{16}$ inch waferboard on trusses spaced 24 inches on center, sheathing often sagged between trusses. This common problem may be cosmetic only, or it may get to a point where failure is a possibility. In this case, corrective action is taken. The most common corrective action is to replace or overlay the sagging sheathing with a thicker sheathing. A less common solution is to provide intermediate supports under the sheathing, working from inside the attic.

FRT Plywood   **Fire Retardant Treated plywood** has been used since the late 1970s, often on attached homes (row or town homes) rather than detached homes. It was used to replace more expensive parapet walls extending through the roofs at party walls where fire-stopping was needed between dwellings. In many areas, the plywood was required 4 feet out from the party wall on either side of the roof. It was frequently, but not always, installed in this location.

How It Works   Chemicals in the wood are designed to char the wood at relatively low temperatures (typically in the early stages of a fire). This charring raises the auto-ignition temperature of the wood. This will help control the spread of a fire. The charring of the wood weakens it, but in a fire situation, this is a secondary issue.

With some types of FRT plywood, the chemicals were activated at excessively low temperatures, (around 150°F) commonly reached in attics. As a result, the wood was weakened even though there was no fire situation.

Implications   The weakened FRT plywood often loses its ability to hold staples. Roof shingles can be blown off in relatively low winds. The sheathing may sag and/or delaminate and can be weak enough that someone walking on the roof could fall through.

Let's look at common sheathing conditions, including those associated with FRT plywood.

8.1 CONDITIONS

Common sheathing problems include –

1. Sag,
2. buckled,
3. delaminated,
4. deteriorated FRT plywood,
5. rot and insect damage,
6. mechanical damage and splitting, and
7. fire damage.

8.1.1 SAGGING SHEATHING

Causes   Sagging sheathing may be caused by –

1. overspanning
2. excess loads (either widespread or concentrated)
3. deteriorated wood (due to rot, fire or FRT deterioration)
4. panel type sheathing installed in the wrong orientation
5. inadequate edge support

Strategy   Be careful with flat and cathedral roofs. Walk carefully on these and pay attention to how spongy they are, whether or not sag is visible. These roofs are much more prone to rot problems, due to condensation caused by a lack of ventilation.

From the outside, look for a wavy pattern across the surface of the roof. From inside, check the sheathing between rafters or trusses.

8.1.2 BUCKLED PLYWOOD, WAFERBOARD, OR OSB

Causes   This is caused by panels being tightly butted together on original installation. No allowance was made for expansion, due to moisture.

Strategy   Look for panels that are crushed slightly at the edges. They may be buckled up or down. This may be a greater problem where there is more moisture, but can occur in any roof.

8.1.3 DELAMINATED PLYWOOD

Causes   This problem of the plies coming apart may be caused by –

1.   poor quality material
2.   rot and/or moisture
3.   deteriorated FRT plywood

Strategy   Again, this is a problem that is often (but not always) associated with flat or cathedral roofs. In conventional attics, it may also be found where there is poor venting, good insulation and lots of moist air leaking into the attic.

8.1.4 DETERIORATED FRT PLYWOOD

Cause   As discussed earlier, the chemical reaction causes the charring and weakening of the plywood, due to normal attic temperatures.

Strategy   Sometimes there are labels (stamps) on the plywood that are visible from the attic that identify it as FRT plywood. However, these may not be visible.

While this plywood is rarely found in detached houses, it is common in town or row houses built in the 1970s and 80s. The FRT plywood may be near the party walls, but you should look at all the sheathing.

Look for evidence of roofing nails or staples that have come loose. Look for delaminating plywood. Look for darkened color on the underside of the plywood. This may look like mold or mildew. Look for white dust. These are the salts of the chemicals, creating a type of efflorescence.

8.1.5 ROT AND INSECT DAMAGE

We talked about this in 3.1.6.

8.1.6 MECHANICAL DAMAGE OR SPLITTING

We talked about this in 3.1.7.

8.1.7 FIRE DAMAGE

We talked about this in 3.1.8 on page 43.

► 9.0 SEISMIC AND WIND RESISTANCE

Earthquakes and hurricanes are significant problems in some parts of North America. Earthquake risks are highest in California, Nevada, Alaska, Hawaii and Puerto Rico. Hurricane risks are greatest in the southeastern USA.

Similar Problems
Earthquake and hurricane forces are different, but similar in some ways. We'll look at earthquake issues first, then discuss wind problems. Our discussions are introductory and there is much more information available. Those of you who inspect in vulnerable areas have strong motives to develop your knowledge beyond this discussion.

9.1 EARTHQUAKE

Goal
The goal is to have a home stay in place during an earthquake. One code body states the goal as having homes sustain damage that can be repaired in the event of minor or moderate quakes, and remain standing long enough to allow occupants to get out during a major quake. An earthquake of over 7.5 on the Richter scale is a major quake.

House As A Unit
During an earthquake, the house should act as a unit, with the foundations, floors, walls, and roof moving together. Problems arise when these move independently of each other.

Risk Factor
Unreinforced masonry buildings and structures are more vulnerable to earthquake damage than wood frame homes. Wood frame homes with **shearwalls** are better than ordinary wood frame buildings. Homes with the structural components tied together and tied to the foundation are better than conventionally framed houses. Single story homes are better than two story homes.

Common Problems
Failure modes during quakes typically include –

• Posts moving off piers
• Beams moving off posts
• Cripple walls falling off foundations
• Masonry chimneys collapsing

Two Strategies The two critical strategies in reducing earthquake damage are –

• tying the house structural components together and
• using **shearwalls** to minimize racking of the structure.

Tying Homes Together

Special fasteners are used, both during new construction and in upgrading existing homes. The hardware includes **sill anchors** (mechanical wedge-type in retrofit situations), hangers, **hold downs (tie downs)**, **post caps**, straps and **hurricane clips (hurricane ties)**. Wood members can also be used to tie components together.

Securement The fasteners may be nailed, bolted or embedded in concrete. Engineers, manufacturers and designers have differing opinions about the type, size, location and number of fasteners required in any situation. The goal is to tie the building together to prevent lateral movement or overturning. The sills should be tied to foundations or floor slabs, posts should be tied to piers, beams should be tied to posts, floors should be tied to sills, walls should be tied to floors and sills, and roofs should be tied to walls.

Bracing Posts Adjacent posts in sub-grade areas may be supported with 2 by 4 diagonal braces to help resist lateral forces.

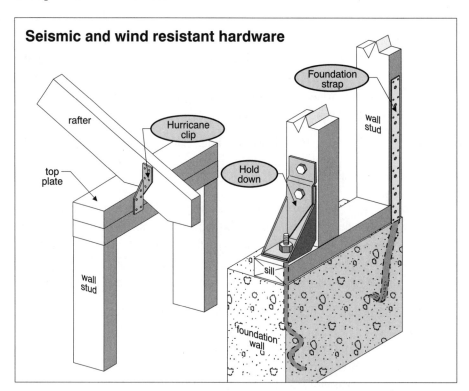

Shearwalls

Shearwalls help wood frame walls resist racking due to the strong lateral forces that occur during earthquakes. Shearwalls are typically $3/8$ to $1/2$ inch plywood or waferboard. They must extend the full height of the wall to be effective. Doors and windows interrupt shearwalls.

Exterior Walls   Shearwalls are typically the exterior walls of a wood frame home. Some interior walls on large homes may also be shearwalls.

Details   The plywood or waferboard panels may be installed on the inner or outer faces of stud walls. They are not needed on both. The panels are installed vertically, except on cripple walls less than four feet tall. Gaps of roughly 1/8 inch are left around all edges of panels to allow for expansion due to changes in moisture content. Without these gaps, the panels may buckle when they swell.

Securement   Panel edges are nailed every 4 to 6 inches, depending on the designer and the situation, and every 12 inches in the field of the panels. All four edges of panels must rest on something solid such as sills, studs, rim joists, top plates or blocking.

Hold Downs   **Hold downs** are provided at each corner of the home and at each end of every shearwall. Hold downs are heavy L-shaped brackets that secure the shearwall to the foundation. Hold downs are usually secured with bolts.

Cripple Walls   **Cripple walls** are short wood frame walls that span from the foundation to the first floor. They are vulnerable to earthquakes because they have little resistance to lateral forces. Cripple walls can be converted to shearwalls from the inside by adding plywood or waferboard panels to the studs. Stud spaces are typically vented into the sub-grade area with $1/2$ inch diameter holes at the top and bottom of each stud cavity.

Other earthquake protection

Strap Appliances Down   Heavy appliances such as water heaters, furnaces, refrigerators, washing machines and stoves may be strapped to the building to keep them in place.

Special Gas Valves   Gas valves that shut off automatically if the gas line ruptures can be provided near the gas meter in earthquake prone areas.

Chimneys   Unreinforced masonry chimneys are common on old homes and there is no easy way to improve their resistance to earthquake. Some people put $3/4$ inch plywood on attic floors to prevent bricks falling off chimneys from coming through ceilings into the home.

9.1.1 CONDITIONS

Earthquake resistance is a regional issue, and is handled differently from place to place. You should become familiar with accepted good practice in your area for both new and existing homes. You may not want to write up a lack of earthquake resistant features as defects, but may prefer to describe them as improvements that can be made. The issues you raise may include the following –

1. Fasteners   - missing
               - incomplete
               - ineffective
               - suspect

2. Shearwalls   - missing
               - incomplete
               - ineffective
               - suspect

Causes

Fastener or shearwall deficiencies may be the result of original construction or improper installation of retrofit systems.

Implications

The implications are higher risk of damage to or collapse of the home during earthquakes.

Strategy

The first step is to research your area to determine widely accepted good practice. As you perform your inspection, you may be able to find fasteners in several places and you may see shearwall panels on cripple walls. A visual inspection however, will not usually give you enough information to be conclusive about the work. Don't go out on a limb.

You may be able to tell the client you saw no evidence of earthquake protection work, some amateurish evidence, or some evidence of good work. You may recommend that the client take measures to improve protection or further evaluate the earthquake resistance of the home.

9.2 HURRICANES

Earthquakes impose lateral forces on homes, for the most part. Hurricanes also exert lateral forces, but also impose uplift forces. While similar to earthquakes in many respects, hurricanes and other high winds present separate problems.

Regional Issue

Hurricanes are regional issues, and there are other wind-related problems such as twisters and tornadoes that are also somewhat regional. We'll focus on hurricanes in this discussion. The southeastern United States is the most prominent hurricane area in North America. Several devastating hurricanes have occurred in this area over the last 10 years and building officials, insurance companies, builders and homeowners have all started to look at homes differently as a result.

Key Issues Considerable investigation and research has been done after these hurricanes, and much has been learned about the mechanisms of failure. Hurricanes usually carry heavy rains and much of the damage from hurricanes is caused by water. Wind is not the only issue, but often creates the openings that allow water into homes. Many believe the three key issues in hurricane resistance for homes are –

• The roof sheathing must be well secured to the roof framing
• The roof framing must be well secured to the walls
• Openings like doors and windows must be protected from flying debris

Deck Nailing Roof sheathing should be nailed at 6 inch centers along panel edges and at 12 inch centers in the field. Sheathing at overhangs is often nailed at 4 inch centers because wind forces can be greater here.

Hurricane Clips Hurricane clips or straps are used to secure roof framing to walls. Straps are also used to fasten wall top plates to the walls themselves.

Openings Openings can be protected through special impact resistant windows, or shutters, plywood covers or some other shielding protection on the outside.

Roof Bracing Truss roofs can be strengthened with wood braces on the webs and the chords. Gable end walls have proven vulnerable to hurricane winds, and can also be strengthened with braces in the attic.

Wind Resistant Shingles Asphalt shingles are often blown off roofs during hurricanes and other high winds. Manufacturers have been making efforts to increase the wind resistance of roofing materials. Some areas are calling for mopped-in underlayment beneath shingles where the risk of shingle loss is significant.

Concrete Tiles Concrete tiles have also blown off roofs in hurricanes. These are worse than composition shingles because the heavy tiles become dangerous projectiles. Improved installation techniques are being encouraged, including full and effective mortar beds for concrete tiles.

Hip Roofs Designers are being encouraged to move from gable roofs to hip roofs since hips are less likely to fail.

Garage Doors Garage doors have been a problem because they blow in easily. Stronger doors, hardware and tracks are a partial solution.

9.2.1 CONDITIONS

Since hurricanes are regional issues, and since building practices to resist hurricanes are changing, you will need to research good practices in your area. Learn what retrofits are recommended, and what changes are practical for existing homes. If you inspect new homes, you also need to stay current with accepted practices for new construction.

Problems, or improvement possibilities you may report include –

1. Bracing - missing
   - incomplete
   - ineffective
   - suspect

2. Framing fasteners - missing
   - incomplete
   - ineffective
   - suspect

3. Protection for openings - missing
   - incomplete
   - ineffective
   - suspect

Causes   The causes of these problems are original construction which did not address these issues or amateurish improvement efforts.

Implications   The implications of these problems is increased risk of damage or destruction during hurricanes.

Strategy   You will need to find out what the accepted good practices are and, to the extent possible, identify their presence or absence during the inspection. You probably won't be able to be conclusive. Don't guess. You may say you saw no evidence, some evidence or considerable evidence of hurricane protection measures, and may recommend work or further investigation. As with earthquake protection, you may choose to report these issues as potential improvements rather than deficiencies.

Structure
M O D U L E

QUICK QUIZ 6

☑ INSTRUCTIONS

• You should finish reading Study Session 6 before doing this Quiz.

• Write your answers in the spaces provided.

• Check your answers against ours at the end of this Section.

• If you have trouble with this Quiz, re-read the Session and try the Quiz again.

• If you do well, move on to Field Exercise 2.

1. What is the difference between a wood I-joist and traditional lumber?

_____

_____

2. It is acceptable to notch a bird's mouth into the bottom plate of an I-joist.

   True ☐   False ☐

3. Is it acceptable for wood I-joists to lean against each other at the peak the way rafters can?

_____

4. In both plank and panel roof sheathing, vertical joints should not run continuously up one rafter or one truss. Adjacent vertical joints should be staggered. Explain why.

_____

_____

5. Give three possible causes of sagging sheathing.

_____ _____ _____

6. What is FRT plywood and where was it commonly used?

_____

_____

7. List five types of hardware that may be used to improve the ability of a home to resist earthquakes.

_____

_____

_____

_____

_____

8. Describe a shearwall, mentioning materials, fastening and location.

_____

_____

9. Name three key issues in hurricane resistance for houses.

_____

_____

_____

If you had no trouble with the Quiz then you are ready for Field Exercise 2.

Key Words:

- **Wood _I_ Joists**
- **Bird's mouths**
- **Toe bearing**
- **Ridge beam**
- **Panel type roof sheathing**
- **Plank type roof sheathing**

- **Edge support for sheathing panels**
- **H clips**
- **Tongue and groove**
- **FRT plywood**
- **Delaminated plywood**

► 10.0 INSPECTION TOOLS

1. **Flashlight**

   To examine dark area, such as crawlspaces.

2. **Screwdriver/Awl**

   To probe suspect surfaces.

3. **Moisture Meter**

   To identify high moisture content in building materials.

4. **Tape Measure**

   To evaluate foundation height and thickness against grade height, for example.

5. **Plumb Bob**

   Is used to quantify leaning or bowing wall conditions.

6. **Mason's Level**

   To help quantify out-of-plumb situations.

► 11.0 INSPECTION CHECKLIST

Location Legend   N = North   S = South   E = East   W= West
B = Basement   1 = 1st story   2 = 2nd story   3 = 3rd story

LOCATION	CONDITION	LOCATION	CONDITION
	RAFTERS		**TRUSS**
	• Sagging		• Truss uplift
	• Concentrated loads		• Sag
	• Spliced		• Buckled webs/braces missing
	• Weak framing at openings		• Missing webs
	• Rafter spread		• Modified improperly
	• Rot		• Weak connections
	• Warped		• Endbearing
	• Mechanical damage		• Notches/holes
	• Split		• Mechanical damage
	• Fire damage		• Rot
	• Insects		• Insect damage
	• Weak connections/birdsmouth cuts		• Fire damage
	• Endbearing		
	• Too small/overspanned		**SHEATHING**
	• Ridge sag		• Sag
	• Bearing on ridge board		• Buckled
			• Delaminated plywood
	COLLAR TIES		• Too thin
	• Need lateral bracing		• FRT plywood deterioration
	• Missing		• Mold/mildew
	• Weak connections		• Rot
	• Buckling		• Insect damage
	• Mechanical damage		• Fire
	• Rot		• Weak connections
	• Insect damage		
	• Fire damage		**I JOISTS**
			• Birds mouths
	KNEE WALLS/PURLINS		• Toe bearing/endbearing
	• Removed/needed		• No ridge beams
	• Single top plate/sag		• Notched
	• Buckling		• Weak connections
	• Purlins sagging		• Rot
	• Purlins installed on side		• Insect damage
	• Mechanical damage		• Fire damage
	• Insect damage		
	• Rot		**SEISMIC**
	• Fire damage		• Fasteners - missing
	• Weak connections		- incomplete
			- ineffective
			- suspect
			• Shearwalls - missing
			- incomplete
			- ineffective
			- suspect
			HURRICANE
			• Bracing problems
			• Fastener problems
			• Opening protection problems

► 12.0 STRUCTURE INSPECTION PROCEDURE

INSPECTION PROCEDURE

This outline provides a general approach to inspecting structures. You may have to modify this, based on field conditions.

---

1. Before You Start

Control
- Remind yourself that you must be in control of the inspection process. Do not allow yourself to be distracted.

Neighborhood
- You should know what to expect from the area.
- What type of construction is common in the area?
- Are the houses low, medium or high quality?
- Is the area subject to chronic flooding?
- Are expansive soils a problem?
- Are unstable ravines an issue?
- Is the area built on fill?
- Are termites or other wood boring insects common?
- Does the climate lend itself to concealed rot of wood structural members?

---

2. What Are You Looking At?

Construction Type
Identify the type of structure and identify the foundation/footing system, as well as the floor, wall and roof construction.

Materials
Look at the construction materials. Are they what you would expect?

Access
How much of the structure is accessible?

Additions And Modifications
Look for such things as additions, porches which have been enclosed, or other building modifications. Compare to neighboring houses to look for changes that may have been made.

Construction Sequence
Envision the construction sequence. In what order were things put together? These can help identify problems.

What's Missing? Are all the pieces there? This is one of the most difficult things to observe.

3. What To Look For

Inside And Outside

Backtracking Is Okay

The structural inspection involves looking at both the inside and outside of the building. It does not matter where you start but you should be prepared to back-track. Many inspectors are reluctant to go back and take a second look at the outside, for example, if they have already toured it. However, new information that you learn on the inside of the building often demands that you go back outside. You do not have to apologize for backtracking. Many inspectors use a double tour approach to all inspection items.

Movement

Good structures do not move. You are looking for movement. Structural reports often include words like **lean**, **sag**, **bow**, **crack** and **heave**.

Common Conditions

Related Movement

You should know the proper installation methods and common conditions for each material and component. Look for conditions suggesting present or future non-performance. However, do not focus on individual components in isolation. There is a relationship that must be considered. For example, if the floors are not level, this means that the foundations may have moved, joists may have deflected, or beams and columns may have moved. With structural issues there is a cause and effect relationship between various components. It is unusual for one structural component to move in isolation.

Landscape And Close-up Views

Use a **macroscopic** and **microscopic** approach. With structures, this is particularly important. When you are two feet from a wall, it is tough to pick up a subtle lean or bulge. When you are fifty feet from a wall, it is tough to pick up hairline cracks.

Weak Points

Pay particular attention to weak points such as connections, points where additions join original construction, porches that have been closed to form living quarters, evidence of fire damage, evidence of substantial re-arrangement of the structure, inaccessible crawlspaces, mudsills, wood/soil contact, etc.

What's Missing? Remember to look for what is not there, but should be.

Assembling Clues

When looking at the structure, you are usually adding up a series of clues.

- Does each new piece of information reinforce or contradict your initial impression? Do not reject any point that does not fit your theory as a **red herring**. Consider all of the information before forming a conclusion.
- What do the majority of the clues suggest?
- What could have caused the inconsistent clues to appear and still fit the description? As you zero in on the most probable scenario, take a step back and see what else may have caused it.
- Is your theory the only possible one?

Analyzing
Cracks

When looking at cracks some inspectors sketch the problems and then ask themselves a series of questions. The process goes like this:

1) Make a sketch of all the movement you noted
2) Note these things:
   • Length
   • Continuous through components?,
   • Orientation and shape (horizontal, vertical, diagonal or random)
   • What has moved ?
   • In what direction?
   • Are there other related conditions (e.g., leaning)?
   • Is it still moving?
   • Why did it move?

Implications

Once you have concluded what has happened, then you have to answer the "So what?" question.

   • What are the implications of the movement that you have seen?

   - Is it typical settlement?
   - Is the house about to collapse?
   - Is it somewhere in between?

Details And
Big Picture

As a general strategy, you have to look for and at specific items, but you must also take a more passive look at the house and let it tell you its story. Do not make the house fit the parameters of your first impression. You need to be open-minded in the truest sense. It is one of the challenges of being a home inspector. You must be both –

   • meticulous and detail-oriented
   • conceptual and big-picture oriented.

Deduction
Versus
Observations
Results In
Opinion
Versus Fact

Recognize that in most cases you can't see everything. Most of your analysis is going to be by deduction rather than direct observation. Therefore, an element of doubt is built in. Make it clear to your client where you are not reporting a fact, but offering an opinion based on indirect and incomplete evidence.

4. Conclusions and Reporting

Evaluate
Performance

Is the structure doing its job? Is it **staying put**?

Your Suspicions

Which of the materials or methods are suspect?

Recom-
mendations

What needs to be done – replace, repair, investigate further, monitor, or is no action recommended?

Priority

If improvements are necessary, are they urgent?

Is there a life safety issue?

Cost Estimates If you provide estimates of cost, what are these likely to be? Where there is a possibility that what you see is the tip of a much larger iceberg, say so.

Limitations • What restricted your inspection?
• Was there limited access?
• Were items concealed?
• Has recent decorating eliminated some of the historical clues that are available?
• Did storage and furnishings get in the way?
• Were roof joists, ceiling joists, etc. concealed by insulation?
• Did insulation above the top of ceiling joists prevent you from making your way through the entire attic?

Let your client know in writing how you inspected various areas. Did you crawl through crawlspaces and attics or simply look at them from the access hatch?

Last Look After you finish your structural inspection, ask yourself, "What did I miss?" Take one last macroscopic look at the house to make sure everything fits what you have already seen.

Structure
MODULE

FIELD EXERCISE 2

☑ INSTRUCTIONS

You should complete everything up to Quiz 6 before doing this Exercise.

In this Exercise you will inspect the roof structure of eight to ten houses. The roof structure should be trusses rather than rafters.

For each house do A, B and C below.

Allow yourself roughly ½ an hour for each house. You will need daylight.

Part A - Exterior Inspection

For this section you will be inspecting the roof from the exterior. Step back from the house and observe the roof plane. Look for any signs of rafter or ridge sag. Continue around the house and make note of any other irregularities in the structure.

Part B - Gaining Access

The next step is to gain access to the attic space. Identify all attic hatches. Open the hatch, being careful not to damage the finish. Decide whether you will enter the attic space or inspect the attic from the hatch. Is there clear access? Is there anything that would be dangerous about entering the attic? Is it possible that you could damage the house by entering the attic? Decide and document your reasons.

Part C - Interior Inspection

Whether you are inspecting the attic from the hatch or from inside the attic, make a list of all the structural components that you can. Refer back to the Study Sessions if you see a component you don't recognize.

Were you able to identify any of the problems that were discussed in the text? If so, make a list.

_____ _____ _____

_____ _____ _____

► 13.0 BIBLIOGRAPHY

STRUCTURE	AUTHOR/S	PUBLISHERS
Architectural Graphic Standards	Charles George Ramsey/ Harold-Reeve Sleeper	*John Wiley & Sons*
The Handbook of Building Construction	George A. Hool/ Nathan C. Johnson	*McGraw – Hill*
The New Science of Strong Materials	J.E. Gordon	*Pelican*
Structures	J.E. Gordon	*Plenum Press*
Permanent Wood Foundations	Gary J. Gibson	*Sure – West Publishing Inc.*
Diagnosing & Repairing House Structure Problems	Edgar O. Seaquist	*McGraw – Hill*
Wood Design Manual	Compilation	*Canadian Wood Council*
Building Failures, Diagnosis & Avoidance, 2d Ed.	W.H. Ronsom	*E. & F.N. Spon, London*
Design of Wood Structures	Donald E. Breyer	*McGraw – Hill*
Residential Foundations: Design, Behaviour, and Repair	Robert Wade Brown	*Van Nostrand Reinhold*
		Van Nostrand Reinhold
Rough Framing Carpentry	Mark Currie	*Craftsman*
A Visual Dictionary of Architecture	Francis D.K. Ching	*Publishing Ventures Inc.*

Also: 1. Applicable Building Codes to your area. Many codes have companion publications that contain explanations and/or illustrations. These can be very helpful. Examples are:

National Building Code of Canada	Compilation	*National Research Council of Canada*
CAB • One and Two Family Dwelling Code	Compilation	*The Council of American Building Officials*
Uniform Building Code	Compilation	*International Conference of Building Officials*

Note: Copies of U.S. building codes available from: Southern Building Codes Congress International (SBCCI), 900 Montclair Road, Birmingham, AL, 35213 Council of American Building Officials (CABO), 5203 Leesburg Pike, Suite 708, Falls Church, VA, 22041

Building Official Codes Administrators International (BOCA), 4051 West Flossmoor Road, Country Club Hills, IL, 60478
International Conference of Building Officials (ICBO), 5360 Workman Mill Road, Whittier, CA, 90601

2. Periodicals such as those listed below often address structural topics:

The Old House Journal	Periodical	*Builderburg Group, Inc.*
The Journal Of Light Construction	Periodical	*Time*
Fine Homebuilding	Periodical	*The Taunton Press*
Building Performance: Hurricane Andrew in Florida Observations, Recommendations and Technical Guidance	Federal Emergency Management Association	Federal Emergency Management Association
APA Homeowners Guide for Earthquake Safeguards	American Plywood Association	American Plywood Association

► ANSWERS TO QUICK QUIZZES

Answers to Quick Quiz 1

1. True

2. True

3. False

4. True

5. 1. The access is blocked
   2. You might damage property
   3. It might be dangerous

6. 1. Collapse duct work
   2. Put your foot through the ceiling
   3. Fall through a ceiling
   4. Disturb an electrical connection

7. 1. A sag in the rafter or ridge system
   2. Dishing of the roof surface
   3. Spreading of rafters or the top of the walls

8. 1. Poor end bearing
   2. Weak connections
   3. Rot or insect damage
   4. Mechanical damage
   5. Fire damage
   6. Cracks or sagging of interior finishes

9. They might be loose or unstable

10. More snow will accumulate on the roof.

Answers to Quick Quiz 2

1. 1. Carry live loads of wind, rain, snow and people
   2. Carry dead loads of roof sheathing, roof coverings and roof equipment
   3. Support dead loads of insulation and ceiling finishes
   4. Laterally support building walls
   5. Create an attic space, ventilation space and support for soffits and fascia

2. 1. Rafters are sloped structural members on steep roofs that support sheathing and run from the roof peak down to the eaves. They may be 2 by 4 to 2 by 10's and are typically spaced 12 to 24 inches on center.

   2. Roof joists are horizontal or nearly horizontal framing members on low sloped roofs that carry the sheathing, roof covering and live loads above to walls or beams. Roof joists can be thought of as low sloped rafters. Some roof joists also carry ceiling finishes.

3. Ceiling joists are horizontal members that support insulation and ceilings. They are used with rafters and may support attic floors. Ceiling joists often tie the bottom ends of opposing rafters together to make a structurally sound triangle of the roof assembly.

3. Ceiling joists help prevent rafters and the tops of walls from being pushed outward by live loads on the roof. Ceiling joists are often in tension, running from the bottom of one rafter to another. They must be continuous to resist these forces.

4. A hip rafter is a rafter that forms a roof hip and supports the jack rafters on either side. The hip rafter follows the line of the hip.

A valley rafter follows the line of the valley in a roof and supports the jack rafters on either side. Hip and valley rafters are typically one size larger than other rafters in the roof structure.

Jack rafters are short rafters that either have their top end at a hip rafter or their bottom end at a valley rafter.

5. The span of a rafter is determined by its horizontal projection.

6. A ridge board does not carry rafter loads. A ridge beam does. A ridge beam will prevent rafter spreading. A ridge board will not. A ridge board is typically 1 by x material. A ridge beam is typically at least 2 by x material. Ridge beams require vertical supports below. Ridge boards do not.

7. Condensation and resultant rot is a chronic problem with flat and cathedral roofs.

Answers to Quick Quiz 3

1. Sagging rafters may be due to:
- Rafters overspanned or undersized
- Too many layers of roofing materials
- Excessive loads

2. Sagging rafters cause a dishing in the entire roof surface and/or a sag at the ridge. Sheathing sag is a repetitive pattern across the roof between rafters, trusses or roof joists.

3. Rafter spread may be caused by:
- Ceiling joists running parallel to rafters
- Ceiling joists not well connected to rafters
- Ceiling joist splices not secure
- Rafters not well secured to the structure
- Ceiling joists removed to create cathedral ceilings.

4. Rafters are less likely to spread when there is a ridge beam because the rafters hang on this structural member. With a simple ridge board, the rafters are not prevented from dropping at the ridge. A ridge beam, if properly installed, helps prevent the rafters from dropping or spreading.

5. End bearing should be 1½ inches.

6. Headers and trimmers (doubling of rafters) strengthen the roof around openings for dormers, skylights, etc. This is similar to the headers and trimmers created in floor systems at stairwell openings.

7. Condensation tends to be more uniform and wide spread than leakage. Condensation is uniform laterally across the roof. Leaks tend to run down sloped roof surfaces following gravity.

Answers to Quick Quiz 4

1. Collar ties help prevent rafter sag.

2. Collar ties should be located halfway up the rafters.

3. Because collar ties are in compression, they may buckle. Lateral support helps to prevent buckling.

4. 4 in 12.

5. Knee walls and purlins both provide mid-point support for rafters. Knee walls provide their support by transferring the loads down to ceilings joists and walls or beams below. Purlins act as beams running along the underside of rafters. The top plate of a knee wall may sag if it is a single plate and if the studs are not lined up with the rafters above.

Answers to Quick Quiz 5

1. A chord is part of the perimeter of a truss. Webs are the internal members.

2. Trusses are further apart than most rafters. Trusses are often 24 inches on center and some common plywood and waferboard sheathings are not thick enough to span 24 inches without sagging under live load.

3. Trusses may sag because of:
- Excess load
- Overspanning
- Weak connections
- Cut or damaged webs or chords

4. Truss uplift.

5. Drywall may sag because ½ inch drywall cannot span the 24 inches between trusses without sagging, especially if the drywall has been wet as a result of condensation, or during construction and finishing.

6. King post, queen post, fink, howe, fan, belgian or doublefink, scissor, mono, pratt, warren, gable end.

7. Attach moldings to ceilings but not walls, and allowing the ceiling drywall to float are common solutions for truss uplift.

8. Either.

Answers to Quick Quiz 6

1. Wood I-joists are engineered and manufactured wood systems that have a top and bottom chord and a web that joins them.

2. False.

3. No.

4. The roof is stronger if vertical joints are staggered. Vertical joints are weaknesses in the roof panel. Lining up all the weakness will tend to make the roof act as several smaller panels rather than one large one.

5. Sheathing may sag due to:
   - Overspanning
   - Excess loads
   - Deteriorated wood
   - Panel type sheathing installed in the wrong direction
   - Inadequate edge support

6. Fire Resistant Treated (FRT) plywood is typically used in row or town home close to the party walls to avoid building parapet walls. A chemical treatment in the wood was designed to char the wood at relatively low temperatures raising the auto-ignition temperature of the wood, helping to control the spread of fire.

7. Sill anchors, hold downs (tie downs), straps, hangers, post caps and hurricane clips (ties)

8. Shearwalls are $^{3}/_{8}$ to $^{1}/_{2}$ inch plywood or waferboard nailed to exterior (and sometimes interior) stud walls of home to resist the lateral forces of earthquakes and prevent racking. They must extend the full wall height without interruption to be effective. They are nailed every 4 to 6 inches at panel edges and every 12 inches in the field of the panels. All edges must rest on solid wood framing or blocking. Hold downs should be provided at each corner and each end of the shearwall.

9. Roof sheathing must be well secured to roof framing.

   Roof framing must be well secured to wall framing.

   Openings for doors and windows must be protected against flying debris.